THE RECENT MAMMALS OF IDAHO

Bull Yellowstone Moose *(Alces americanus shirasi)*. Photographed at
Hoodoo Lake in the Selway Primitive Area, Idaho County, Idaho, by
K. D. Swan.

Courtesy: U.S. Forest Service

THE RECENT MAMMALS
OF IDAHO

BY

WILLIAM B. DAVIS

CONTRIBUTION FROM
THE MUSEUM OF VERTEBRATE ZOOLOGY
UNIVERSITY OF CALIFORNIA
BERKELEY

The CAXTON PRINTERS, Ltd.
Caldwell, Idaho
April 5, 1939

Printed and bound in the United States of America by
The CAXTON PRINTERS, Ltd.
Caldwell, Idaho
52685

CONTENTS

LIST OF ILLUSTRATIONS

KEYS

INTRODUCTION

Idaho is so situated geographically that the faunas of the north Pacific Coast, of the Rocky Mountains, and of the Great Basin meet there, each contributing in greater or lesser degree to the composite fauna of the state. Despite this zoological attractiveness, little was published on the mammals of Idaho prior to Merriam's report, "Results of a Biological Reconnoissance of south-central Idaho" (North American Fauna, no. 5, 1891). Lewis and Clark, who traversed a small sector of the area on their expedition to the Pacific in 1804-06, were the first to record observations on the mammals found within the present boundaries of the state. Eighteen years later, Alexander Ross, a fur trader and trapper for the Hudson's Bay Company, explored the "Snake Country" and, in 1855, published in his "The Fur Hunters of the Far West" some of what he observed about beaver and buffalo there (see Davis, 1935). In 1833, John K. Townsend crossed the southern part of Idaho on his way to the Pacific. While in the state, he collected the type specimens of two kinds of mammals and recorded observations on a few of the larger species in his "Narrative of a Journey across the Rocky Mountains to the Columbia River ... ", published in 1839.

Nearly forty years later, in 1872, C. Hart Merriam, then a youth of sixteen, accompanied the party of the Hayden Survey of the Territories as naturalist. This party traversed the eastern portion of Idaho in a north-south direction. While there, Merriam collected and preserved fifteen species of mammals, as set forth in his published account of 1873. Perhaps an interest aroused on this early trip was the incentive for his later explorations in the state. The scientific results of these he published, as already indicated, in 1891. The new information that has appeared since is scattered and is contained, for the most part, in an article (Whitlow and Hall, 1933) which has reference to a small area in southeastern Idaho, and in numbers of the North American Fauna series wherein restricted groups of mammals are treated.

In addition to C. Hart Merriam and his associates, Vernon Bailey, Basil Hicks Dutcher, and Clark P. Streator, many others have collected mammals in Idaho. Among the more recent workers are William T. Shaw, who collected in the vicinity of Moscow from 1922 to 1925; Adrey E. Borell and Raymond M. Gilmore, who spent the summer of 1930 collecting at several localities in Washington and Adams counties for Ralph Ellis; in the summer of 1932, Alden H. Miller, Robert T. Orr, and Dean Blanchard collected at a number of localities in the western and northern portions of the state; Raymond M. Gilmore spent from July to October, 1935, collecting in Fremont and Clark counties for the American Museum of Natural History; David H. Johnson, Henry S. Fitch, and Dale Arvey, in July, 1937, obtained 55 mammals in the southwestern corner of the state in Owyhee County. I spent parts of four summers, 1934-37, and from December 21, 1935, to January 11, 1936, collecting and making observations on the mammals in the southern half of the state. At various times in my field work I have been assisted by Allan Upton (1934), Elmer Aldrich (1935), Howard Twining (1935), Willis Pequegnat (1936), Joe Donohoe (1936), and Walter Clark (1937). Other specimens have been collected from time to time by staff members of the United States Bureau of Biological Survey. Those who have been especially active in this respect are Luther J. Goldman, Stanley G. Jewett, Stanley E. Piper, and L. E. Wyman. These all, then, have had a part in bringing the present book to completion and along with others deserve credit for whatever merit it may have.

It is a particular pleasure to acknowledge the help received from those associated with the Museum of Vertebrate Zoology. Indeed, without the assistance of Miss Annie M. Alexander and Oscar P. Silliman, the work probably never would have been completed. Almost the same may be said for the guidance received there from Joseph Grinnell and E. Raymond Hall. To the latter and David H. Johnson I am further indebted for seeing the work through the press. Then, too, from James H. Gipson and his associates, The Caxton Printers, I acknowledge invaluable assistance.

Arthur H. Howell and Stanley G. Jewett, of the Biological Survey, and Wharton Huber, Associate Curator in the Academy of Natural Sciences of Philadelphia, supplied me with critical information that could not have been gotten otherwise; Amos H. Eckert, former State Game Warden of Idaho, and William Keubli, Clayton, Idaho, supplied me with certain of the rarer fur-bearing species.

The data for this report were compiled from a study of 3106 specimens, original field notes of my own and those of other workers, and published works. The bulk of the specimens examined is deposited in the California Museum of Vertebrate Zoology, Berkeley; others are in the Charles R. Connor Museum, Pullman, Washington; the Bureau of Biological Survey collection, Washington, D. C.; the National Museum, Washington, D. C.; the Los Angeles Museum, Los Angeles, California; the Academy of Natural Sciences of Philadelphia, Pennsylvania; the Carnegie Museum, Pittsburgh, Pennsylvania; the American Museum of Natural History, New York; the zoological collections of Brigham Young University, Provo, Utah; the Rocky Mountain Spotted Fever Laboratories' collection, Hamilton, Montana; and in the private collections of Ralph Ellis, Berkeley, California; David MacKaye, Santa Cruz, California; William T. Shaw, Fresno, California; and W. E. Snyder, Beaver Dam, Wisconsin. To the persons in charge of the above collections, I wish to express my appreciation for the privilege of examining certain of the specimens contained therein. Assistance in the preparation of this publication was rendered by personnel of Works Progress Administration O.P. No. 465-03-3-193. To many others, whose names are too numerous to mention here individually, I am similarly grateful for assistance they so freely gave me in other ways.

THE RECENT MAMMALS OF IDAHO

Relief map showing the principal topographic features of Idaho.

GEOGRAPHY OF THE STATE

In traveling the length of Idaho from north to south, one is impressed with the marked topographic, biotic, and climatic differences that exist at the two extremes of the state. In the north, one is constantly amid mountains covered with varied and luxuriant stands of conifers and mesophytic shrubs. The central portion is extremely rugged; the highest mountains in the state, many of them over 11,000 feet in altitude, are found there, and much of the region is comparatively inaccessible and therefore little known. In the south, particularly on the Snake River Plains, the land is gently rolling or nearly flat and, except in cultivated areas, is covered mostly with xerophytic vegetation. Some of this region consists of barren basaltic outcroppings.

The Snake River Plains extend in a broad crescent from Oregon eastward nearly across the state toward Yellowstone National Park. In many places the valley is 80 miles or more in width; it is nearly 300 miles in length, and slopes gradually from an altitude of near 6000 feet at its eastern end to 2100 feet in the vicinity of Weiser. Through this broad valley, following in general its greater curvature, flows the Snake River, the only large river in the state that drains westward from the central Rocky Mountains to the Columbia River. Interposed at intervals along its course are many falls, rapids, and steep-walled canyons which have been carved through fields of sheet basalt. In its course across southern Idaho, only one important stream, Big Wood River, enters the Snake from the north, whereas numerous streams, draining from the Raft River, Albion, Goose Creek, and Bruneau mountains, are contributary from the south.

Geologically, the Snake River Valley is old. Except for the extensive fields of lava between King Hill and Idaho Falls on the north side of the river, much of its floor consists of fluviatile and lacustrine deposits which, for ages, have been carried down by the streams from the surrounding mountains. As evidenced by exposed sedimentary deposits along the Payette River and elsewhere, at an earlier time, thought to be at the beginning of the Tertiary, the

Snake River Valley was fully 1000 feet lower in elevation than at present. At some time in the Tertiary, now judged to be in the Miocene (see Buwalda, 1924:572), the river was blocked, as a result of volcanism or by elevation of the land, in the region where it now enters the Seven Devils Canyon between Oregon and Idaho. One result was the formation of a huge lake, known to geologists as Lake Payette (not to be confused with the now existing Payette Lake in Valley County), which extended northward and eastward in Idaho to near the present site of Ashton, and southeastward to near Bear Lake. In time the lake became filled with deposits brought down from the mountains and by volcanic dust. These sedimentary deposits are known as the Payette Formation. Subsequent volcanism, intermittently continued to Recent time, is thought to explain the occurrence of numerous strata of sheet-lava alternating with sedimentary deposits which now are conspicuous in the steep-walled gorge near Twin Falls.

At a later time, and in a part of its former bed, Lake Payette was replaced by Lake Idaho, whose easternmost limit was near Shoshone Falls. This second lake is judged to have been in existence in the Pliocene and Pleistocene epochs. In the area west of Shoshone Falls evidence of the former existence of this lake comprises bench marks, and deposits of silt, sand, and other sediments in which numerous aquatic and land-dwelling vertebrates are now found as fossils. As I shall point out later on, these lakes and the general east-west course of the Snake River have had important bearing on the present distribution of mammals in the southern half of the state of Idaho.

At some time during the existence of these two lakes, other smaller lakes were present in regions where they now are absent or are much reduced in size. One of them in Pleistocene time was Bear Lake. Later it was replaced by the present-day Bear Lake, which occupies a part of the older lake bed. Another is thought to have occupied the Salmon and Pahsimeroi valleys in the central portion of the state. This lake, if the geologic evidence is correctly interpreted, existed at about the time that Payette Lake was at its highest level. None of these smaller lakes seems to have influenced the migration and dispersal of mammals in Idaho as did lakes Payette and Idaho.

Volcanism played an important part in sculpturing the eastern half of the Snake River Valley as we see it today. Although the most extensive flows are north of the Snake River, volcanism occurred to the south and east as well. In the region from Gooding east to near Pocatello, extensive barren fields of lava mark the sites where this geologic activity was most pronounced. In the region of the Craters of the Moon National Monument, some of the flows are thought to be no older than 250 years.

Most of the uplifts giving rise to the mountains in Idaho date back probably to the Jurassic or earlier. The mountains south of the Snake River, for the most part, are round-topped and much eroded, with alluvial piedmont plains; those in the central part of the state are high, exceedingly rugged, and steep-sided, a condition which suggests considerable faulting. In the north the mountains are lower, less precipitous, and show scourings and moraines left by the Great Ice Sheet which, in the Pleistocene, extended south in Idaho at least as far as Coeur d'Alene Lake. Many of the lakes in northern Idaho probably resulted directly from the action of this large body of ice.

The altitude of Idaho varies from 710 feet, on the Snake River at Lewiston, to 12,655 feet, at the top of Mt. Borah in the Pahsimeroi Mountains. The mean elevation of the Snake River Plains is near 4000 feet, that of northern Idaho is near 3000 feet, with most of the valleys near 2000 feet. The central portion is the "backbone" of the state; the valleys average near 5000 feet in elevation, and the general average for that region is near 7000 feet. It is here that most of the streams which empty into the Snake River in its northward course arise. In general, the eastern boundary of Idaho is higher than the western. Tin Cup Valley, east of Grays Lake at the Idaho-Wyoming border, is slightly over 5700 feet; the elevation at the opposite side of the state at nearly the same latitude is 2100 feet. These facts are reflected in the direction of flow of the rivers. As previously mentioned, the Snake River flows from east to west in southern Idaho and from south to north in the region where

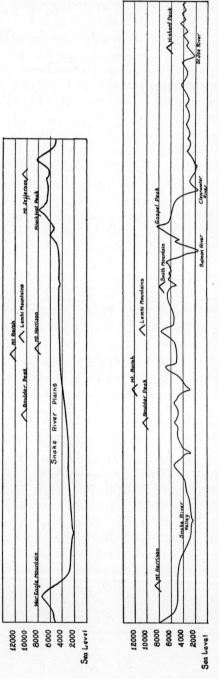

FIG. 1. Profile sections of Idaho. Top.—Section from west to east through the Snake River Valley in the southern part of the state. Bottom.—Section from south to north taken near longitude 117 degrees W.

it constitutes the western boundary of the state. The Salmon River and its many tributaries flow north, then west. Most of the other larger rivers assume a similar course; all of them, except those in the extreme northern part of the state, converge toward Lewiston, the lowest place in the state. The profile sections (fig. 1) are helpful in visualizing these general trends.

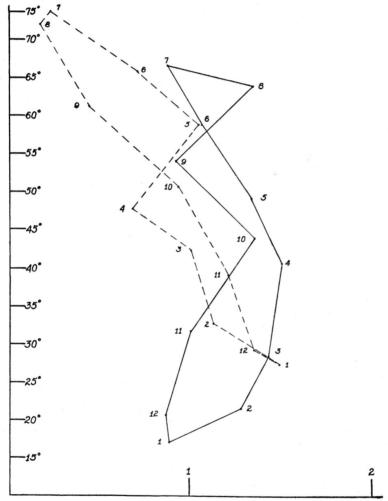

FIG. 2. Hythergraphs for Montpelier (solid lines) in southeastern Idaho and Payette (dotted lines) in southwestern Idaho. Temperature is represented in degrees Fahrenheit, precipitation in inches. Numbers beside points in the figures designate months of the year.

Because the state is situated inland from the oceans, its climate is typically continental, cold in winter and hot in summer. Considerable variation in climate is found in different parts of the state, however. The northern "panhandle" is typically humid, with an average annual rainfall of 30 inches and with cold winters and moderate summers. The central mountainous portion is considerably drier, with less than 10 inches of precipitation annually, and with mild summers and cold winters. Killing frosts often occur in June and August in the higher valleys. The Snake River Valley as a whole experiences cold winters and hot, dry summers; the average annual rainfall there is near 10 inches. In the western part of the valley, near Payette, the summers are extremely hot and dry; the winters, however, are mild, a circumstance which is due in part to the low elevation. The hythergraphs (figs. 2 and 3) illustrate in graphic form the average monthly temperature and precipitation in localities selected to show extremes of climatic variation in the state.

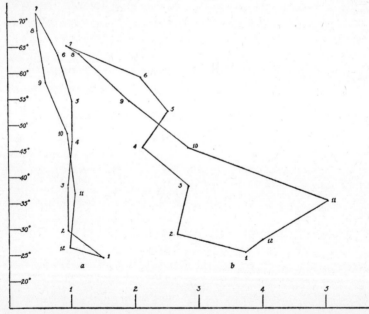

Fig. 3. Hythergraphs for Rupert (a), in Snake River Valley in southern Idaho, and Sandpoint (b), in the panhandle. Temperature is represented in degrees Fahrenheit, precipitation in inches. Numbers beside points in the figures designate months of the year.

FLORAL PROVINCES

Three distinct floral provinces occur in Idaho, (1) the
Northern Rocky Mountain region, (2) the Central Rocky
Mountain region, and (3) the Great Basin region. The accounts of the coniferous associations in the first two of these
provinces are adapted from Frothingham (1909).

THE NORTHERN ROCKY MOUNTAIN REGION includes part
of southern British Columbia, northeastern Washington,
northern Idaho, and northwestern Montana. In its relatively
humid climate, as compared with that farther south, several
species typical of the Pacific Coast meet the Rocky Mountain trees, and a heterogeneous composition of the forest is
the result. The coast species, which here extend eastward
to the Rocky Mountains, are western white pine, giant arborvitae, lowland fir, western hemlock, and probably the
coast form of the Douglas fir. Associated with these species,
either mixed or in pure stands, are yellow and lodgepole
pines, Engelmann spruce, alpine fir, and the Rocky Mountain Douglas fir, all of which range farther south and east
in the Rocky Mountains.

The most characteristic forest associations in this region
are (1) an alpine fir association, (2) a white pine association, (3) a lodgepole pine association, and (4) a yellow pine
association. The alpine fir association occupies upper slopes
and high ridges, and hence is not continuous. It is composed chiefly of alpine fir, with white-bark pine, Engelmann spruce, and, near its lower limits, a mixture of
Douglas fir, lodgepole and western white pines, western
larch, and aspen. The stand is open and parklike at high
altitudes, but becomes dense lower down and gradually
changes into the next association.

The white pine association occupies protected situations
and moist soils with heavy stands of western white pine
mixed in widely varying proportions with western larch,
giant arborvitae, Douglas fir, lodgepole pine, lowland fir,
and western hemlock. Western larch predominates over
limited areas, and in many places forms an important type.

The lodgepole pine association here usually is a temporary one which has succeeded western white pine after fires. The young stands are dense and crowded, but as they mature they become more open. The forest is largely pure lodgepole pine, especially on poor, shallow soils; on deep and moist soils, however, a large proportion of Douglas fir, lowland fir, larch, and Engelmann spruce is often mixed with the lodgepole pine.

Characteristic of the yellow pine association is an open, pure stand situated in relatively dry areas at low altitudes. In moist localities the forest becomes dense and contains, in addition, Douglas fir, lowland fir, western larch, and lodgepole pine. In swampy situations at low altitudes there is often a "cedar swamp" association composed of giant arborvitae, either in pure stands or in mixture with white pine, larch, hemlock, Douglas fir, or lowland fir.

As mentioned in part above, the climate of the Northern Rocky Mountain region is humid, with abundant precipitation during the growing season. Daily and seasonal ranges of temperature are not excessive as a rule, and seasonal extremes of 90 degrees and –25 degrees F. are rarely exceeded. The growing season is approximately 150 days. Killing frost sometimes occurs in July and August, and in winter there are occasional prolonged periods of intense cold. Snowfall is moderate in amount.

THE CENTRAL ROCKY MOUNTAIN REGION is characterized by the predominance of the lodgepole pine association. This forest is best developed in the central part of Idaho. Here, as elsewhere, there are different, distinct associations correlated with altitude. Those of widest distribution in this region, beginning with the highest, are (1) an alpine fir association, of alpine fir, Engelmann spruce, and other less important alpine trees, becoming in the lower portions a nearly pure spruce forest, (2) a lodgepole pine association, covering whole watersheds with pure, unbroken stretches of lodgepole pine, interspersed with occasional small unmixed stands of Douglas fir, (3) a Douglas fir association, sometimes in extensive pure stands, but more often mixed with lodgepole pine, Engelmann spruce, and alpine fir above, and with yellow pine below, and (4) a lowland yellow

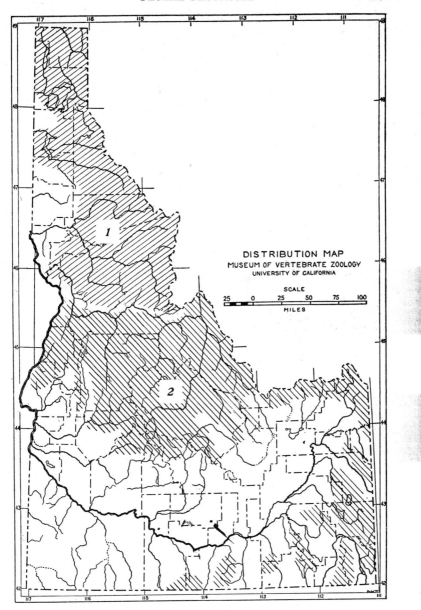

FIG. 4. Map showing the distribution of coniferous forests in Idaho.
1. Northern Rocky Mountain area, 2. Central Rocky Mountain area
(adapted from Frothingham).

pine association. Besides these, there are large, even-aged, pure stands of aspen which come in densely on fresh soils of burns.

In this region daily and seasonal ranges of temperature are great, precipitation is small or moderate, and the growing season often is less than 90 days. The winters are long and severe, with heavy snowfall and frequent periods of extreme cold during which the temperature sometimes falls to –30 degrees or even –40 degrees F. The summers are hot, and in some parts of the region are dry. The annual precipitation in the Douglas fir zone is from 15 to 25 inches, largely in the form of snow; in other areas it is as low as 7 inches. In general, more snow falls on the western than on the eastern sides of the mountains.

In the lower valleys of both these regions, the riparian growth often consists of balm of Gilead, black cottonwood, Bebb willow, Scouler willow, dogwood, and birch. The understory shrubs consist mainly of blueberry, raspberry, salmonberry, serviceberry, gooseberry, and currant.

THE GREAT BASIN REGION, including all of the Snake River Plains, the numerous fingerlike valleys that drain into it, and most of the foothills and piedmont plains south of the Snake River in Idaho, is dominated by sagebrush and other xerophytic plants. East of Shoshone Falls, where the average elevation is near 4300 feet, little else but sagebrush is found. In alkali soils, however, saltbush may occur. The lower foothills support a growth of juniper and mountain mahogany. Toward the west, in the old Idaho Lake basin where the altitude is under 3000 feet, saltbush often occurs in pure stands. More often, the stands are mixed, consisting of various species of sagebrush, saltbush, and greasewood. Along intermittent streams, pure stands of sagebrush (*Artemisia tridentata*) often reach a height of five or six feet. Along permanent streams, the riparian growth usually consists of pure stands of peach-leaved willow, or of mixed stands of willow, cottonwood, and wild rose. In certain areas, particularly toward the west and north, the narrow-leaved cottonwood is found in nearly pure stands.

The climate of this region is dry, with usually less than 10 inches of precipitation annually. Daily and seasonal ranges of temperature are excessive; seasonal extremes may vary from 110 degrees to –45 degrees F. The growing season is approximately 120 days or less, depending upon altitude. Killing frosts sometimes occur as late as May 15 and as early in the fall as September 21. Snowfall is never excessive, but prolonged periods of intense cold in winter are common.

In the following summary of the principal trees and shrubs of Idaho, those starred with an asterisk occur largely in the region under which they are listed.

NORTHERN ROCKY MOUNTAIN REGION

SHRUBS	TREES
Amelanchier alnifolia	*Abies grandis
Bossekia parviflora	Abies lasiocarpa
Ribes parvum	*Cornus instoloneus
Ribes saxosum	*Larix occidentalis
Ribes vicosissimum	*Pinus monticola
Rubus strigosa	Pinus murrayana
Philadelphus lewisii	Pinus albicaulis
*Vaccinium caespitosum	*Pinus ponderosa
	Picea engelmannii
	*Populus balsamifera
	Populus trichocarpa
	*Pseudotsuga taxifolia
	Pseudotsuga mucronata
	*Salix bebbiana
	*Salix scouleriana
	*Thuja plicata

CENTRAL ROCKY MOUNTAIN REGION

SHRUBS	TREES
As in the region above except where starred.	Abies lasiocarpa
	Picea engelmannii
	*Pinus albicaulis
	*Pinus flexilis
	*Pinus murrayana
	*Pseudotsuga mucronata
	Populus trichocarpa

GREAT BASIN REGION

SHRUBS	TREES
*Artemisia tridentata	*Cercocarpus ledifolius
*Artemisia arbuscula	*Cercocarpus parvifolius
*Artemisia nova	*Juniperus scopulorum
*Artemisia spinescens	*Juniperus utahensis
*Atriplex nuttalli	*Populus angustifolia
*Atriplex spinescens	*Salix amygdaloides
*Grayia spinescens	*Pinus monophylla
*Sarcobatus vermiculatus	
Rosa sp.	

DISTRIBUTIONAL AREAS IN IDAHO

It is because any serious consideration of the problem of distribution of mammals must take into account the physical and biotic features of the environment, that I have summarized, in the previous sections, the more important topographical, geological, climatic, and floral aspects of Idaho. Each was treated as an entity there, whereas no such divorced condition really exists in nature. Instead each affects profoundly the nature, and often the fate, of the other. In the following paragraphs, therefore, I shall attempt to correlate the isolated facts presented earlier with those I have been able to gather about mammalian distribution in Idaho. I would have the reader know, however, that I have been unable to visit all parts of Idaho personally. I have not visited the extreme northern, and the nearly inaccessible central mountainous, parts of the state, and for information concerning those areas I have had to rely upon the field notes and published works of others. The information available concerning the central portion is discouragingly meager; it is the least known part of Idaho.

Of the 141 kinds of mammals occurring in Idaho, 15 are widely distributed throughout the state. These occur from the humid, cool, northern region southward to the hot, arid Great Basin. A few are aquatic, or semi-aquatic, in habit and hence are not subjected to the extreme of high temperature to which land-dwelling forms are exposed. Others are large herbivorous species that are seminomadic in habit; still others are carnivores, each of which enjoys a relatively large home territory and has a long cruising radius. Fifty-six kinds appear to be limited in their distribution primarily by climatic factors, largely temperature, while the remaining 70 kinds may be assignable to three or, possibly, five areas, the limits of which are determined not by climate alone, but by the *interaction* of climatic, geographic, edaphic, and biotic factors, each of which, alone, may affect each of the kinds of mammals differently.

Each of these areas appears to constitute a natural assemblage of plants and animals which is peculiar to it, and

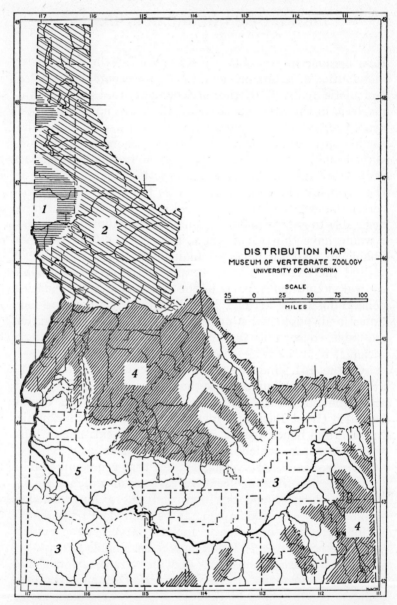

FIG. 5. Map showing biotic areas in Idaho. 1. Columbian Plateau,
2. Northern Rocky Mountain, 3. Northern Great Basin, 4. Central
Rocky Mountain, 5. Payette. The bounds of the Payette Biotic Area
are indicated by broken lines. Compare with figure 4.

hence may be considered as a faunal-floral unit. These units are analogous to the "faunal areas" of Grinnell (1914), but, unlike them, are not necessarily determined primarily by humidity. More nearly to convey this concept, the term "biotic area"* is here proposed. By this term I do not wish to imply that the particular assemblage of plants and animals necessarily *originated* or *evolved* in the area in question, although some of the individual kinds may have done so. I do wish to convey the idea, however, that within each of the biotic areas there exists *at the present* an assemblage of plants and animals which has become recognizably distinct from assemblages in adjoining areas.

An index to the degree to which various groups of mammals vary is found in the number of recognizably different races within each species or higher category. As is pointed out below in the summary of Orders and Families, the rodents far outnumber all other kinds of mammals in the number of geographic races. This group, therefore, is thought to exhibit the greatest genetic plasticity and potentiality for variation. It is primarily upon the distribution of this group of mammals and that of certain dominant or highly restricted birds and plants that these biotic areas have been outlined (see map, fig. 5).

These areas, listed in order from north to south, may be referred to as (1) the Northern Rocky Mountain Biotic Area (referred to below as northern biotic area), (2) the Central Rocky Mountain Biotic Area (referred to below as central biotic area), and (3) the Northern Great Basin Biotic Area (referred to below as Great Basin).

In addition to these three well-defined areas, two others less well differentiated (at least in Idaho) may be recognized, namely, (1) the Columbian Plateau Biotic Area, and (2) the Payette Biotic Area. The Columbian Plateau, which enters Idaho for a short distance in the vicinity of Lewiston, appears to be inhabited by a group of mammals, birds, and plants which might warrant its recognition as a distinct area. I have insufficient data to confirm this suggestion,

---

* Since writing this section, I find that Clark (1937), independently, coined and used this term with a similar meaning in connection with an ecologic study of North Coast Ranges in California.

however. The Payette Biotic Area, thought of here as that area in southwestern Idaho and northeastern Oregon which is characterized by deep lacustrine deposits known as the Idaho and Payette formations, also may be a distinct biotic unit. The fact that the mammals *Sorex preblei, Citellus m. vigilis, Thomomys t. townsendii, Dipodomys m. preblei, Onychomys l. fuscogriseus, Reithrodontomys m. nigrescens,* and possibly *Lepus c. wallawalla* are geographically limited to that area suggests the presence there of an area of differentiation. Additional work in this region, particularly in its Oregon portion, is needed to verify the impression given by these meager data. Because of insufficient material, I have not considered the Columbian Plateau Biotic Area in detail. For the same reason the Payette Biotic Area is here treated as a portion of the Great Basin Biotic Area.

Northern Rocky Mountain Biotic Area

This area, comprising the northern portion of the state, is a southward extension of a more extensive area occupying the greater part of southeastern British Columbia, northwestern Montana, and portions of northeastern Washington. Its southern limits in Idaho appear to be in the vicinity of the Salmon River where it transects the state into northern and southern parts (see profile, fig. 1). Topographically, the region is mountainous, traversed by numerous rivers, and dotted with lakes. The larger lakes, Coeur d'Alene, Pend Oreille, and Priest, are in the northern half. The climate is humid, with abundant precipitation during the growing season. Locally, as much as 40 inches of precipitation, much of it in the form of snow, may fall in a single year. Daily and seasonal ranges of temperature are not extreme, as a rule, but in winter there are occasional periods of intense cold; seasonal extremes of 90 degrees and –25 degrees F. are seldom exceeded. The average length of the frostless season, as computed from tables given by Livingston and Shreve (1921), is 132 days (May to September), although killing frosts sometimes occur in July and August.

In discussing the forest trees of this region, Frothingham (1909) states that in its relatively humid climate, as compared with that farther south, several species typical of the Pacific Coast meet the Rocky Mountain trees, and a great diversity in the composition of the forest results. The coast species are western white pine, giant arborvitae, lowland fir, western hemlock, and probably the coast form of Douglas fir. Associated with them either as pure stands or in mixture are yellow and lodgepole pines, Engelmann spruce, alpine fir, and the Rocky Mountain Douglas fir, all of which in Idaho attain their greatest importance in the following biotic area.

Associated with these forest trees are such shrubs as blueberry, huckleberry, and salmonberry, and, during the breeding season, such birds as western winter wren (*Nannus hiemalis pacificus*), varied thrush (*Ixoreus naevius meruloides*), western bluebird (*Sialia mexicana occidentalis*), chestnut-backed chickadee (*Penthestes rufescens rufescens*), Grinnell mountain chickadee (*Penthestes gambeli grinnelli*), Bohemian waxwing (*Bombycilla garrula pallidiceps*), Vaux swift (*Chaetura vauxi*), and Merrill song sparrow (*Melospiza melodia merrilli*). Mammals restricted largely to this area are: Alaskan little brown bat, British Columbia marmot, gray-tailed chipmunk, Coeur d'Alene chipmunk, broad-footed flying squirrel, Coeur d'Alene pocket gopher, Drummond meadow mouse, Kootenai jumping mouse, Bangs pika, and mountain caribou.

Central Rocky Mountain Biotic Area

The Central Rocky Mountain Biotic Area is thought of as that area, occupied by the Rocky Mountains in western Montana and central Idaho, which extends from the Salmon River southward to southeastern Idaho and southwestern Wyoming. A narrow projection, broken into numerous isolated sections, extends from the Rocky Mountains westward along the southern border of the state.

Topographically, this area is mountainous in character and includes the highest elevations in the state. Along its southern limits, numerous tongues of the Great Basin sage-covered plains project northward on the valley floors. There are several small lakes in the central and southeastern parts. The climate is relatively arid; precipitation, consisting largely of snow, is from 7 to 25 inches yearly. The winters are long and severe, with heavy snowfall and frequent periods of extreme cold, at which times the temperature often falls to –30 degrees or even –40 degrees F. The summers are hot, for the most part dry, and frosts occur frequently during this season at higher altitudes. The average length of the frostless season is less than 60 days.

The area is characterized by a preponderance of lodgepole pine which, at middle altitudes, covers whole watersheds with pure, unbroken stands. At higher elevations, Engelmann spruce and alpine fir are dominant. The Rocky Mountain Douglas fir is found occasionally in extensive pure stands, but more often it is mixed with the above three kinds of trees. In addition, there are large, pure stands of aspen of uniform age which come in densely on fresh soil after burns. Associated with these forest trees are a number of shrubs and montane perennial and annual herbs, and, in the breeding season, such birds as the black rosy finch (*Leucosticte atrata*), Rocky Mountain pine grosbeak (*Pinicola enucleator montana*), mountain bluebird (*Sialia currucoides*), pink-sided junco (*Junco mearnsi*), and other montane species.

Mammals restricted to this area, or found there more often than elsewhere, are: Idaho grizzly bear, black bear, hoary marmot, gray-tailed ground squirrel, yellow-tailed ground squirrel, Idaho spotted ground squirrel, brown pocket gopher, Sawtooth white-footed mouse, Idaho red-backed mouse, Wasatch meadow mouse, Idaho jumping mouse, Lemhi pika, Seven Devils pika, Yellowstone moose, and Rocky Mountain goat.

Northern Great Basin Biotic Area

This area, comprising the Snake River Plains and the arid plateaus in southwestern Idaho, northwestern Utah, northern Nevada, northeastern California, and eastern Oregon, is considered a part of the Great Basin. Physiographically, however, most of the area, and all of it in Idaho, is separated from the Great Basin proper which has no drainage to the sea. Topographically, the area in Idaho is an undulating plain bisected into northern and southern portions by the Snake River. Its northern and eastern limits are well defined by the mountains which rise abruptly from the plain. In a number of places, fingerlike valleys project from the plains into the mountain masses. Such valleys are those of Big Lost River, Big Wood River, Birch Creek, Blackfoot River, Lemhi River, and Raft River. A broken western extension of the Rocky Mountains interrupts the continuity of the southeastern portion of this area in Idaho and separates, in part, the portion in Idaho from that farther south in Nevada and Utah. Much of the plains from Mountain Home eastward is covered with discontinuous fields of lava, some of which, especially in the vicinity of the Craters of the Moon National Monument, are thought to be only a few hundred years old.

Precipitation here normally is less than 15 inches yearly; about two thirds of it falls in the form of snow. The winters, as a rule, are moderately cold; occasional prolonged periods of extreme cold are experienced, at which time the temperature may drop to as low as −45 degrees F. The summers are hot and for the most part dry; precipitation during the frostless season, May to September, usually is less than 3 inches. Daily and seasonal extremes of temperature seldom exceed 110 degrees and −15 degrees F.

The dominant vegetation of the area is xerophytic, consisting of several species of sagebrush (*Artemisia*) which, in favorable uncultivated regions, form pure, dense stands. Associated with *Artemisia tridentata* are salt sage, small salt sage, hop sage, rabbit brush, two species of juniper, and, in the foothills, mountain mahogany. Several kinds of birds are thought to be restricted to the area in the breeding season. Among them are: sage hen (*Centrocercus urophasianus*), Nevada red-winged blackbird (*Agelaius phoeniceus nevadensis*), Brewer blackbird (*Euphagus cyanocephalus cyanocephalus*), Nevada loggerhead shrike (*Lanius ludovicianus nevadensis*), Nevada sage sparrow (*Amphispiza belli nevadensis*), Brewer sparrow (*Spizella breweri breweri*), American raven (*Corvus corax sinuatus*), and green-tailed towhee (*Oberholseria chlorura*).

Mammals typical of the area are: western canyon bat, Snake River Valley raccoon, little spotted skunk, Nevada long-eared desert fox, Nevada mantled ground squirrel,

Great Basin chipmunk, Townsend pocket gopher, Idaho pocket mouse, Columbian kangaroo rat, short-tailed grasshopper mouse, canyon mouse, Nevada wood rat, and desert black-tailed jack rabbit.

Within each of the above described biotic areas the mammals are not continuously distributed; many races are adapted, and largely restricted, to certain definite associations or habitats. Associations found in one or more of the biotic areas may be defined as follows:

1. *Marsh Association.*—Marshes are typical of all three biotic areas, but especially so of the Great Basin where isolated springs are surrounded by higher, dry, sage-covered land. In them are found such hydrophytic plants as sedges, cattails, and reeds, and such birds as coots, red-winged and yellow-headed blackbirds, marsh wrens, and yellow-throats. Mammals inhabiting the marsh proper usually are muskrats only. This association, in most instances, merges imperceptibly with the meadow, and as a result certain meadow-dwelling species, particularly the semi-aquatic meadow mice, may temporarily extend their ranges into the marsh.

2. *Meadow Association.*—In each of the mountainous biotic areas this association may be subdivided into (1) Valley Meadows, and (2) Alpine Meadows. Valley meadows usually are under 5000 feet in elevation, and especially in the northern part of the state they frequently are less than 2000 feet. Inhabiting meadows in each of the three areas are such grass-dwelling or grass-eating mammals as ground squirrels (of the big-eared type), meadow mice, pocket gophers, jumping mice, and shrews. In alpine meadows, the voles *Clethrionomys, Phenacomys,* and *Microtus richardsoni* replace the lowland-dwelling meadow mice; ground squirrels often are absent, but jumping mice are usually present in greater numbers than in the Valley Meadow Association.

3. *Prairie Association.*—Here grassland species predominate. In the northern biotic area many of the camas prairies may be considered as typical of this association. In the central biotic area, this association is lacking for the most part. Camas Prairie in Camas County, and another Camas Prairie in Jefferson County are on the border line between

the central biotic area and the Great Basin, but the presence in the former of the Columbian ground squirrel and of the yellow-tailed ground squirrel in the latter favor placing them with the Central Rocky Mountain area. In the Great Basin, this association consists largely of rolling hills and valleys covered with bunch and June grass inhabited by *mollis* ground squirrels and several kinds of prairie-dwelling birds. Mammals inhabiting this association in each of the three biotic areas consist chiefly of ground squirrels (*mollis* in the Great Basin, *columbianus* in the north), pocket gophers, and the carnivores that prey upon them.

4. *Chaparral Association.*—This association in the northern and central biotic areas comprises the mesophytic shrubs—syringa, huckleberry, blueberry, raspberry, gooseberry, currant, and serviceberry, which harbor a variety of birds and such mammals as white-footed mice, snowshoe rabbits, and chipmunks. It occurs usually in the valleys or on semi-open hillsides where it constitutes an understory cover in the open coniferous forests. In the Great Basin area the shrubs are xerophytic, consisting of sagebrush, greasewood, salt sage, rabbit brush, and mountain mahogany. Depending upon the nature of the soil, this association includes kangaroo rats, pocket mice, and, depending upon the nature of the chaparral itself, white-footed mice, pygmy rabbits, and black-tailed jack rabbits, and, of birds, the sage thrasher, Brewer sparrow, sage sparrow, and loggerhead shrike.

5. *Deciduous Woodland Association.*—Along most of the watercourses at lower elevations in all three biotic areas, the riparian growth consists largely of cottonwoods and willows. In the northern and central areas, dogwood, birch, and alder may occur. Associated with such trees are a number of kinds of summering birds (flycatchers, warblers, and vireos) and, of mammals, chipmunks, tree squirrels, flying squirrels, and certain species of bats. At higher elevations, these trees are replaced in burned-over areas by dense, even-aged, nearly pure stands of quaking aspen which harbor deer, snowshoe and white-tailed hares, and, in the understory vegetation, the smaller rodents—white-footed mice, jumping mice, and the *mordax* meadow mouse. Here

the Richardson grouse is found most commonly and, in summer, mountain bluebird, Audubon warbler, alder flycatcher, juncos, and several species of woodpeckers.

6. *Coniferous Association types.*—In the northern biotic area, the coniferous forest consists of several different associations: (1) Alpine Fir Association. This occurs at higher elevations and consists of alpine fir, white-bark pine, Engelmann spruce, and, near its lower limits, a mixture of Douglas fir, lodgepole pine, western white pine, western larch, and aspen. (2) White Pine Association. This association, consisting of heavy stands of western white pine mixed in widely varying proportions with western larch, giant arborvitae, lowland fir, western hemlock, Douglas fir, and lodgepole pine, occupies the protected situations and moist soils. (3) Yellow Pine Association. This is characterized by yellow pine in an open, pure forest occupying relatively dry ground at low altitudes. (4) Lodgepole Pine Association. In most instances this is a temporary association which has succeeded western white pine after fires.

I am not sufficiently well acquainted with the ecology of the various species of birds and mammals in northern Idaho to state with assurance their distribution in terms of associations. We do know that in the forested areas the more common mammals are red squirrels, flying squirrels, red-backed mice, and, in broken forests, deer, snowshoe hares, Canada lynx, pine marten, and white-footed mice.

In the central biotic area, the Lodgepole Pine Association is dominant, often covering hundreds of square miles at middle altitudes without interruption. In it are found typically the red squirrel, pine marten, red-backed mouse (*C. g. idahoensis*), and porcupine. The hairy woodpecker, Cassin purple finch, western tanager, and red-breasted nuthatch are typical birds. At higher elevations, the Alpine fir association again is encountered, and, where the forest is open near timberline, mantled ground squirrels and mountain sheep occur. Below the lodgepole pine, a Douglas Fir Association occurs in scattered localities. Most often the stand consists of mixed Douglas fir, lodgepole pine, and alpine fir; occurring here are *amoenus* chipmunks, flying squirrels, white-footed mice, and occasionally red squirrels.

7. *Rock Association.*—Although few plants definitely are associated with rock ledges and outcroppings, many kinds of birds and mammals are. In the Great Basin area, basaltic outcroppings and "rim rocks" are conspicuous features of the landscape. Often, little else but herbs and a few junipers, sagebrush, and mountain mahogany break the monotony of the barren rocks. Here the Nevada wood rat, canyon mouse, Idaho pocket mouse, yellow-bellied marmot, cottontail, bobcat, and *minimus* (*consobrinus* excepted) chipmunks are at home. Associated with them are such birds as the Pacific nighthawk, American raven, canyon wren, rock wren, and white-throated swift. At higher elevations, in all three biotic areas, pikas, mantled ground squirrels, marmots, mountain goat, and mountain sheep are found. Birds occurring there are the black rosy finch, golden eagle, and rock wren.

Climate and distribution.—A cursory examination of the world-wide distribution of birds and mammals indicates that climate is an important physical element in controlling the presence or absence of certain kinds in the various parts of the world. Temperature seems to be of prime, humidity of secondary, importance, particularly as regards the larger taxonomic units over areas of considerable extent; winds, fogs, clouds, and other meteorological phenomena play minor roles and influence the minutiae which, in part, differentiate animals of the lowest taxonomic category, subspecies or geographic race. When one considers smaller areas, the state of Idaho for instance, and smaller taxonomic units, that is, geographic races, correlation between geographic distribution and climatic conditions, particularly temperature, is less obvious or is absent.

In Idaho, climate has important bearing on the distribution of birds and mammals, but, because the state comprises a relatively small area as compared with that of the North American continent as a whole, the precise effects of the individual components of climate are not readily perceived. Because the entire state lies in the North Temperate Zone, it lacks the contrast that would be present if it lay in more than one major temperature zone.

The most obvious biogeographical divisions of the state are the biotic areas outlined above. Each is thought to be delimited, not by any *one* climatic factor, but by the *interaction* of *all* elements constituting climate with the physiographic and biotic constituents of the area. Looked at in this way, climate *in its entirety* may be considered one of the principal factors responsible for a biotic area and consequently delimiting the distribution of those mammals in it which have become adapted to, and restricted by, conditions present there. To me, climate is not the *immediate* factor controlling the distribution of birds and mammals in Idaho. Rather, it is an *ultimate*, relatively less critical factor which combines with others, such as topography, altitude, geology, and soil, to influence the distribution of vegetation, which in turn influences to a greater or less degree the distribution of each kind of bird and mammal.

Each element constituting climate is thought not to affect a given area equally. Temperature may be the most critical in one instance, humidity in a second, direction of prevailing winds in a third; or, the effects of any two or more elements in combination may outweigh the effects of another element or combination of elements, and therefore be more critical in producing a given climatic set-up. In illustration, let us consider the distribution of plants and mammals in the small area comprising Mt. Harrison. This isolated mountain lies south of the Snake River in the vicinity of the town of Albion, where it rises steeply from the Snake River Valley (4300 feet) to a height of over 9000 feet. The prevailing winds are from the west; snowfall in winter averages four feet on the mountain itself and about two feet on the lower foothills. More snow falls on the western than on the eastern slope. Considering humidity in terms of annual precipitation, the higher parts of the western slope should favor a growth of coniferous forest, but none occurs there. A seemingly obvious explanation for its absence on that slope is that a higher average summer temperature, produced by that part of the mountain receiving nearly direct rays of the sun at the hottest part of the day, causes an early, rapid melting of the snow, and consequent rapid run-off. By mid-June, snow is practically absent from the west side of the mountain, whereas on the east side patches of it remain until mid-July. Winter winds, often at blizzard velocities, remove some of the heavy snowfall from the west side and transport it to the east side, where it may accumulate in sheltered places to a depth of 15 or 20 feet. In this instance, then, western exposure, high average summer temperature, and a prevailing westerly wind outweigh the combined effects of high altitude and greater annual snowfall in producing the climatic set-up on the western side of the mountain. Moreover, this climatic set-up is thought to be responsible for the lack of coniferous forests and the presence, instead, of sagebrush from the valley below to near the top.

The eastern side of the mountain is furrowed by two

deep canyons which lie in an almost east-west direction. In Howells Canyon, the northernmost of the two, conifers are restricted to the north-facing slope. The south-facing slope, exposed as it is to the nearly direct rays of the sun throughout a greater part of the year, is covered with sage-brush from the top to near the bottom of the canyon, where a stream supplies the conditions necessary for existence of conifers. The north-facing slope of the mountain, however, is devoid of coniferous trees except in the canyon in which Land Creek flows. Much of the slope is as high as the north-facing slope of Howells Canyon, and, because the two slopes are parallel and less than a mile apart, the total annual amount of heat and precipitation received on each would appear to be about the same. In seeking an explanation for the differences in vegetation on the two slopes, one finds that the north slope of the mountain is exposed to the full sweep of the high winter winds, whereas the north-facing slope of Howells Canyon is partly protected by the peak of the mountain. Thus the snow is removed from the exposed slope while the other retains at least its normal fall. Here, then, the effect of high winter winds has counteracted the combined effects of supposedly equal temperature and precipitation.

These circumstances are reflected in the distribution of the birds and mammals on the mountain. For example, *amoenus* chipmunks, porcupines, Cassin purple finches, pine siskins, ruby-crowned kinglets, and olive-backed thrushes are common on the north-facing slope of Howells Canyon and on the eastern side of the mountain in general wherever coniferous forests are found; seldom are they encountered in other areas. The *minimus* chipmunk, pygmy rabbit, gray-tailed and red-tailed ground squirrels, sage thrasher, green-tailed towhee, and Brewer sparrow are commonly seen in the sage-covered areas and seldom, or never, in the forest. Some species of both birds and mammals are less restricted and occur with nearly equal frequency in both areas. Stated differently, the ranges of those birds and mammals, on Mt. Harrison, which are restricted to a particular set of environmental conditions are not delimited by any *one* of several climatic factors, but rather by the biota as a whole, the nature of which is determined by slope exposure, altitude, substrate, and climate *in its entirety,* any one of which may predominate under certain circumstances.

In comparing the biota at Payette in the Great Basin biotic area with that at Sandpoint in the Northern Rocky Mountain biotic area, both of which places are near 2000 feet in elevation, marked differences in the component species are observed. Among the rodents there is no overlap in the ranges of subspecies, that is to say, no subspecies occurring at Payette is found at Sandpoint, and *vice versa.* Altitude may be ruled out as an explanation of the differences. Latitude doubtless has some effect because the two localities are slightly more than 4 degrees apart. Soil probably does not play an important part because at both localities it is of lacustrine origin. The most obvious explanation is that the climate of the two regions differs markedly. The hythergraphs (figs. 2, 3) show that the range of average monthly temperatures is less than 10 degrees F. greater at Payette than at Sandpoint; month by month, except in June, July, and August, it is nearly identical, but in those three months, especially in July, the hottest month of the year in each instance, the temperature at Payette averages nearly 9 degrees higher. The total annual precipitation at the two localities, however, is as 10:32; in July the precipitation at Sandpoint is equal to that received at Payette in the wettest months, January excepted. This situation suggests that at Sandpoint a higher humidity has greatly modified the effects of temperature, and that high humidity is largely responsible for the distinct biota of the northern part of the state.

Considering the state as a whole, we find that a sharp break in climatic conditions occurs where the central mountainous areas meet the Snake River Plains. It is along this line that an abrupt change in the mammalian fauna is found. Thirty-one geographic races whose affinities lie with those mammals occupying the Great Basin pass little, if at all, beyond this line. Another sharp break occurs along the east-west course of the Salmon River. Near here is the line of demarcation which separates the northern Rocky Mountain elements from those farther south. Thus, the three biotic areas are thought to be delimited by climatic conditions, and more especially by the interaction of the climatic factors (each of which is more or less modified by the others) with the physiographic features of the areas.

To summarize: Climate, in its entirety, interacting with the physical and biotic features of the area, is thought to be important in delimiting the distribution of mammals in Idaho. Because temperature appears to affect principally larger taxonomic units over large areas (usually larger than the entire state of Idaho; a temperate zone, for instance), its effect as an agent limiting the distribution of certain mammals *in Idaho* is usually not of an *immediate,* but rather of an *ultimate,* nature. In other words, temperature is thought to be less limiting, therefore less critical, in determining the presence or absence of certain mammals in Idaho; associational restriction, type of substrate, and relative humidity are thought to be *more* restricting, therefore *more critical,* in delimiting the ranges of the different kinds.

Snow and distribution.—In southern Idaho, as in most of the Great Basin proper also, snow seems to be an essential factor in determining the distribution of several kinds of mammals. It not only provides the necessary moisture in those places where the minimum essential amount is present for continuous existence of certain species, but it also serves as the highway, so to speak, for their dispersal. Pocket gophers do not hibernate (evidence the numerous earth cores found in spring when the snow melts) : they are active throughout the year. In those regions where snow accumulates on the ground to a sufficient depth, pocket gophers burrow through it. Because digging in snow is relatively easy, it is conceivable that pocket gophers, equipped as they are for continued fossorial labors, may travel considerable distances in this manner over areas that are impassable by them during the dry season, and do so in comparative safety. Food is available in winter in the form of green shoots enveloped in the snow.

In years of heavy snowfall, the maximum of essentials for life may be present in areas which, during another part of the year or climatic cycle, may be lacking even in minimum essentials, but which may, in times of plenty, act as "stepping stones" from one permanently habitable area to another some distance removed. An indication that such movements possibly do occur is the presence in summer of old mounds and earth cores in areas that are inhospitable to pocket gophers at that season. I found such evidence in May, 1934, in a barren waste area near Riddle, Owyhee County, approximately one and one-half miles from the nearest sign of activity (at Indian Creek) of this rodent at that time of year. Several traps set in burrows in the barren area yielded nothing, whereas traps set along Indian Creek caught three gophers. This circumstance suggests that in the previous winter when snow was deep, pocket gophers had occupied the area which was inhospitable to them in summer. If pocket gophers can travel the distance suggested by these observations, it is possible that even greater distances are traversed under optimum conditions. Of course, time is the essence of such progress.

This behavior on the part of pocket gophers leads to the question of the origin of colonies now isolated, often by several miles of inhospitable territory, from the nearest colony of like kind. Should each one be considered as a remnant of a once continuous population, or can their presence be explained otherwise? I am of the opinion that some of the now isolated colonies could have, and probably did, originate by migration through snow as suggested above. Others may have been isolated by changing geographic and climatic conditions, but since one cannot distinguish such colonies from those that have become established relatively recently by invasion of the area, perhaps both factors have been operative. The original stock may have been isolated by geographic and climatic changes, subsequent dispersal having taken place by migration through the snow.

This same principle perhaps may explain the presence of other nonhibernating kinds such as *Sorex, Microtus,* and *Lepus townsendii* in areas where they apparently are isolated by inhospitable territory surrounding them. In winter, *Microtus* are active and travel considerable distances through or under snow. Borell and Ellis (1934) record that in the Ruby Mountains, Nevada, these mice were restricted to the vicinity of water in summer. In winter, however, their burrows, under three feet of snow, led over areas which in summer were too dry and open to be occupied. In early spring, the population in a given area probably is widespread, but as the season advances and progressively drier conditions prevail, the wintering animals and the young of the year are forced to leave portions of the winter and early spring range and concentrate in the vicinity of water where green vegetation still is available. As the season progresses, the population pressure and resulting increased competition for food and shelter must be extremely great. Perhaps this circumstance gives impetus to spreading out as soon as snow is sufficiently deep to provide the necessary protective cover. Such movements would be greatest in regions where the summers are dry and hot and the winters cold and with heavy snowfall. In regions where green grass, in quantity, is available at all seasons, periodic contractions and expansions of range of *Microtus* would not result, at least from the same cause.

The map showing the distribution of *montanus* meadow mice in Nevada (Hall, 1935) reveals a highly discontinuous range. Some populations are so far removed geographically from their nearest neighbors of like kind that they must, with surety, be considered relics of a former, nearly continuous distribution. In Idaho, particularly in the Great Basin part, the distribution of this lowland species also is discontinuous, but in no instance of which I am aware can an isolated population be considered relict with surety. More likely, all such populations are affected directly by cyclic climatic oscillations; in favorable winters the entire population in the southern part of the state may be in more or less direct contact; at other times, when conditions are more adverse for meadow mice, territory formerly occupied may become uninhabitable. Marshes come and go in southern Idaho; meadow mice inhabiting them probably behave likewise. At any rate, differences among the various populations of *Microtus montanus* examined from southern Idaho are little, if any, greater than those found among individuals from a single locality. This homogeneous condition of the populations over wide areas suggests frequent interbreeding among the different, now isolated, populations. Snow of sufficient depth and duration would permit the necessary migrations for this to occur.

E. Raymond Hall tells me that he often has seen burrows of shrews in the snow in Kansas; and Jackson (1928), quoting Nelson, says that after snow falls *Sorex* travel from place to place by forcing a passage under the snow, and frequently keep so near the surface that a slight ridge is left to mark their passage. On the ice of the Yukon River in Alaska, Nelson traced a ridge of this kind more than a mile, and he was repeatedly surprised to see what a direct course the shrews could make for long distances under the surface of the snow. It is highly probable that in southern Idaho, and in the Great Basin in general, *Sorex* utilize this method of traveling from one isolated region, across territory which might be inhospitable in summer, to reach another habitable region some distance away. At least, this hypothesis explains the occurrence of shrews in certain, apparently inaccessible, areas.

To the white-tailed jack rabbit, a boreal species in the Great Basin area, snow, of course, is not a medium through which to travel. Rather, the presence of snow probably removes a limiting factor, possibly temperature or aridity, or both, enabling the animals to descend from one isolated mountain mass, cross a valley which in summer is inhospitable, and reach another boreal region some distance away. In southern Idaho, this species is restricted to the mountains in summer, but in winter it descends to the valleys. As spring approaches and the upward migration begins, some individuals which descended from a given mountain and survived the winter may not return whence they came. Also these creatures are more or less nomadic in habit and, as far as I have been able to determine, never establish permanent "home territories." Opportunity thus provided for cross-breeding may explain the homogeneity of the white-tailed jack rabbit population throughout the Great Basin.

To summarize: An essential factor in the distribution of nonhibernating mammals that are dependent upon any combination of cover, humidity, and relatively low temperature for existence in semiarid regions may be snow of sufficient depth, plus the element of time, to permit movement from one habitable area across an intervening inhospitable region to another habitable area some distance removed.

Associational areas and distribution.—Saunders (1921) considers associations (or habitats) the most fundamental of distributional units. Certainly, this concept is basic in explaining the distribution of most mammals in Idaho. These units vary according to the nature of the biotic area or areas in which they are included. Certain kinds of mammals are not restricted by circumstances limiting a single association, but rather are so constituted that they are able to succeed well in two or more. The species *Peromyscus maniculatus*, for example, occurs in nearly all the associational areas in the state. I, personally, have taken them in marsh, meadow (both valley and alpine), prairie, chaparral, deciduous woods, coniferous forests (here usually at or near the periphery), and rocky outcroppings; *Microtus mordax* occurs in marsh, meadow (usually alpine), chaparral, and deciduous woods associations. The Wandering Shrew, likewise, is not sharply delimited by any one particular association. These, and other, exceptions do not invalidate the general principal stated above; they merely show that it does not apply in all instances. Most kinds, particularly of rodents, are restricted to one association. On the peripheries of any associational area, a certain amount of "spilling over" is to be expected because (1) two adjacent associations are seldom sharply defined, and (2) the population pressure exerted on the occupants of an association usually is sufficient to induce "exploration" for additional suitable territory. Spilling over, as determined by catches in traps, is particularly noticeable after the young of the year have swollen the numbers of a population.

Examination of any associational area reveals that two major constituents are concerned: (1) organic, and (2) inorganic, each present and exerting its influence on the mammals there in varying degrees, depending on the nature of the association in question. Each constituent plays some part in determining whether or not a given kind of mammal can succeed. Grinnell (1914), in discussing the "associational restrictions" of animals along the lower Colorado River, considers that the following three elements of the habitat are of most importance in the order named, varying, of course, with the inherent nature of the animal concerned: (1) Kind of food supply afforded, (2) presence of safe breeding places, and (3) presence of places of temporary refuge.

Each of the above-named elements *must* be present in the area inhabited in quantity, or to a degree, sufficient to permit any given kind of animal to succeed, but the *relative importance of each* depends ultimately upon the animal under consideration. From observations in southern Idaho, and elsewhere, I am led to believe that the kind of food acceptable to each of many kinds of mammals does not, except within wide limits, constitute *the* major limiting factor under normal conditions. The degree to which the kind of food is important in distribution (as distinct from mere existence) depends upon several conditions: (1) the inherent nature of the animal itself, (2) climatic conditions at the time the animal is being studied, (3) the ease of availability of food to the animal, that is, the *distance* between the refuge den and the food supply, and (4) the amount of food available.

Over 50 per cent of the kinds of mammals in Idaho, and a far greater percentage of the individuals, are rodents. These, bridging the gap in the food chain from the vegetation on which they feed to the predators, have relatively poor powers of defense and rely either upon running or upon the nearness of refuges for protection. A partial degree of racial safety is provided by their higher reproductive ratio as compared with kinds better equipped for self-preservation, but, even so, *individual protection* must be provided for in order that racial safety may be maintained.

By way of illustration, the marmot (*Marmota flaviventer*), widely distributed in southern Idaho, may be cited. In elevation, it ranges from 2000 feet along the western course of the Snake River to over 8000 feet in the mountains. This circumstance places it in association with alpine food plants at one altitudinal extreme of its range, and with xerophytic kinds at the other. Such a distribution cannot be explained on the basis of the distribution of certain food plants, nor upon a given set of climatic conditions. Instead, the presence or absence of suitable rocky refuge sites is thought to be most important. Of course, food, in the nature of green herbs, must be present, but where food of a kind acceptable to them is present and rock piles or outcroppings are absent, no marmots occur. In this particular instance, and in others which are cited below, the order of importance of the three elements of habitat is precisely the reverse of that given by Grinnell (*ibid.*). It might be said that the distribution of marmots in Idaho is more closely correlated with the *inorganic* than with the organic elements consti- tuting habitat.

The distribution of *Microtus* in Idaho is another case in point. We might set up the question: Is the presence of *Microtus* in a given area correlated primarily with the presence of suitable food plants, or is it determined pri- marily by the presence of suitable *vegetational cover* in which the animals can enjoy a relative degree of safety? Trapping records and observation show that their presence or absence in a given area has a high positive correlation with the presence or absence of suitable cover. Where food in the form of green grass is present, but not of sufficient height to afford protection, *Microtus* usually are absent. Food, again, seems to be of secondary importance, but, un- like the marmot, with these rodents the organic, rather than the inorganic, constituent of the associational area is more important.

Furthermore, with certain of the ground squirrels, *Citellus columbianus* for instance, the presence or absence of meadow land in which they can burrow and seek food in the near vicinity of their refuges apparently is a more critical factor in their distribution than the mere presence of food. Kangaroo rats occur most abundantly in Idaho in areas where the soil is sandy or, if otherwise, easily worked even though the same types of food plants may be present in as great, or even greater, quantity in an adjacent area where soil conditions are adverse. Pygmy rabbits occur most commonly in areas where sagebrush or other xero- phytic shrubs are present in sufficient numbers and size to offer adequate protection; the kind of food available seems not to be as critical in determining their distribution as is the kind of *cover*.

On the other hand, certain kinds of mammals seem to be limited in distribution by the presence of particular food plants. Beavers, for instance, appear to be limited to areas in Idaho where willows, cottonwoods, or quaking aspen occur. Red squirrels probably are restricted to coniferous forests chiefly because the nuts of these trees constitute the most important item of their diet.

The above examples illustrate, I think, that the element of the habitat which is *most* critical for the existence of any animal depends upon the inherent nature of that animal and its ability for, and method of, self-preservation. In other words, some kinds are limited chiefly by the presence or absence of adequate cover, others by the presence or absence of certain kinds of food, and a third class, particularly among birds, by the presence or absence of suitable sites in which to rear the young. The examples illustrate, also, that certain kinds of mammals whose most important limiting factor seems to be adequate cover depend primarily upon vegetation (biotic, or organic factors); others rely chiefly upon the substrate (inorganic, or edaphic factors).

The following tabulation indicates certain species of mammals which, in their respective habitats, are thought to be limited predominantly by the kind of factor under which each is listed.

EDAPHIC FACTORS	BIOTIC FACTORS (other than animal life)
Marmota flaviventer	*Citellus armatus*
Eutamias dorsalis	*Citellus columbianus*
Thomomys talpoides	*Citellus beldingi*
Thomomys quadratus	*Eutamias minimus*
Thomomys townsendii	*Tamiasciurus hudsonicus*
Perognathus parvus	*Glaucomys sabrinus*
Dipodomys ordii	*Reithrodontomys megalotis*
Dipidomys microps	*Phenacomys intermedius*
Onychomys leucogaster	*Clethrionomys gapperi*
Peromyscus crinitus	*Microtus montanus*
Neotoma lepida	*Microtus mordax*
Neotoma cinerea	*Microtus richardsoni*
Ochotona princeps	*Zapus princeps*

Further analysis of the biotic component of habitat or association reveals that competition among the species therein affects distribution. This is especially true when two species compete for a common food supply. Gause (1937), by experimental methods, has demonstrated the truth of two important principles of distribution, namely, (1) that two species or races occupying *identical* ecologic niches cannot occur in the same habitat area, and (2) that two species or races occupying *different* ecologic niches in a habitat may live together there indefinitely in essentially stable equilibrium when each occupies the niche where it is more efficient. Although his experimental animals were microscopic, he gives assurance that what has long been accepted to be true by deduction, has been proved true, in the animals he used, by experiment and mathematical analysis.

Perhaps ground squirrels in southern Idaho are subjects of an experiment in nature which will test the first of these two principles as well as did Gause's experiment with micro-organisms. Ecologically, I have been unable to detect appreciable differences between *Citellus armatus* and *Citellus beldingi oregonus* where I have observed them in close proximity to one another. Both are restricted largely to the vicinity of water where green vegetation is available until midsummer or later. Each occurs in the mountain valleys and near the tops of the mountains; likewise, both are successful in the valleys at lower elevations. Food acceptable to each is identical as far as I can tell from observation; neither is very tolerant of dry conditions, but both exist, in relatively small numbers, amid sagebrush in nearly typical desert areas. Seemingly, the two species are nearly identical in habits and habitat preference.

The map (fig. 8) shows that these two species in Idaho occupy complementary portions of the southern part of the state and that their ranges meet in the vicinity of Mt. Harrison. There both frequently occur in the same fields. The range of *armatus* does not extend west of Mt. Harrison, that of *oregonus* terminates in the Raft River Valley a few miles to the east so that the overlap, or perhaps better stated interdigitation, of the ranges of the two is about 20 miles in extent. To the east of Raft River Valley *armatus* alone is found, while only *oregonus* occurs to the west of Mt. Harrison. The environment for at least 50 miles to the east and west of Mt. Harrison is surprisingly uniform.

Study of their distribution in the twenty-mile zone of overlap shows that although the two species occur in the same fields *they occur in different parts of them*. There is little, if any, overlap in the territories of adjacent colonies of the two species, and interbreeding between them is extremely rare. Whether one of the species will ultimately replace the other remains to be seen. Mr. T. B. Murray, who has charge of rodent control work in Idaho, has gained the impression that in the past 18 years *oregonus* has been moving slowly, but steadily, eastward. If this be true, *oregonus* may eventually supplant *armatus* in southern Idaho.

The present discontinuous distribution of *Citellus elegans* suggests that in the past it occupied a nearly continuous range, including much of northern Nevada, southern Idaho, and southwestern Wyoming, and that much of its former range has been usurped by the ecologically similar, if not identical, invaders, *armatus* and *oregonus*. Where I have found *elegans* in close proximity to either of the other two, I have been unable to detect appreciable ecological differences. Moreover, the present distribution of both *armatus* and *oregonus,* as I shall discuss in more detail later, convincingly demonstrates that these two species are recent immigrants to southern Idaho, whereas *elegans* seems to be relict. Perhaps we have here an illustration in nature of the last stages in the replacement of one species by an ecologically similar, but better adapted, species. From the above, we may conclude that ecologically similar species tend to complement each other in range. I know of no instance where the ranges of two species of pocket gopher or of big-eared ground squirrel are coincident, or nearly so; invariably, they are complementary.

Several species in Idaho illustrate the second principle, namely, that ecologically dissimilar species can successfully occupy the same habitat area. One need only examine any association to see this principle illustrated. In the meadow along Cassia Creek near Elba, pocket gophers, big-eared

ground squirrels, meadow mice, and cottontails live in more
or less stable equilibrium because each one is well adapted
to a particular part of the habitat, that is, to a particular
ecologic niche. Meadow mice inhabit the more marshy areas
where the others, burrowing animals except possibly the
cottontail, are excluded because of the presence of surface
water or a very high water table which prevents burrowing; pocket gophers burrow in the semi-moist places;
ground squirrels occupy the higher, and therefore drier,
parts of the meadow; cottontails are found most commonly
near the willow thickets along the creek.

The Snake River and distribution.—As previously stated,
the Snake River flows from east to west in southern Idaho
and transects the Great Basin region of the state into northern and southern parts. Except for more extensive volcanism in the northern portion, the two sections are nearly
identical in altitude, climate, vegetation, and composition
of the soil. The river, from a point near American Falls
west to Oregon, averages 600 feet in width and seldom
freezes completely over in winter except at the few places
where the water is comparatively quiet. At an earlier time,
much of the Snake River Valley was occupied by a vast
lake, and we are fairly certain that for thousands of years
either the river or the now vanished lakes, or the two in
combination, extended completely across southern Idaho in
an east-west direction. Furthermore, the river is not of the
meandering type with constantly shifting channels; shifts
that have occurred in the river bed involve a gradual movement toward the south. This shift is thought to have been
effected in part by the greater volcanic activity north of
the river, a circumstance which probably accounts for its
now crescentic outline.

Aside from Grinnell's (1914) and Goldman's (1937 b)
work on the Colorado River, no one, so far as I am aware,
has attempted to analyze the effects of a large river on the
distribution of mammals in America. I have had this problem in mind throughout the course of my study and have
collected at localities on opposite sides of the river with
the purpose of finding out if the mammals on the two sides
were alike or different; in other words, to discover what

effect the river has as a barrier to geographic movements of mammals. Briefly stated, I have found that hibernating, land-dwelling mammals which are closely restricted to a definite home territory and do not ordinarily swim are different on the two sides of the river; also, that burrowing kinds usually are different on the two sides. On the other hand, nonburrowing, nonhibernating kinds, in every instance of which I am aware, are the same on the two sides. In other words, the Snake River is a physical barrier to the geographic movements of only certain kinds of mammals; for others it seems not to be a barrier, or at any rate its effect is not apparent.

The most striking example of the river's action in restricting the geographic movements of mammals is afforded by the big-eared ground squirrels *Citellus armatus* and *Citellus beldingi oregonus*. The map (fig. 8) showing the distribution of these two species in Idaho reveals that *oregonus* is restricted to the south side of the river from near Albion west to Oregon; I know of no individual of this species which has crossed, unaided by man, to the north side. In seeking for an explanation of this distribution, we find that throughout the extent of the range of *oregonus* in Idaho the Snake River averages 600 feet in width; moreover, where it is narrow, the banks are precipitous and consist of basalt on which no ground squirrels occur. That the factor which limits the northward distribution of *oregonus* in Idaho is the *width* of the river and not interspecific competition, which might prevent *oregonus* from gaining a foothold on the north side, is evidenced by the fact that no ecologic counterpart of *oregonus* occurs on the north side where territory apparently suited to its needs is available.

The distribution of *armatus* gives even more convincing evidence that the *width* of the river is of prime importance in restricting the movements of these squirrels. From Albion northeastward to near Idaho Falls, the Snake River is as wide, or nearly so, as it is farther west in the range of *oregonus*. Between these two localities, *armatus* occurs *only on the southeast side of the river*. Above Idaho Falls, however, where the river divides into numerous smaller tributaries (50 to 100 feet in width), *armatus* occurs on

both sides of the streams, and, circumventing the Lost
River Desert, its range extends westward to the Big Lost
River and Pahsimeroi valleys and northward into Montana.

The distribution of *mollis* ground squirrels, likewise, is
influenced by the presence and relative width of the Snake
River. In western Idaho where the river constitutes the
boundary between Idaho and Oregon, the ground squirrels
(*C. m. idahoensis*) are markedly different from those (*C.
m. vigilis*) occurring on the Oregon side of the river. Here,
only the river separates populations of the two races, and
there is little, if any, crossing from one side of the river
to the other. In the upper end of the Snake River Valley,
from Idaho Falls to Blackfoot, however, crossing of the
river where it is broken up into a number of smaller tributaries is evidenced by intergradation between *C. m. mollis*
and *C. m. artemesiae.* Here we are dealing with a U-shaped
chain of intergrading races of a single species. The open
part of the U is in the western end of the valley where the
races are markedly different on the two sides of the river;
the closed part is near the upper end of the valley where
intergradation indicates that crossing of the river has been,
and probably is being, accomplished.

The distribution of other ground squirrels contributes
evidence which supports the hypothesis that the Snake
River, where it is of relatively great width, impedes the
geographic movements of ground squirrels. In the region
where the river flows through the Seven Devils Canyon and
constitutes the boundary between Idaho and Oregon, we
find *Citellus columbianus ruficaudus* on the Oregon side of
the river, whereas *Citellus columbianus columbianus* occurs
on the Idaho side. Also, in this same region, *Citellus brunneus* occurs on the Idaho side of the river; as far as I am
aware, no closely related species or race occurs on the
Oregon side.

In searching for an explanation of why the relative
width of the Snake River should affect the distribution of
ground squirrels and not that of certain other kinds of
mammals, *Peromyscus maniculatus* or *Microtus montanus*
for example, several possible reasons come to mind. In the
first place, ground squirrels hibernate. In winter at the

times when the river is frozen over and would permit ground squirrels to cross from one side to the other over the ice, as it does permit other mammals to do, the ground squirrels are hibernating underground. They do not emerge in spring much, if any, earlier than the time when the ice breaks up. In spring and early summer when the squirrels are most active, open water, at flood stage for part of the time, prevents crossing. In autumn when the river is low and might permit mammals to cross where sand bars are exposed, or to swim the then much narrower channel, the squirrels again are hibernating. Thus, when conditions of the river are favorable for crossing, the squirrels are dormant; when the squirrels are active and when population pressure is highest, the condition of the river prevents them from crossing.

In the second place, ground squirrels ordinarily do not swim, even though they can do so with apparent ease, as I learned from experiments made to test their swimming abilities. Nevertheless, two hundred yards is a long distance for any terrestrial mammal to swim in swiftly, or even moderately, flowing water; even some of the strong swimmers hesitate to cross such wide streams. This circumstance alone would tend to prevent crossing where the river is wide. Toward the headwaters where the streams are only 50 to 100 feet in width, the squirrels probably cross by swimming, or on natural bridges, fallen trees, artificial or natural dams, which, for the most part, are lacking farther west. I have found no evidence that man-made bridges across the river have (as yet) aided ground squirrels to cross from one side to the other.

Furthermore, ground squirrels are colonial and pretty much restricted to a definite, relatively small, home range. Nomadic tendencies appear to be lacking, except, perhaps, in young of the year which seek out places in which to become newly established. This circumstance influences the behavior pattern of the animals, for one instinctive reaction in time of danger is to seek out the home burrow.

Some squirrels, marmots for instance, are the same on the two sides of the river in spite of the fact that they hibernate. They differ from ground squirrels, however, in that they *do not hesitate to enter water.* Hamilton (1934) and others have pointed out their ability to swim; also, that they enter water voluntarily. Near Hagerman, Idaho, I found individuals on a small rocky island in the river which they could have reached unaided only by swimming, because at that place the river does not freeze over nor does it recede sufficiently in summer to allow them to cross the channel on a relatively dry substrate. In addition, they inhabit rock piles and rocky canyons, and where the river is narrowest west of Idaho Falls it flows through basalt-walled canyons. Here it may be no wider than 50 feet. This circumstance, combined with their swimming ability, probably permits them to cross the river in certain places with relative ease.

Additional evidence that the Snake River, where it is relatively wide, restricts the geographic movements of certain kinds of mammals is found in the distribution of pocket gophers in southern Idaho. The maps (figs. 18 and 19) graphically illustrate that where the river is wide a given race of pocket gopher (*T. t. townsendii* excepted) does not occur on both sides of the river. *Thomomys quadratus* is restricted wholly to the south side of the Snake River from near Blackfoot westward to Oregon; another species, *Thomomys talpoides*, occurs southward to the river, but has not crossed. I know of no instance where either species has crossed to the opposite side of the river. Bailey (1936) records *Thomomys fuscus fuscus*, the race herein referred to as *Thomomys talpoides fuscus*, from the Oregon side of the Snake River, but specimens that I have examined from Oregon near the localities whence Bailey's specimens came are definitely *quadratus*, the species I should expect to occur there. Toward the upper part of the Snake River Valley where the streams are much smaller than the main river, both *talpoides* and *quadratus* occur on *both sides of the streams.*

In the region where pocket gophers do not cross, the river averages 600 feet in width, snowfall usually is light, and the river seldom freezes over completely except in certain places where the water is relatively quiet. Toward the headwaters, however, the streams are smaller (50 to 100 feet in width), the winters are severe, and snow may accumulate to a depth of 4 feet or more and remain on the ground for several months; here crossing does occur, as indicated by the presence of each species on both sides of the river. In one region circumstances prevent pocket gophers, which are active throughout the year, from crossing the river, while in the other, conditions favor movements back and forth across the streams. It will be recalled that pocket gophers burrow readily through snow and, at least theoretically, are able to travel some distance in this manner. We might say, then, that in regions where winters are severe and snowfall is heavy, rivers do not permanently restrict the geographic movements of pocket gophers, whereas in regions where winters are relatively mild and snowfall is light, a large river permanently restricts their geographic movements.

As I have pointed out below in the general account of the Family Geomyidae, *Thomomys townsendii* likewise is limited in its geographic movements by the Snake River, particularly in regions where it is wide. This is not evident on the distributional map, however.

Thus, the Snake River affects the distribution of ground squirrels and pocket gophers *in exactly the same way.* Where the river is wide (600 feet), neither has been able to cross from one side of the river to the other; toward the headwaters, however, where the streams are smaller (50 to 100 feet), crossing appears to have been accomplished with little if any difficulty.

The distribution of each of the following kinds of mammals in southern Idaho is thought to be limited by the Snake River in that portion where it averages 600 feet in width.

LIMITED ON THE SOUTH (Occurs north of the river)	LIMITED ON THE NORTH (Occurs south of the river)
Citellus columbianus columbianus	*Citellus beldingi oregonus*
Citellus brunneus	*Citellus armatus*
Citellus mollis idahoensis	*Citellus mollis vigilis*
Citellus mollis artemesiae	*Citellus mollis mollis*
Eutamias minimus pictus	*Ammospermophilus leucurus leucurus*
Thomomys talpoides fuscus	*Eutamias minimus scrutator*
Thomomys townsendii townsendii	*Thomomys quadratus quadratus*
	Thomomys quadratus bridgeri
	Thomomys townsendii owyhensis

In each instance where the range of a species or geographic race listed above includes also territory along the headwaters, the river there has little, if any, apparent effect as a barrier to its geographic movements. That is, the *same kinds* of mammals *occur on both sides* of the smaller streams, whereas farther west, where the river is wide, *different kinds* occur on the two sides.

Mammals to which the river does not act as a barrier are active the year round, typically nonfossorial, and, in some instances, strong swimmers. Movement from one side to the other is thought to occur largely in winter when the river may be frozen over in places. That *ice*, of sufficient thickness and duration, completely bridging the river is essential for such movements to occur is evidenced by the distribution of *Dipodomys ordii columbianus* in Idaho as compared with that farther west where the Columbia River constitutes the boundary between Oregon and Washington.

Kangaroo rats lack completely the ability to swim (Grinnell, 1922) and, hence, must cross the river by some other means. In southern Idaho where the river freezes over more often than does the Columbia River near Wallula, Washington, kangaroo rats occur on both sides of the Snake River. Moreover, no appreciable differences could be detected in specimens from the two sides, a circumstance suggesting frequent crossing of the river and intermingling of populations. However, along the Columbia River, kangaroo rats are known to occur only on the south side. Since the Columbia River seldom, if ever, freezes completely over in the region where kangaroo rats occur along its south bank, their complete absence in Washington north of the river leads to the conclusion that lack of ice in winter has prevented them from crossing.

Many kinds of mammals probably swim across the river. Coyotes, jack rabbits, meadow mice, marmots, and shrews take to water readily and perhaps could swim across the river, especially in autumn when it is low. Each of the above-named kinds, marmots excepted, is active in winter and could then cross on the ice. I have found tracks of rabbits and coyotes in the snow where these animals had crossed the river on the ice. Cottontails are found in winter on many of the islands in the river when ice permits them to cross from the mainland. They do not become established permanently there, however, because at flood stage the islands usually are inundated.

A second way in which the Snake River affects the distribution of animals is by serving as a "highway of dispersal" for certain aquatic and semiaquatic species. Beaver, muskrat, mink, and otter, among mammals, and white pelican, California and ring-billed gulls, double-crested cormorant, and ducks of many kinds, among birds, find here an environment which permits them to penetrate an otherwise nearly desert area.

Racial history and distribution.—If we assume nature to be ever changing, it is pertinent to recall that, of the 141 kinds of mammals occurring in Idaho, many are widespread, whereas others are more or less limited to definite biotic or associational areas, and that the geographic movements of some kinds are definitely stopped by the Snake River although those of others are not. These circumstances, considered along with what is known of the present distribution of these same kinds *outside* the bounds of Idaho, and the fossil record taken into account, give basis for judging of migrational trends.

The fossil record reveals that certain kinds of mammals, present in Idaho in the Pleistocene, today are extinct, while others now occur only in places outside the state. In the Pliocene and Pleistocene a shrew, *Blarina* (see Gazin, 1933 b), a fox, *Urocyon* ? (see Gazin, 1935), and a lemming mouse, *Synaptomys* (see Wilson, 1933), occurred in Idaho, whereas *Blarina* now occurs only east of the Rocky Mountains, *Urocyon* in a more southern region, and *Synaptomys* to the north of Idaho. Among other kinds that formerly lived in Idaho but now extinct or found in North America only as introduced by man, are the ground sloth, saber-toothed tiger, elephant, and camel.

Because of the incompleteness of the fossil record, comparison of a list of the mammals known at any one time in the past with a list of those now living indicates only a few of the changes that have occurred. Some of these changes reflect the effect of time, whereas others are concerned with space, in the sense of geographical shifts over land areas. The insight thus afforded us into the history of the Recent fauna suffices at least to show that it consists of (1) kinds which have *migrated* in, or are migrating in, from outside regions, and (2) a certain core that has been there at least since the Pleistocene or, perhaps, earlier.

The pocket gophers probably belong in the latter category. Fossil animals from deposits at Hagerman (Upper Pliocene or Lower Pleistocene) closely resemble the present-day *Thomomys quadratus* in size and tooth structure (see Wilson, 1933). The deposits in which the remains were found are on the *south* side of the Snake River in an area where the only pocket gopher living today is *quadratus*. If the late geological history of the region and present distributional tendencies on the part of pocket gophers have been interpreted correctly, these pocket gophers must have occupied a range *only* on the south side of the Snake River and Pleistocene Lake Idaho precisely as *quadratus* does today. Of course, the lake no longer exists, but the river does. Perhaps this Pliocene or Pleistocene pocket gopher, *Thomomys gidleyi*, gave rise directly to *T. quadratus*, for the changes required for it to have done so are slight. If so, the evidence is that *Thomomys quadratus* is an old, long-established resident of southern Idaho south of the Snake River.

Near American Falls, fossil remains of a large pocket gopher, referred to *Thomomys townsendii* (see Gazin, 1935), have been found in gravels which are thought to have been deposited at a time later than were the beds near Hagerman. I have not examined these remains, but I judge they will be found to be close to the race, *T. t. similis*, living in that area today. The colony of *similis* today is completely isolated and fully 150 miles removed from the nearest population of Townsend pocket gophers. We know from our study of present-day pocket gophers that two kinds do not occur in the same area; they complement one another in geographic range, and I infer that the same territorial relationship existed between different species of pocket gophers in Pliocene and Pleistocene times. If so, and if the *quadratus-gidleyi* stock continuously occupied the territory on the south side of the Snake River *between* the ranges of *T. t. similis* near Pocatello and *T. t. owyhensis* in Owyhee County, it may be inferred that the ancestors of *similis* reached the region near Pocatello by migrating along a route other than along the Snake River. This seems probable because the lava fields north of the Snake River (in existence since the Miocene) are absolute barriers to pocket gophers of all kinds. As pointed out in the species account of *similis,* the most logical course seems to have been from the *south* by way of the western and northern shores of Pleistocene Lake Bonneville and its outlet, Red Rock Pass, to the Snake River. Thus, we consider *T. t. similis* to be an old resident of Idaho, although it may not have been established there for as long as has *T. quadratus* and its predecessor, *T. gidleyi.*

The present distribution and differentiation of the ground squirrel, *Citellus mollis,* in Idaho strongly suggest a long-time residence for it too (for details, see accounts of the subspecies of *mollis*). Its present distribution outside Idaho, particularly the presence of an isolated race *north* and *west* of the Columbia River in Washington, supports this view. In fact, the species probably has been resident in much of the area it now occupies since at least early Pleistocene.

The peculiar, highly discontinuous distribution of another ground squirrel, *Citellus elegans,* combined with its differentiation into three geographic races, and considered in the light of what we know about the present distribution of *Citellus armatus* and *Citellus beldingi oregonus* in Idaho, suggests a long-continued occupancy of parts of Idaho. Moreover, the suggestion is that *elegans* has had to give way before the ecologically similar, but perhaps more aggressive and better adapted, *armatus* and *oregonus. Ochotona princeps,* the pika or cony, likewise occupies a highly discontinuous range, and it, too, seems to be a long-established resident of Idaho.

Turning now to kinds of mammals that are late immigrants, a third kind of ground squirrel, *Citellus beldingi oregonus,* is worthy of consideration. In Idaho it lives entirely south of the Snake River from Raft River Valley westward to Oregon. It is unknown from the north side of the river where territory suited to its needs is unoccupied by an ecologically similar kind. This fact and the manner in which its range meets that of its ecologic counterpart, *Citellus armatus,* south of the Snake River near Albion, suggest that *oregonus* is a migrant, from the southwest, which has moved in recently and found the river impassable. Otherwise, it probably would occupy a range on both sides of the river as do *Citellus mollis* and *Citellus elegans.* Likewise, *Citellus armatus,* as judged from its present distribution alone, seems to have moved into Idaho from the southeast, or, perhaps, the east, and it, also, has found the Snake River a barrier except toward the headwaters.

The present distribution of the kangaroo rat, *Dipodomys ordii,* particularly along the Columbia River where it constitutes the boundary between Oregon and Washington, suggests that it is of southern origin. It has not been found on the north side in this area where the river seldom, or never, freezes over, although *Citellus mollis,* which is definitely limited by a river the size of the Columbia, occurs on both sides. This suggests that the kangaroo rat migrated in from the south and reached Idaho and Oregon *after* the ground squirrel had crossed the relatively dry river channel, possibly when the river was blocked farther upstream in northeastern Washington by ice sometime in the Pleistocene.

Likewise, the present distribution of *Neotoma lepida, Peromyscus crinitus, Onychomys leucogaster, Reithrodontomys megalotis, Ammospermophilus leucurus,* and other rodents, particularly in regions outside the state, suggests southern origin and a relatively late migration into Idaho.

Other species appear to have been derived from the north in relatively recent time. One of these, a vole, *Phenacomys intermedius,* is restricted now to boreal situations. It occurs in the mountainous parts of Idaho and elsewhere, but it is unknown from the mountainous parts of southern Idaho and from the entire Great Basin, despite special search made for it in the two last-mentioned areas. This negative evidence, to me, strongly supports the view that it did not occur in the Rocky Mountains in the Pleistocene, because had it been there then, and especially as a lowland form which later retreated to a boreal environment, as Howell (1926) suggests, relict colonies would be expected today on the higher mountains in the Great Basin. A probable explanation for its absence today from southern Idaho and the Great Basin proper is that it migrated from the east into the area it now occupies in Idaho and adjoining states *after* desert conditions came into existence and isolated the higher mountains farther south where it could live were it able to reach them.

The red-backed vole, *Clethrionomys gapperi*, in Idaho and in adjoining states occurs under much the same sort of conditions. The genus is absent from southern Idaho west of the Bannock Mountains and from all the mountains in the Great Basin. This distribution bespeaks a recent migration from the north and east into Idaho after the Pleistocene, because the species occurring in Idaho today, *gapperi*, is known from Pleistocene cave deposits in Pennsylvania, a situation which attests its presence in North America before, or in, the Ice Age.

These examples illustrate the principle that the mammalian fauna of Idaho has been, and probably still is, changing. We might summarize as follows: The present distribution of mammals in Idaho reflects the past geographic movements of the individual kinds. Some kinds living there today are old residents; others have moved in only recently, some from the south, some from the north, and all now are in process of adjustment. Some kinds, *Citellus elegans* for instance, have had to give way in part before incoming migrants; others (*Synaptomys* and *Blarina*) are entirely gone from the state.

MUSEUMS CONTAINING TYPE SPECIMENS
FROM IDAHO

Academy of Natural Sciences of Philadelphia, Pa. 2
Museum of Comparative Zoology, Cambridge, Mass. 1
Museum of Vertebrate Zoology, Berkeley, Calif. 8
Museum of Zoology, University of Michigan, Ann
    Arbor, Mich. 1
Ralph Ellis collection, Berkeley, Calif. 1
United States National Museum, Washington, D. C. 29
Unknown 1

TYPE LOCALITIES IN IDAHO

In all, 43 specific and subspecific names are known to have been based on Idaho-taken mammals. For each of these, there is given below, first the name used in the original description accompanied by the name of the author and, second, the citation to the date and place of publication. The name in current use, where different from that given in the original description, is given in square brackets. Within each genus the species and geographic races are listed in the chronological order of their description.

Under *Type* there is given the sex, approximate age, and nature of the specimen (skin, skull, or both) ; its catalog number; the name of the collection in which deposited; locality where taken; date taken and name of the collector together with his original field number. Then follows, under *Remarks,* reasons for restatement of the type locality when the one given differs from that previously published.

Sorex dobsoni Merriam, N. Amer. Fauna, no. 5, p. 33. July 30, 1891. [*Sorex vagrans monticola* Merriam.]

Type.—Female, adult, skin and skull; no. 24274/31678, U. S. National Museum (Biological Survey collection) ; Alturas Lake, 7200 feet, Sawtooth Mountains, Blaine County; collected October 3, 1890, by C. Hart Merriam and Vernon Bailey, original no. 1929.

Remarks.—In the original description, the type locality is given as "Sawtooth or Alturas Lake, Sawtooth Mountains, Idaho." Alturas Lake is the name applied to this lake on the 1928 ed. of the U. S. Geologic map of Idaho. This same change, that is, substituting Alturas Lake for Sawtooth Lake, is made in the restatement of the type locality for each of the species and races described from that locality.

Sorex idahoensis Merriam, N. Amer. Fauna, no. 5, p. 32. July 30, 1891. [*Sorex cinereus cinereus* Kerr.]

Type.—Female, adult, skin and skull; no. 23527/30945, U. S. National Museum (Biological Survey collection); Timber Creek, 8200 feet, Lemhi Mountains, Lemhi County; collected August 26, 1890, by C. Hart Merriam and Vernon Bailey, original no. 1674.

Remarks.—Merriam (1891:5) applied the name "Salmon River Mountains" to that range separating the Lemhi and Pahsimeroi valleys. These mountains now are known as the Lemhi Mountains, and the name Salmon River Mountains has been restricted to that range northwest of, and parallel to, the Salmon River, between Middle Fork and Salmon River proper. The Timber Creek is tributary to the Lemhi River, joining that stream near the present town of Junction, Lemhi County. The location of the collecting station where the above type specimen was taken is approximately 13 miles south of Junction. The type specimen of the following species was collected at that station also.

Sorex vagrans similis Merriam, N. Amer. Fauna, no. 5, p. 34. July 30, 1891. [*Sorex obscurus obscurus* Merriam. Renamed by Merriam, December 31, 1895.]

Type.—Female, adult, skin and skull; no. 23525/30943, U. S. National Museum (Biological Survey collection); Timber Creek, 8200 feet, Lemhi Mountains, Lemhi County; collected August 26, 1890, by Basil Hicks Dutcher, original no. 1670.

Remarks.—See under *Sorex idahoensis*.

Ursus idahoensis Merriam, N. Amer. Fauna, no. 41, p. 54. February 9, 1918.

Type.—Male, adult, skull only ?; no. 187,888, U. S. National Museum; North Fork of Teton River, possibly in Fremont County; collected September 23, 1874, by Richard Leigh.

Remarks.—The exact type locality is not known. The specimen might have come from the south side of the river, in which event the type locality would be in Madison County or Teton County.

Arctomys columbianus Ord, Guthrie's Geography, 2nd Amer. ed., vol. 2, pp. 292, 303. 1815. Based on the "Burrowing Squirrel" of Lewis and Clark. [*Citellus columbianus columbianus* (Ord).]

Type.—No type specimen was designated; Ord's description was based upon an earlier one by Lewis and Clark who collected and preserved specimens of this squirrel. None of their specimens is known to be in existence today.

Type Locality.—Camas prairie about two miles north of Kamiah, in Idaho County, 1921 feet elevation.

Remarks.—The original description by Ord was based on the account of the "Burrowing Squirrel" given in the Paul Allen edition of Lewis and Clark's Journals, 1814. Two years later Rafinesque described this squirrel under the name *Anisonyx brachiura* and his description was drawn from the same account of the "Burrowing Squirrel" by Lewis and Clark. Although specimens were collected and preserved by Lewis and Clark, it was not until 1891 that Merriam established the true identity of the "Burrowing Squirrel."

Merriam (1891:41) designated the type locality as "Camas prairie between the forks of the Clearwater or Kooskooskie." Miller (1924:

186), following Merriam in part, gives it as "Camas prairie between the forks of the Clearwater and Kooskooskie, about 40 miles from Moscow, Lincoln County." This animal was first taken by Lewis and Clark in 1806 when they were encamped at Camp Chopunnish. In regard to the location of this site, Wheeler (1904:268) says, "Their camp was on the east, or right, bank of the Kooskooskie River north of Commearp..., or Lawyer's Canon Creek." This locality is about two miles north of the present town of Kamiah.

The first record of this species is an entry by Clark in the Journals of Lewis and himself (Thwaites ed., 5:36) May 14, 1806, in which he says: "About Meridian Shannon came in with...2 squirrels common to this country." Lewis (Journals, 5:70) states, under date May 27, 1806: "...I preserved the skins of several of these animals with the heads, feet, and legs entire." The accounts from which Ord drew his description were entered in the Journals this same day, that is, May 27, 1806.

Citellus idahoensis Merriam, Proc. Biol. Soc. Washington, vol. 26, p. 135. May 21, 1913. [*Citellus mollis idahoensis* Merriam.]

Type.—Female, adult, skin and skull; no. 168290, U. S. National Museum (Biological Survey collection); Payette, at junction of Payette and Snake rivers, Payette County; collected April 23, 1910, by Stanley G. Jewett, original no. 17.

Remarks.—Since the publication of the original description of this race, a new county, Payette, has been created.

Citellus leurodon Merriam, Proc. Biol. Soc. Washington, vol. 26, p. 136. May 21, 1913. [*Citellus mollis mollis* (Kennicott).]

Type.—Male, subadult, skin and skull; no. 169031, U. S. National Museum (Biological Survey collection); Murphy, in hills of southwestern Idaho west of Snake River, Owyhee County; collected May 30, 1910, by Stanley G. Jewett, original no. 112.

Citellus mollis artemesiae Merriam, Proc. Biol. Soc. Washington, vol. 26, p. 137. May 21, 1913.

Type.—Male, adult ?, skin and skull; no. 23489/30907, U. S. National Museum (Biological Survey collection); Birch Creek, ten miles south of Nicholia, in Clark County; collected August 9, 1890, by Vernon Bailey, original no. 1573.

Remarks.—Through the courtesy of Mr. Arthur H. Howell I have been supplied with a summary of the itinerary of Merriam's expedition of 1890. The summary was taken from Bailey's journal and catalog, excerpts of which follow: "August 2. Moved camp to Birch Creek, about ten mi. south of Nicholia, where Birch Creek has cut through the upper bank of lava rock and makes a gap through rocky banks 275 feet high. August 5. Bailey took his horse and rode down Birch Creek about 25 mi. to J. R. Richards' ranch. August 6-8. Trapping about ranch and in sink of Birch Creek. Returned to base camp. August 8-10. In camp on Birch Creek." Since the type specimen was collected August 9, it doubtless came from the vicinity of their base camp.

Citellus mollus (typographical error for mollis) pessimus Merriam, Proc. Biol. Soc. Washington, vol. 26, p. 138. May 21, 1913. [Citellus mollis artemesiae Merriam.]

Type.—Male, adult ?, skin and skull; no. 23925/31330, U. S. National Museum (Biological Survey collection) ; Big Lost River, seventeen miles southeast of Arco, Butte County; collected July 23, 1890, by Clark P. Streator, original no. 53.

Remarks.—Merriam's party spent from July 21 to 24, 1890, on Big Lost River about fifteen miles southeast of the old town of Arco. At the time the railroad was built from Blackfoot to Mackay, about 1902, Arco was moved about three miles up the river to its present site. The deserted railroad station of Pioneer is seventeen miles in a direct line southeast of Arco and is very near the type locality.

Citellus townsendii brunneus A. H. Howell, Proc. Biol. Soc. Washington, vol. 41, p. 211. December 18, 1928. [Citellus brunneus A. H. Howell.]

Type.—Female, adult, skin and skull; no. 201963, U. S. National Museum (Biological Survey collection) ; New Meadows, Adams County; collected July 11, 1913, by L. E. Wyman, original no. 178.

Citellus elegans aureus, new subspecies described in present volume.

Type.—Male, subadult, skin and skull; no. 71965, Mus. Vert. Zool.; Double Springs, sixteen miles northeast of Dickey, Custer County; collected July 20, 1936, by J. A. Donohoe, original no. 71.

Tamias minimus melanurus Merriam, N. Amer. Fauna, no. 4, p. 22. October 8, 1890. [Eutamias minimus pictus (Allen).]

Type.—Male, adult, skin and skull; no. 23048/30494, U. S. National Museum (Biological Survey collection) ; west side of Snake River near Blackfoot, Bingham County; collected July 17, 1890, by Vernon Bailey and Basil Hicks Dutcher, original no. 1451.

Eutamias ruficaudus simulans A. H. Howell, Jour. Mammal., vol. 3, p. 179. August 4, 1922.

Type.—Female, adult, skin and skull; no. 28487/40591, U. S. National Museum (Biological Survey collection) ; Coeur d'Alene, Kootenai County; collected June 1, 1891, by Clark P. Streator, original no. 881.

Eutamias amoenus cratericus Blossom, Occas. Papers Mus. Zool., Univ. Michigan, no. 366, p. 1. December 21, 1937.

Type.—Female, adult, skin and skull; no. 78001, Mus. Zool., Univ. Mich.; Grassy Cone, 6000 feet altitude, Craters of the Moon National Monument, Butte County; collected October 3, 1936, by Phillip M. Blossom, original no. 1262.

Sciurus richardsoni Bachman, Proc. Zool. Soc. London, 1838, p. 100. [*Tamiasciurus hudsonicus richardsoni* (Bachman).]

Type.—No. 293, Academy of Natural Sciences of Philadelphia; Wildhorse Creek, head of Big Lost River, Custer County; collected August 12, 1834, by J. K. Townsend (see Bachman, 1839:67). Mr. Wharton Huber, Associate Curator at the Academy of Natural Sciences of Philadelphia, states (letter of May 15, 1935): "Sex not noted—Mounted specimen removed from board. In very fair condition except tail broken and tip of same missing. Skull still in skin. From the size of the teeth it is probably an immature animal."

Remarks.—Bachman (*ibid.*) states that the label of the type specimen bore the date "August 12, 1834." On this date Townsend, a member of Nathaniel J. Wyeth's second expedition to the "Oregon," was on the upper reaches of Big Lost River. Recourse to Wyeth's Journal (Young ed., 1899:228) makes it possible to establish with fair accuracy where he was on the day in question.

Wyeth's party spent the night of August 11 three miles below (downstream from) what is now known as the junction of the North Fork and Summit Creek branches of Big Lost River. Excerpts from the log of August 12 follow: "Moved 3 miles up the creek ... at which place the creek divides into about equal parts the one going south I took ... followed this up one mile and a branch going E 3 miles farther ... another E 4 miles farther ... looked so bad camped...." From the above description, it appears that Wildhorse Creek was ascended into what is now known as the Devils Bedstead country near Hyndman Peak.

Sciuropterus alpinus bangsi Rhoads, Proc. Acad. Nat. Sci. Philadelphia, 1897, p. 321. June, 1897. [*Glaucomys sabrinus bangsi* (Rhoads).]

Type.—Male, subadult ?, skin and skull; no. 6959, E. A. and O. Bangs collection (now no. 6959, Mus. Comp. Zool.); collected March 8, 1897, by Harbison and Bargamin near Raymond, Idaho County.

Remarks.—The type locality as given by Rhoads, Miller, and others is no more restricted than "Idaho County." Harbison and Bargamin were then living at Raymond (see Rhoads, *ibid.*), and it appears probable that the type specimen came from near the town of Raymond, which was an old mining camp, with post office, situated at the junction of Seigal Creek and Red River, near 4400 ft., 4.5 mi. SE Elk City; post office was discontinued in or about 1902.

Glaucomys bullatus A. H. Howell, Proc. Biol. Soc. Washington, vol. 28, p. 113. May 27, 1915. [*Glaucomys sabrinus bangsi* (Rhoads).]

Type.—Female, adult, skin and skull; no. 24271/31675, U. S. National Museum (Biological Survey collection); Alturas Lake, Blaine County; collected September 28, 1890, by Vernon Bailey and Basil Hicks Dutcher, original no. 1883.

Castor canadensis taylori, new subspecies described in present volume.

Type.—Female, adult, skin and skull; no. 67588, Mus. Vert. Zool.; Big Wood River, near Bellevue, Blaine County; collected in April, 1935, by J. M. Wright, original no. 1137 of W. B. Davis.

Geomys townsendii Bachman, Jour. Acad. Nat. Sci. Philadelphia, vol. 8, p. 105. 1839. [*Thomomys townsendii townsendii* (Bachman).]

Type.—Skin and skull; no. 147, Academy of Natural Sciences of Philadelphia; near Nampa, Canyon County; collected by J. K. Townsend in late August ?, 1834.

Remarks.—For a discussion of the type locality, see Bailey (1915: 43) and Davis (1937:152). In regard to the type specimen, Mr. Wharton Huber, Associate Curator at the Academy of Natural Sciences of Philadelphia, states (in letter of May 15, 1935) that it was "originally a mounted specimen, sex not noted—Now made into a very good skin—Skull removed and practically perfect except tips of upper incisors broken off and left lower incisor broken off about ¼ inch from tip."

Thomomys clusius fuscus Merriam, N. Amer. Fauna, no. 5, p. 69. July 30, 1891. [*Thomomys talpoides fuscus* Merriam.]

Type.—Female, adult, skin and skull; no. 24267/31671, U. S. National Museum (Biological Survey collection); mountains near Summit Creek, head of Big Lost River, Custer County; collected September 23, 1890, by Basil Hicks Dutcher, original no. 1847.

Remarks.—The type locality as stated by Merriam (1891:70) is "From mountains at head of Big Lost River." Careful reading of his accounts (*ibid.*) reveal that the party ascended Summit Creek, which is the middle fork of Big Lost River, and crossed the mountains to Trail Creek. It indicates that Dutcher remained in these mountains, probably at or near the pass, for a few days. It was during this time that he collected the type specimen. In view of this, the mention of the area near Summit Creek seems justifiable as a means of more definitely placing the exact type locality.

Thomomys idahoensis Merriam, Proc. Biol. Soc. Washington, vol. 14, p. 114. July 19, 1901. [*Thomomys talpoides idahoensis* Merriam.]

Type.—Male, adult, skin and skull; no. 23482/30900, U. S. National Museum (Biological Survey collection); Birch Creek, ten miles south of Nicholia, in Clark County; collected August 8, 1890, by Clark P. Streator, original no. 129.

Remarks.—Since the appearance of Bailey's (1915) work on the pocket gophers, two new counties have been created in east-central Idaho; the type locality lies in what is now Clark County.

Thomomys pygmaeus Merriam, Proc. Biol. Soc. Washington, vol. 14, p. 115. July 19, 1901. [*Thomomys talpoides pygmaeus* Merriam.]

Type.—Male, adult, skin and skull; no. 55271, U. S. National Museum (Biological Survey collection); Montpelier Creek, about ten miles northeast of Montpelier, 6700 feet altitude, Bear Lake County; collected July 29, 1893, by Vernon Bailey, original no. 4150.

Thomomys nevadensis atrogriseus Bailey, Proc. Biol. Soc. Washington, vol. 27, p. 118. July 10, 1914. [*Thomomys townsendii townsendii* (Bachman).]

Type.—Male, adult, skin and skull; no. 181196, U. S. National Museum (Biological Survey collection); Nampa, Canyon County; collected March 15, 1913, by L. E. Wyman, original no. 35.

Thomomys townsendii owyhensis Davis, Jour. Mammal., vol. 18, p. 154. May 14, 1937.

Type.—Female, adult, skin and skull; no. 67490, Mus. Vert. Zool.; Castle Creek, eight miles south of Oreana, Owyhee County; collected May 22, 1935, by William B. Davis, original no. 1260.

Thomomys townsendii similis Davis, Jour. Mammal., vol. 18, p. 155. May 14, 1937.

Type.—Female, adult, skin and skull; no. 46507, Mus. Vert. Zool.; Pocatello, Bannock County; collected November 10, 1928, by Wayne B. Whitlow, original no. 182.

Perognathus parvus idahoensis Goldman, Proc. Biol. Soc. Washington, vol. 35, p. 105. October 17, 1922.

Type.—Male, adult, skin and skull; no. 236394, U. S. National Museum (Biological Survey collection); Echo Crater, Craters of the Moon National Monument, twenty miles southwest of Arco, Butte County; collected June 14, 1921, by Luther J. Goldman, original no. 2752.

Onychomys leucogaster brevicaudus Merriam, N. Amer. Fauna, no. 5, p. 52. July 30, 1891.

Type.—Male, adult, skin and skull; no. 23086/30532, U. S. National Museum (Biological Survey collection); Blackfoot, Bingham County; collected July 15, 1890, by Vernon Bailey and Basil Hicks Dutcher, original no. 1442.

Reithrodontomys megalotis nigrescens A. H. Howell, N. Amer. Fauna, no. 36, p. 32. June 5, 1914.

Type.—Male, adult, skin and skull; no. 201616, U. S. National Museum (Biological Survey collection); Payette, Payette County; collected June 9, 1913, by L. E. Wyman, original no. 98.

Remarks.—Payette County has been created since Howell published his description.

Hesperomys crinitus Merriam, N. Amer. Fauna, no. 5, p. 53. July 30, 1891. [*Peromyscus crinitus crinitus* (Merriam).]

Type.—Male, adult, skin and skull; no. 24255/31659, U. S. National Museum (Biological Survey collection); Shoshone Falls, north side Snake River, Jerome County; collected October 10, 1890, by C. Hart Merriam and Vernon Bailey, original no. 1945.

Remarks.—Merriam and his associates collected on the north side of the river at this locality in what is now Jerome County.

Peromyscus maniculatus serratus, new subspecies described in present volume.

Type.—Female, adult, skin and skull; no. 72330, Mus. Vert. Zool.; Mill Creek, fourteen miles west of Challis, 8370 feet altitude, Custer County; collected July 27, 1936, by W. B. Davis, original no. 2290.

Phenacomys orophilus Merriam, N. Amer. Fauna, no. 5, p. 66. July 30, 1891. [*Phenacomys intermedius intermedius* Merriam.]

Type.—Female, adult, skin and skull; no. 23856/31256, U. S. National Museum (Biological Survey collection); Timber Creek, 10,500 feet altitude, Lemhi Mountains, Lemhi County; collected August 28, 1890, by C. Hart Merriam and Vernon Bailey, original no. 1710.

Evotomys idahoensis Merriam, N. Amer. Fauna, no. 5, p. 67. July 30, 1891. [*Clethrionomys gapperi idahoensis* (Merriam).]

Type.—Female, adult, skin and skull; no. 24283/31687, U. S. National Museum (Biological Survey collection); Alturas Lake, east base of Sawtooth Mountains, Blaine County; collected October 4, 1890, by C. Hart Merriam and Vernon Bailey, original no. 1936.

Arvicola (Mynomes) macropus Merriam, N. Amer. Fauna, no. 5, p. 60. July 30, 1891. [*Microtus richardsoni macropus* (Merriam).]

Type.—Female, adult, skin and skull; no. 23887/31291, U. S. National Museum (Biological Survey collection); Pahsimeroi Mountains, head of Pahsimeroi River, 9350 feet altitude, Custer County; collected September 16, 1890, by C. Hart Merriam and Vernon Bailey, original no. 1803.

Remarks.—Merriam applied the name Pahsimeroi Mountains to "a group of lofty, rugged, snow-marbled peaks, arranged in the form of a double or triple amphitheater, surrounding the source of the Pahsimeroi River." The name now is applied to the whole range from that area north to the Salmon River.

Arvicola (Mynomes) mordax Merriam, N. Amer. Fauna, no. 5, p. 61. July 30, 1891. [*Microtus mordax mordax* (Merriam).]

Type.—Male, adult, skin and skull; no. 24231/31635, U. S. National Museum (Biological Survey collection); Alturas Lake, Blaine County; collected September 29, 1890, by C. Hart Merriam and Vernon Bailey, original no. 1903.

Arvicola (Mynomes) nanus Merriam, N. Amer. Fauna, no. 5, p. 63. July 30, 1891. [*Microtus montanus nanus* (Merriam).]

Type.—Male, adult, skin and skull; no. 23853/31253, U. S. National Museum (Biological Survey collection); Pahsimeroi Mountains, head of Pahsimeroi River, 9350 feet altitude, Custer County; collected September 16, 1890, by C. Hart Merriam and Vernon Bailey, original no. 1809.

Zapus princeps idahoensis Davis, Jour. Mammal., vol. 15, p. 221. August 10, 1934.

Type.—Male, adult, skin and skull; no. 54845, Mus. Vert. Zool.; five miles east of Warm Lake, 7000 feet altitude, Valley County; collected July 9, 1932, by Robert T. Orr, original no. 660.

Ochotona uinta lemhi A. H. Howell, Proc. Biol. Soc. Washington, vol. 32, p. 106. May 20, 1919. [*Ochotona princeps lemhi* A. H. Howell.]

Type.—Female, adult, skin and skull; no. 23543/30961, U. S. National Museum (Biological Survey collection); Timber Creek, Lemhi Mountains, ten miles south of Junction, Lemhi County; collected August 19, 1890, by Clark P. Streator, original no. 174.

Remarks.—Howell (*ibid.*) gives the type locality as "Lemhi Mountains (10 miles west of Junction)." Under date of April 11, 1935, Mr. Howell furnished me with a synopsis of the itinerary of Merriam's expedition which states that on August 19, 1890, camp was on "West side of Timber Creek Valley, a mile from the creek on one of the little streams that flows into it," and that collecting was done in the mountains above camp. Timber Creek is *south* and slightly west of Junction.

Ochotona schisticeps goldmani A. H. Howell, N. Amer. Fauna, no. 47, p. 40. August 21, 1924. [*Ochotona princeps goldmani* A. H. Howell.]

Type.—Male, adult, skin and skull; no. 236408, U. S. National Museum (Biological Survey collection); Echo Crater, Craters of the Moon National Monument, twenty miles southwest of Arco, Butte County; collected June 18, 1921, by Luther J. Goldman, original no. 2754.

Ochotona princeps howelli Borell, Jour. Mammal., vol. 12, p. 306. August 24, 1931.

Type.—Male, adult, skin and skull; no. 8744, Ralph Ellis collection; summit Smith Mountain, 7500 feet altitude, near head of Bear Creek, south end of Seven Devils Mountains, Adams County; collected July 16, 1930, by Raymond M. Gilmore, original no. 1325.

Ochotona princeps clamosa Hall and Bowlus, Univ. Calif. Publ. Zool., vol. 42, p. 335. October 12, 1938.

Type.—Male, adult, skin and skull; no. 78100, Mus. Vert. Zool.; N. rim Copenhagen Basin, 8400 feet altitude, Bear Lake County; collected July 21, 1937, by William B. Davis, original no. 2645.

Lepus californicus depressus Hall and Whitlow, Proc. Biol. Soc. Washington, vol. 45, p. 71. April 2, 1932. [*Lepus californicus deserticola* Mearns.]

Type.—Female, adult, skin and skull; no. 47066, Mus. Vert. Zool.; one-half mile south of Pocatello, Bannock County; collected December 7, 1930, by Wayne B. Whitlow, original no. 442.

Lepus idahoensis Merriam, N. Amer. Fauna, no. 5, p. 76. July 30, 1891. [*Sylvilagus idahoensis* (Merriam).]

Type.—Male, adult, skin and skull; no. 24045/31461, U. S. National Museum (Biological Survey collection); head of Pahsimeroi Valley, near Goldburg, Custer County; collected September 16, 1890, by Basil Hicks Dutcher, original no. 1816.

Remarks.—Merriam's party spent the day of September 16, 1890, traveling down the *upper* part of the Pahsimeroi Valley.

Odocoileus virginianus ochrourus Bailey, Proc. Biol. Soc. Washington, vol. 45, p. 43. April 2, 1932.

Type.—Male, adult, skin and skull; no. 159353, U. S. National Museum (Biological Survey collection); Coolin, south end of Priest Lake, Bonner County; collected December 27, 1908, by Frank Lemmer, miscellaneous catalog no. 7483.

Remarks.—A large buck five or six years old, skull with antlers, and skin in full winter pelage.

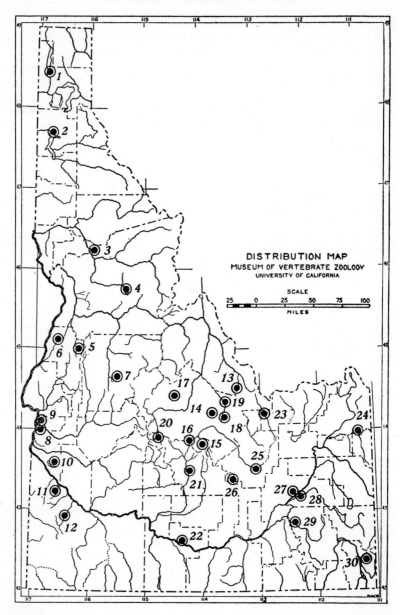

DISTRIBUTION MAP
MUSEUM OF VERTEBRATE ZOOLOGY
UNIVERSITY OF CALIFORNIA

SCALE
25   0   25   50   75   100
MILES

Fɪɢ. 6.

TYPE LOCALITIES IN IDAHO

1. Coolin, south end of Priest Lake, Bonner County.
2. Coeur d'Alene, Kootenai County.
3. Camas Prairie about 3 miles north of Kamiah, Idaho County.
4. Raymond, Idaho County.
5. New Meadows, Adams County.
6. Summit Smith Mountain, Adams County.
7. Five miles east of Warm Lake, Valley County.
8. Payette, at junction of Payette and Snake rivers, Payette County.
9. Payette, Payette County.
10. Nampa, Canyon County.
11. Murphy, in hills of southwestern Idaho, Owyhee County.
12. Castle Creek, 8 miles south of Oreana, Owyhee County.
13. Timber Creek, 8200 feet, Lemhi Mountains, Lemhi County.
14. Double Springs, 16 miles northeast of Dickey, Custer County.
15. Wildhorse Creek, head of Big Lost River, Custer County.
16. Mountains near Summit Creek, head of Big Lost River, Custer County.
17. Mill Creek, 14 miles west of Challis, Custer County.
18. Pahsimeroi Mountains, head of Pahsimeroi River, Custer County.
19. Pahsimeroi Valley, near Goldburg, Custer County.
20. Alturas Lake, Blaine County.
21. Big Wood River, near Bellevue, Blaine County.
22. Shoshone Falls, north side of Snake River, Jerome County.
23. Birch Creek, 10 miles south of Nicholia, Clark County.
24. North Fork Teton River, Fremont County.
25. Big Lost River, 17 miles southeast of Arco, Butte County.
26. Echo Crater, Craters of the Moon National Monument, Butte County.
27. West side Snake River, near Blackfoot, Bingham County.
28. Blackfoot, Bingham County.
29. Pocatello, Bannock County.
30. Montpelier Creek, about 10 miles northeast of Montpelier, Bear Lake County.
31. (Not shown on map) North rim Copenhagen Basin, 8400 feet, Bear Lake County.

GAZETTEER OF LOCALITIES

In compiling the gazetteer I have attempted to include all localities from which specimens have been examined or recorded. Geographical place-names have been altered considerably in the past forty years so that many old names in Idaho are difficult, or impossible, to locate on modern maps. Some of the old mining camps at which specimens were collected no longer exist. For all localities that can be found readily on any recently printed map, I have given first the name of the locality, followed by the name of the county in which it now (1937) is situated, and the elevation (exact when known, otherwise estimated as indicated by the word "near" preceding).

For localities more difficult, or impossible, to find on recent maps, I have endeavored to give in each instance a precise location by section, township, and range, or by a verbal description and explanation of its former or present position. I was unable to locate a few of the place names for localities where specimens were taken many years ago.

I have had recourse to all the published topographic, Forest Service, and water-supply maps of Idaho; also, the 1926 revised edition of the United States Geological Survey map of Idaho.

Aberdeen, Bingham County, 4404 ft.; E side American Falls Reservoir; Sec. 33, T. 5 S., R. 31 E.
Acequia, Minidoka County, near 4100 ft.
Acequia, 2 mi. E of, Minidoka County, near 4100 ft.
Acequia, 3 mi. SE of, on S side Snake River, in Cassia County, near 4100 ft.
Albion, Cassia County, 4750 ft.
Albion, 4 mi. NW of, Cassia County, near 4300 ft.
Albion, 4 mi. S of, Cassia County, near 5300 ft.; collecting done on Howell Creek.
Albion, 6 mi. SE of, Cassia County, near 5300 ft.; collecting done on road to Elba.
Alridge, Bingham County, 5300 ft.; SW ¼ Sec. 26, T. 2 S., R. 38 E.
Alturas Lake, Blaine County, 7000 ft.; in Sawtooth Mountains at head of Salmon River.
American Falls, Power County, 4404 ft.
American Falls, 4 mi. NE of, Power County, near 4400 ft.

American Falls, 3 mi. SW of, Power County, near 4400 ft.; collecting done along U. S. Highway 30.

American Falls, 5 mi. SW of, Power County, near 4300 ft.; collecting done along U. S. Highway 30.

American Falls, 19 mi. SW of, on S side Snake River, Power County, near 4300 ft.; collecting done at old Bonanza Bar.

American Falls, 4 mi. NW of, Power County, near 4400 ft.; collecting done on W side of reservoir.

American Falls, 10 mi. WNW of, Power County, 4500 ft.; collecting done in Sec. 31, T. 6 S., R. 30 E.

American Falls, 16 mi. NW of, in Bingham County, near 4700 ft., in T. 5 S., R. 29 E.

American Falls, 19 mi. NW of, in Bingham County, near 4700 ft., in T. 5 S., R. 29 E.

Antelope Valley, Custer County, 6308 ft. On U.S.G.S. topo. sheet, 1932 ed., this valley is called Antelope Flat; located about 16 mi. SE Challis.

Arco, Butte County, near 5313 ft. The old town of Arco, moved about 1902, was about 3 miles downstream from its present site.

Arco, 3 mi. SE of, Butte County, near 5000 ft.; collecting was done along railroad.

Argora, Clark County, near 7000 ft. On Medicine Lodge Creek, 8.5 mi. S Idaho-Montana line and 20 mi. due W of Spencer.

Arimo, Bannock County, near 4500 ft.; located 6 mi. S McCammon on Marsh Creek.

Ashton, Fremont County, near 5000 ft.

Atlanta, Elmore County, 5500 ft.; in Sawtooth Mountains on Middle Fork Boise River.

Baker Creek, 12 mi. N Ketchum, Blaine County, near 7000 ft.; tributary to Big Wood River from SW.

Bald Mountain Ranger Station, 13 mi. S Idaho City, in Elmore County, near 5800 ft.

"Bannock County"; badgers labeled as such were collected in the northeastern portion of the county.

Bannock Creek, 4 mi. S Portneuf River, Power County, near 4400 ft.; creek now drains from the south into the American Falls Reservoir.

Bargamin Creek, 50 mi. SE Grangeville, Idaho County, near 5000 ft.; creek crosses T. 27 N., R. 11 E.

Barrett's Ranch, 9.5 mi. E Pocatello, Bannock County, near 5500 ft.; on W fork Rabbit Creek.

Bear Creek Ranger Station, 1 mi. N of, SW slope Smith Mountain, Adams County, 5400 ft.; located near head of Bear Creek at old Frenchy's Mine about 5 mi. S summit Smith Mountain.

Bear Lake, east side of, Bear Lake County, near 5950 ft.

Bear Park, 35 mi. NE Minidoka, in Blaine County, near 4500 ft.; locality not found on any available map.

Bellevue, Blaine County, near 5000 ft.; on Big Wood River.

Benewah, Benewah County, near 3000 ft.

Berenice, 1 mi. N of, Butte County, near 5300 ft.; near S end of Lemhi Mountains in Little Lost River Valley.

Big Butte, in southeastern Butte County, near 4800 ft.

Big Hole Mountains, 8 mi. NE Swan Valley, Bonneville County, near 6000 ft.; collecting done on Pine Creek.

Big Hole Mountains, summit of, 7 mi. SW Victor, Teton County, near 7000 ft.

Big Hole Mountains, near Irwin, Bonneville County, near 6000 ft.

Big Lost River, near sink, Butte County, near 4500 ft.

Big Lost River Valley, near Chilly, Custer County, near 6000 ft.

Big Lost River Valley, near Thousand Springs, Custer County, near 6000 ft.; this locality is near Dickey.

Big Lost River, head of (Summit Creek), Custer County, 7895 ft.

Big Wood River, near Bellevue, Blaine County, near 5000 ft.

Big Wood River, 1 to 12 mi. N Ketchum, Blaine County, from 6000 to 6600 ft.; several localities all near the river.

Big Wood River, head of, Blaine County, near 8000 ft.

Birch Creek. Specimens collected in 1890 by Bailey, Dutcher, and Streator near their camp 10 mi. S Nicholia are all labeled "Birch Creek." This locality is near Kaufman at the junction of Pass and Birch creeks, Clark County, near 6000 ft.

Birch Creek, near sink of, Butte County, near 4500 ft.

Birch Creek, 2 mi. SE Kaufman, Clark County, near 6000 ft.; T. 9 N., R. 30 E.; Kaufman is located on Birch Creek 1 mi. below the junction of Pass and Birch creeks.

Birch Creek, 2 mi. NW Kaufman, Clark County, near 6000 ft.

Birch Creek, 10 mi. S Nicholia, Clark County, near 6000 ft.; T. 10 N., R. 29 E.; near junction of Pass and Birch creeks.

Bitterroot Mountains. Probably refers to a locality W of Hamilton, Montana, in Idaho County, Idaho.

Bitterroot Mountains E of Birch Creek. Refers to mountains east of Kaufman, in Clark County, near 7500 ft.

Bitterroot Mountains, head of Clearwater River, Clearwater County. This locality is too indefinite to locate precisely.

Bitterroot Valley. This locality is given by Nelson (1909:112) as being in Idaho. The only Bitterroot Valley of which I am aware is in Montana.

Blackfoot, Bingham County, 4497 ft.

Blackfoot, 3 mi. S of, Bingham County, near 4500 ft.

Blackfoot, W side Snake River, Bingham County, near 4500 ft.

Blackfoot, hills east of, Bingham County. The Blackfoot Mountains rise from the Snake River Valley, 4500 ft., to a height of 7490 ft.

Black Lake, .5 mi. E of, Adams County, 6800 ft.; Sec. 3, T. 21 N., R. 2 W.; 38 mi. due N of Goodrich.

Black Rock, Bannock County. A local name for a locality about 8 mi. SE Pocatello on the Portneuf River, near 4500 ft.

Black Springs, 4 mi. W Ashton, Fremont County, near 5000 ft.

Bliss, 3 mi. W of, Gooding County, near 3800 ft.; collecting done along U. S. Highway 30.

Blue Lake, 14 mi. W Sandpoint, Bonner County, 2300 ft.

Blue Lake, Kootenai County, near 2200 ft.; located in Sec. 23, T. 48 N., R. 3 W. on E side Lake Coeur d'Alene.

Blue Spring Hills, Oneida County, near 6000 ft.; low range of hills 15 mi. W and 5 mi. N Malad.

Boise, 14 mi. SE of, Ada County, near 3500 ft.; collecting done along U. S. Highway 30.

Boise River, 5 mi. W Boise, Ada County, 3000 ft.

Boise River, S fork of. The South Fork is largely in Elmore County; elevation 3000 to 6000 ft.

Boulder Peak, Blaine County. This peak is located directly N of the mouth of Baker Creek, and about 15 mi. NW Ketchum; summit is 10,966 ft.

Bowmont, Canyon County, near 2600 ft.; between Melba and Nampa.

Bridge, Cassia County, near 4300 ft.; on Raft River 10 mi. N Idaho-Utah line.

Bridge (for specimens in Biol. Surv. coll.), Cassia County. According to S. G. Jewett, who collected the specimens, collecting was done on the old "Platt" or "Pratt" ranch in the Black Pine Mountains east of Bridge.

Brown's Bench, Twin Falls County, near 5500 ft.; refers to tableland along the Idaho-Nevada line.

Bruneau, 5 mi. N of, Owyhee County, 2600 ft.; collecting done on S bank of Snake River.

Bruneau, 7 mi. S of, Owyhee County, near 2900 ft.

Bruneau, 30 mi. S of, Owyhee County, near 4500 ft.; near Jacks Creek, tributary to Bruneau River.

Bruneau, 40 mi. S of, Owyhee County, near 5000 ft.; near present town of Tindall.

Bruneau Mountains, Owyhee County; a range of mountains on Idaho-Nevada line; many peaks rise to over 9000 ft.

Burley, Cassia County, near 4100 ft.

Cabinet Mountains, east of Priest Lake. These mountains are known on most maps as the Selkirk Mountains, Boundary County; rise from 2439 ft. at Priest Lake to over 7600 ft.

Cabinet Mountains, NE Lake Pend Oreille, Bonner and Boundary counties; rise from 2051 ft. at Lake Pend Oreille to 6785 ft.

Camas, 20 mi. W of, Jefferson County, near 5000 ft.

Camas Creek, near mouth of, Camas County, near 5000 ft.

Cambridge, 2 mi. S of, Washington County, near 2700 ft.

Camp Tendoy, Bannock County, 13 mi. S Pocatello, near 6300 ft.

Canyon Creek, Madison County, near 5200 ft.; empties into Teton River about 15 mi. E Sugar City.

Cape Horn, Custer County, 6400 ft.; 22 mi. NW Stanley on Middle Fork Salmon River.

Cape Horn, 2 mi. SE of, Custer County, 6500 ft.; on Marsh Creek.

Cape Horn, 5 mi. W of, in Valley County, 7000 ft.; collecting done along road from Stanley to Warm Lake.

Castle Creek, 8 mi. S Oreana, Owyhee County, near 2900 ft.

Castle Creek Ranger Station, S Fork Clearwater River, Idaho County, 1800 ft.; located 2 mi. W mouth Meadow Creek in T. 29 N., R. 4 E.; 11 mi. SE Grangeville.

Castleford, Twin Falls County, near 4000 ft.

Cayuse Creek, 10 mi. N Featherville, Elmore County, near 6000 ft.

Cedar Mountain, 12 mi. NE Moscow, Latah County, 4000 to 4500 ft.; site of Washington State College camp.

Challis, Custer County, near 5400 ft.

Cocolalla, 5 mi. W of, Bonner County, near 4000 ft.

Coeur d'Alene, Kootenai County, 2200 ft.

Coeur d'Alene, 10 mi. S of, Kootenai County; probably near Carlin Bay, near 2200 ft.

Coeur d'Alene Mountains, E of Lake Coeur d'Alene, in Shoshone County.

Collins, Latah County, near 3500 ft.; on Potlatch Creek in NW ¼ Sec. 6, T. 41 N., R. 1 E.

Conant Creek, Fremont County, near 5000 ft.; creek located 1 mi. N Drummond.

Conner Canyon, 4 mi. N Elba, Cassia County, near 7000 ft.; located on SE side of Albion Mountains.

Coolin, Bonner County, 2451 ft.; at S end of Priest Lake.

Copenhagen Basin, Wasatch Mountains, 8400 ft.; Bear Lake County; about 20 mi. W Montpelier.

Copper Basin, SW of Mackay, Custer County, near 6000 ft.

Copper Creek, 6 mi. N Muldoon, Blaine County, near 8500 ft.; tributary to Little Wood River.

Craig Mountains, Lewis County, near 4000 ft.; near town of Craigmont.

Crane Creek, 15 mi. E Midvale, Washington County, 2800 ft.; camp was 6 mi. ENE Crane Creek Reservoir.

Craters of the Moon National Monument, in SE Butte County, extending, at two places, a short way into Blaine County.

Crow Creek, head of, Caribou County, near 9000 ft.; heads on Preuss Mountain.

Cuddy Mountain (see Heath).

Declo, 3 mi. S of, Cassia County, near 4200 ft.

Deer Flat, 5 mi. S Caldwell, Canyon County, 2600 ft.

Dickey, Custer County, near 6000 ft.; located in Thousand Springs Valley above Mackay.

Donnelly, Valley County, 4865 ft.; in Long Valley south of Payette Lake.

Double Springs, 16 mi. NE Dickey, Custer County, near 8000 ft.

Driggs, Teton County, near 6000 ft.

Dry Creek, Targhee National Forest, Clark County, near 7000 ft.; in T. 13 N., R. 40 E., 20 mi. W Trude.

Dry Valley, Caribou County, near 6500 ft.; in T. 7 S., R. 43 E., 19 mi. NE Soda Springs.

Dubois, Clark County, near 6000 ft.

Duck Valley Indian Reservation, Owyhee County, near 5000 ft.; half of the reservation is in Nevada.

Echo Crater, Craters of the Moon National Monument, Butte County, 5850 ft.; in Sec. 29, T. 1 N., R. 25 E.

Edna, Idaho County. Cannot be located on any available map; Postmaster Lola Rossi at Idaho City informed me that the name applies to an old mining camp at an elevation of near 6000 ft., 12 mi. E Idaho City.

Elba, Cassia County, near 4500 ft.; on Cassia Creek in valley between Mt. Independence and Mt. Harrison.

Elba, 4 mi. E of, Cassia County, near 4500 ft.

Elk City, 40 mi. SE of, Idaho County. If the distance and direction be correct, this locality is near the Salmon River in extreme SE Idaho County.

Elk Summit, Valley County; located 8 mi. NW Edwardsburg on Elk Creek, tributary to S fork Salmon River, in T. 21 N., R. 8 E., near 8000 ft.

Emmett, 7 mi. S of, in Ada County, near 3000 ft.; collecting done along road from Emmett to Boise.

Felton's Mill, 11 mi. ENE Moscow, Latah County, near 4000 ft.

Fiddle Creek, Idaho County; 3 mi. S Lucile; tributary to Salmon River from east, near 1600 ft.

Fissure Crater=Fissure Butte, Blaine County, 5877 ft.; in W ½ Sec. 10, T. 1 S., R. 25 E., in SE portion of Craters of the Moon National Monument.

Forney, Lemhi County, near 6500 ft.; on Panther Creek, 26 mi. SW Salmon City.

Fort Boise. The old fort was located near the junction of the Boise and Snake rivers near the present town of Parma, Canyon County, near 2224 ft.

Fort Hall. The old fort was located at what is now the upper end of the American Falls Reservoir, 9 mi. WSW the town which bears the name of Fort Hall; was in what is now Bannock County, near 4400 ft.; following localities refer to new Fort Hall.

Fort Hall, 1 mi. N of, Bingham County, near 4480 ft.

Fort Hall Indian School, 10 mi. N Pocatello, in Bannock County, near 4480 ft.

Fort Sherman, Kootenai County, 2200 ft. The old fort was located at the outlet of Lake Coeur d'Alene, 1 mi. W the present town of Coeur d'Alene.

Freedom, Idaho County, near 1600 ft.; located 8 mi. S Whitebird on the Salmon River.

Fruitland, 3 mi. S of, Payette County, 2300 ft.

Geneva, Bear Lake County, 6171 ft.

Glenns Ferry, Elmore County, near 3200 ft.; collecting was done a few miles north of the town.

Glidden Lakes, Shoshone County; Upper Lake is 5900 ft., Lower Lake is 5643 ft. These lakes are located at the head of Canyon Creek, tributary to the Coeur d'Alene River, about 1 mi. W the Idaho-Montana line and 5 mi. NE Mullan.

Gooding, 4 mi. E of, Gooding County, near 4000 ft.

Goodrich, Adams County, near 3000 ft.

Goose Creek, 15 mi. SW Oakley (11 mi. airline), Cassia County, near 4500 ft.

Goose Creek, 25 mi. SW Oakley (18 mi. airline), Cassia County, near 5000 ft.

Grand View, Owyhee County, 2300 ft.

Grand View, 20 mi. S of, Owyhee County, near 3300 ft.; probably near Jack Creek in T. 8 S., R. 3 E.

Grangeville, Idaho County, near 3200 ft.

Granite Mountain, W slope of, Adams County, 4500 ft.; collecting was done about 9 mi. due N New Meadows, near U. S. Highway 95.

Grays Lake, 10 mi. E of, Bonneville County; probably on Trail Creek, near 6000 ft.

Great Owl Cavern, Craters of the Moon National Monument, in NW ¼ Sec. 13, T. 1 N., R. 24 E., Butte County, 5877 ft.

Green Mountain, Idaho County; located in SE ¼ Sec. 10, T. 28 N., R. 11 E., near 7000 ft.; 16 mi. E and 3 mi. S Elk City.

Hagerman, Gooding County, near 3000 ft.; on Snake River.

Hagerman, 2 mi. S of, Gooding County, near 3000 ft.; collecting done on N side of river near Salmon Falls.

Hagerman, 2 mi. S of, in Twin Falls County, near 3000 ft.; collecting done on S side of river near Salmon Falls.

Hailey, Blaine County, 5342 ft.; on Big Wood River.

Hammett, Elmore County, near 2400 ft.; collecting done 1 mi. NE of the town.

Hammett, rimrock 3 mi. NE of, Elmore County, near 3000 ft.

Heath, 1 mi. NE of, on Brownlee Creek, SW slope Cuddy Mountain, Washington County, 4000 to 4400 ft.

Henrys Lake, Fremont County, near 7000 ft.

Heyburn, 2 mi. E of, Minidoka County, near 4100 ft.

Hill City, 22 mi. N of. If the distance and direction be correct, the locality would be near the S fork of the Boise River in Elmore County, near 4500 ft.

Hollister, 3 mi. N of, Twin Falls County, near 4500 ft.; collecting done along U. S. Highway 93.

Homedale, Owyhee County, 2200 ft.

Hoodoo Lake, Idaho County; lat. 49° 19′ N, long. 114° 39′ W.

Hoodoo Valley, Bonner County, 2230 ft.; Hoodoo Lake is in the center of Hoodoo Valley; about 14 mi. W the S arm of Lake Pend Oreille.

Horse Creek, 38 mi. NW Salmon City, Lemhi County, 7000 ft.

Horse Heaven Pass, Custer County, near 8000 ft.; this low pass lies between Double Springs and the head of the Pahsimeroi River.

Howells Canyon, 6 mi. S Albion, Cassia County, near 6000 ft.; collecting done near mouth of the canyon.

Howells Canyon, 8 to 10 mi. S Albion, Cassia County, near 7000 ft.; collecting done 2 mi. E top Mt. Harrison.

Idaho City, Boise County, 4000 ft.

Idaho Falls, Bonneville County, 4690 ft.

Idaho Falls, 7 mi. W of, Bonneville County, near 4800 ft.

Idavada, 1 to 6 mi. N of, Twin Falls County, near 4800 ft.; collecting done along U. S. Highway 93.

Indian Cove, Owyhee County, near 2600 ft.; on S side Snake River nearly opposite Hammett.

Indian Creek, 4 mi. S Pocatello, Bannock County, near 5000 ft.

Indian Springs, 4 mi. S American Falls, Power County, near 4500 ft.

Inkom, Bannock County, near 4500 ft.

Inkom, 8 mi. NW of, Bannock County, near 5400 ft.

Inkom, 8 mi. S of, Bannock County, 4700 ft.

Iona, Bonneville County, near 4800 ft.; located about 6 mi. NE Idaho Falls.

Ione Valley=Iona Valley ? Probably refers to Ione Valley in Nevada.

Irwin, 10 mi. SE of, Bonneville County, near 5436 ft.

Irwin, 20 mi. NW of, Bonneville County; probably near Antelope, along S fork Snake River, near 5000 ft.

Island Park, Fremont County, near 6500 ft.

Jordan Valley (Oregon), 2½ mi. E, in Owyhee County, Idaho, near 4500 ft.

Junction, Lemhi County, near 6000 ft.; in T. 16 N., R. 26 E., at head of Lemhi Valley.

Junction of Ross Fork Creek and Portneuf River, 10 mi. NW Pocatello, Bannock County; now under water in the American Falls Reservoir.

Juniper, Oneida County, near 4500 ft.; 10 mi. N Utah-Idaho line in NW ¼ Sec. 8, T. 15 S., R. 30 E.

Juniper Basin (or Juniper Lake Basin), Owyhee County, near 4800 ft.; in T. 16 S., R. 1 W.

Juniper Mountains, Owyhee County, 6000 to 8000 ft.; near Idaho-Nevada line in extreme SW corner of county.

Justice Park, 15 mi. SE Pocatello on E fork Mink Creek, Bannock County, near 6300 ft.; in Sec. 22, T. 8 S., R. 35 E.

Kamiah, 2 mi. N of, in Idaho County, 1921 ft.

Ketchum, Blaine County, 5823 ft.

Kingston, Shoshone County, near 2000 ft.

Kuna, Ada County, 2700 ft.

Laidlaw Park, 20 mi. N Kimama, Lincoln County, near 4800 ft.; could not be located on any available map.

Lardo, Valley County, 5002 ft.; about 1 mi. W McCall at southern end of Payette Lake.

Leadore, Lemhi County, near 6000 ft.; at junction of Timber Creek and Lemhi River.

Leesburg, Lemhi County, near 6500 ft.; on Napias Creek, 8 mi. from mouth; about 12 mi. NW Salmon City.

Lemhi, Lemhi County, near 5000 ft.; on Lemhi River in T. 18 N., R. 24 E.

Lemhi Mountains, near head of Birch Creek, Butte County, near 7000 ft.

Lemhi River, head of, near 7000 ft.; near Bannock Pass.

Lemhi River, 18 mi. S Salmon City, near 4200 ft.

Lemhi Valley, near Timber Creek, Lemhi County, near 6000 ft.; near present town of Leadore.

Lemhi Valley, near Agency, Lemhi County, near 5000 ft.; near present town of Tendoy in T. 19 N., R. 24 E.

Lerdo. See Lardo.

Lewiston, Nez Perce County, 710 ft.

Little Cottonwood Creek, mouth of, in NW part of Craters of the Moon National Monument, Butte County, near 5900 ft.

Little Lost River, head of, Custer County, near 8000 ft.

Little Lost River Mountains; a locality given by Merriam (1891); probably on Pass Creek, tributary to Little Lost River, Butte County, near 5500 ft.

Little Lost River Valley, near Howe, Butte County, near 5500 ft.

Little Owyhee River, 4 mi. N Nevada line, Owyhee County, near 4800 ft.

Little Wood River, E fork of, Blaine County, near 6500 ft.

Lochsa River, Idaho County; locality too general to locate precisely.

Loon Creek, near head of, Custer County, near 7500 ft.; about 15 mi. N Stanley.

Lower Glidden Lake. See Glidden Lakes.

Mackay, Custer County, near 5500 ft.

Malad, Oneida County, near 4700 ft.

Malta, 2 mi. S of, Cassia County, near 4300 ft.

Malta, 10 mi. E of, Cassia County, near 4400 ft.

Malta, 14 mi. SE of, on Meadow Creek, Cassia County, near 4400 ft.

Mann Creek, 20 mi. N Weiser, Washington County, near 4000 ft.

Marsh Valley, Bannock County; located 9 mi. S McCammon, on Marsh Creek, near 4600 ft.

McCammon, Bannock County, near 4500 ft.

McKinnis, 7 mi. E of, Shoshone County. Not shown on any available map; according to A. B. Howell, who collected there, the locality is 1 mi. W of main divide, on road from St. Regis, Montana, to Coeur d'Alene, Idaho, at 4600 ft. This locality is 1 mi. W Lookout Pass, and 4 mi. E Mullan.

Meadow Creek, 4 mi. W of, 3000 ft., Boundary County.

Meadow Creek, 14 mi. above mouth of, Idaho County; located about 11 mi. E Elk City in T. 29 N., R. 11 E., near 7000 ft.

Medicine Lodge Creek, Clark County, W of Dubois, 6000 to 8000 ft.

Melba, 2 mi. S of, Canyon County, 2600 ft.; collecting done on Walters Butte.

Menan, Jefferson County, near 4800 ft.

Michaud, Power County, 4430 ft.; located on O.S.L. R.R., 9 mi. WNW Pocatello in NW ¼ Sec. 21, T. 6 S., R. 33 E.

Michaud, 5 mi. NW of, Power County, 4400 ft.

Michaud, 5.5 mi. SW of, Power County, 4450 ft.

Midvale, Washington County, near 2500 ft.

Mill Creek, Custer County; collecting done along the creek (8300 ft.) and in the hills to the east (9500 ft.) ; 14 mi. W Challis.

Minidoka, Minidoka County, near 4300 ft.

Minidoka, 12 mi. NE of, in Blaine County, near 4500 ft.

Mink Creek, 4 mi. SE Pocatello, Bannock County, near 4550 ft.; tributary to Portneuf River.

Mink Creek, 2 mi. from Portneuf River, Bannock County, near 4800 ft.

Mission, Kootenai County, near 2200 ft.; located on N side of S fork of Coeur d'Alene River, 6 mi. W Cataldo, in Sec. 34, T. 49 N., R. 1 W.

Montpelier, Bear Lake County, 5963 ft.

Montpelier Creek, 10 mi. NE Montpelier, Bear Lake County, 6500 ft.

Moody Creek, Madison County, near 5000 ft.; flows into Teton River 3 mi. NE Rexburg.

Moscow, Latah County, 2574 ft.

Moscow, 8 mi. NE of, Latah County, near 3500 ft.

Mount Carlton, Benewah County; could not locate.

Mountain Home, Elmore County, 3150 ft.

Mountain Home, 4 to 5 mi. S of, Elmore County, 3050 ft.

Mt. Harrison, Cassia County; located about 8 mi. S Albion; rises from Snake River Valley, 4300 ft., to near 9000 ft.

Mt. Independence, 5.5 mi. SW Elba, Cassia County; rises from Cassia Creek Valley, 4500 ft., to near 9000 ft.

Mt. Jefferson, 3 to 5 mi. S Montana line, at 6500 ft., Fremont County; located 30 mi. N and 2 mi. W Ashton.

Mullan, Shoshone County, 3245 ft.

Murphy, Owyhee County, 2800 ft.

Murphy, 4 mi. S of, Owyhee County, 3200 ft.

Murphy, 5 mi. SE of, Owyhee County, near 3100 ft.

Murphy, 6 mi. W of, Owyhee County, near 4000 ft.

Murphy, 7 mi. SE of, on Sinker Creek, Owyhee County, 2700 ft.

Murphy, 9 mi. SE of, Owyhee County, near 2700 ft.

Murray, Shoshone County, 3000 ft.

Nampa, Canyon County, 2492 ft.

New Meadows, Adams County, near 3900 ft.; near head of Little Salmon River.

Newton's Ranch, 2 mi. NE Inkom, on Rapid Creek, Bannock County, near 5400 ft.

Nezperce, Lewis County, near 3000 ft.

North Canyon, mouth of, Bear Lake County, near 6300 ft.; near west boundary of Sec. 19, T. 12 S., R. 43 E.

Orchard, Ada County, 3100 ft.

Orofino, Clearwater County, 1016 ft.

Osborne. See Osburn.

Osburn, Shoshone County, 2521 ft.

Owyhee River, forks of, Owyhee County, near 4500 ft.

Owyhee River, South Fork of, 12 mi. N Nevada line, Owyhee County, near 4500 ft.

Packers Meadow, Idaho County, near 7000 ft.; located at head of Lochsa River about 10 mi. SW Lolo Hot Springs, Montana.

Pahsimeroi Mountains, Custer County; mountains separating Big Lost River Valley from the Little Lost River and Pahsimeroi valleys; rise to over 12,000 ft.

Pahsimeroi River, near head of, Custer County, near 9000 ft.; at SE base of Mt. Borah.

Pahsimeroi Valley; lies between Lemhi and Pahsimeroi mountains; the Pahsimeroi River flows near the Lemhi Mountains side of the valley and is the boundary between Custer and Lemhi counties there; altitude from near 5000 ft. at Salmon River to 9000 ft. at head.

Pahsimeroi Valley, near Goldburg, Custer County, near 7000 ft.

Paris, Bear Lake County, 5966 ft.; on W side Bear Lake Valley.

Patterson, Lemhi County, near 5000 ft.; in Pahsimeroi Valley, 18 mi. from Salmon River.

Paul, 3 to 4 mi. NW of, Minidoka County, near 4300 ft.

Payette, Payette County, 2152 ft.

Payette, 2 mi. S of, Payette County, 2150 ft.; collecting done between Payette and Snake rivers.

Payette Lake, 3 mi. W of, in Adams County, 5400 ft.; camp located ¼ mi. above Crook Creek Ranger Station.

Payette Valley, Payette County, near 2200 ft.

Pegram, Bear Lake County, 6031 ft.; on Bear River.

Pettit Lake, Blaine County, 7200 ft.; collecting done at base of mountain 1 mi. above head of lake; also along NW shore of lake.

Pingree, Bingham County, near 4500 ft.; on W side Snake River, 12 mi. SW Blackfoot.

Pingree, 1 mi. E of, Bingham County, near 4500 ft.

Pioneer, 17 mi. SE Arco, Butte County, near 4800 ft.; camp was where the railroad crosses Big Lost River.

Pocatello, Bannock County, 4400 ft.

Pocatello, 3 mi. N of, Bannock County, near 4800 ft.

Pocatello, 8.5 mi. NE of, Bannock County, near 5400 ft.

Pocatello, 9 mi. NE of, Bannock County, near 5800 ft.

Pocatello, 12 mi. NE of, Bannock County, 6300 ft.

Pocatello, 2.5 mi. NW of, Bannock County, near 4400 ft.; collecting done along Portneuf River.

Pocatello, 3 mi. S of, Bannock County, near 5000 ft.

Pocatello, 8 mi. S of, Bannock County, near 5800 ft.

Pocatello, 9 mi. SW of, in Power County, near 6000 ft.

Pocatello, 9.5 mi. SW of, in Power County, near 6000 ft.

Pocatello, 2 to 3.5 mi. SE of, Bannock County, 4475 ft.

Pocatello, 5.5 mi. SE of, Bannock County, 4550 ft.

Pocatello, 11 mi. SE of, Bannock County, near 5000 ft.

Pocatello, 4 mi. E of, Bannock County, near 5000 ft.

Pocatello, 5.5 mi. E of, Bannock County, near 6500 ft.; collecting done on ridge between Rapid and Pocatello creeks.

Pocatello, 9.5 mi. E of. See Barrett's Ranch.

Pocatello Creek, N fork of, 6.5 mi. E Pocatello, Bannock County, near 5500 ft.

Pocatello Creek, 6 mi. from Portneuf River, Bannock County, near 5000 ft.

Portneuf, .5 mi. E of, Bannock County, near 4450 ft.; in Sec. 22, T. 7 S., R. 35 E.

Portneuf, 1 mi. E of, Bannock County, near 4500 ft.

Portneuf River, 1 mi. NW Pocatello, Bannock County, 4400 ft.

Portneuf River, 10 mi. NW Pocatello, Bannock County, 4350 ft.

Potlatch River, in northern Latah County.

Preuss Mountains, on boundary between Caribou and Bear Lake counties; rises from 6000 ft. to near 9000 ft.

Priest Lake, Bonner County, 2450 ft.

Raft River, 1 mi. E Malta, Cassia County, near 4300 ft.

Raft River, 2 mi. S Snake River, Cassia County, near 4100 ft.

Raft River, 20 mi. W of, Cassia County, near 4200 ft.; this locality is near present town of Declo.

Raft River Valley, 10 mi. E Declo, Cassia County, near 4300 ft.; collecting done near Cotterel.

Ramey Creek, 4 mi. S Custer, Custer County, 6180 ft.; a small tributary which empties into Yankee Fork above Sunbeam Dam.

Rapid Creek, 4 mi. NE Inkom, Bannock County, near 6000 ft.

Rapid Creek, 9.5 mi. E Pocatello. See Barrett's Ranch.

Rapid River, Idaho County; located 3 mi. S Riggins near junction of Salmon and Little Salmon rivers, near 1800 ft.

Raymond, Idaho County; an old mining camp at the junction of Seigal Creek and Red River, 4.5 mi. SE Elk City, near 4400 ft.; post office discontinued about 1902.

Reynolds Creek, 12 mi. S Snake River, Owyhee County, 4000 ft.

Riddle, Owyhee County, near 5300 ft.

Riddle, 1 mi. S of, Owyhee County, near 5300 ft.

Riddle, 2 mi. SE of, on Indian Creek, Owyhee County, near 5400 ft.

Riddle, 5 mi. SE of, Owyhee County, near 5600 ft.

Riddle, 15 mi. SW of, Owyhee County, near 5000 ft.

Rogerson, 2 mi. W of, Twin Falls County, near 4500 ft.

Rogerson, 2 mi. E of, Twin Falls County, near 4500 ft.

Rogerson, 3 mi. S of, Twin Falls County, near 4500 ft.

Ross Fork Creek, 11 mi. NE Pocatello, Bannock County, near 6300 ft.

Rupert, 4 to 5 mi. N of, Minidoka County, near 4300 ft.

Rupert, 6 mi. S of, on S side Snake River in Cassia County, near 4200 ft.

Salmon City, Lemhi County, 3956 ft.

Salmon Creek, 8 mi. W Rogerson, Twin Falls County, near 4500 ft.; camp at Salmon Creek Reservoir.

Salmon River, Middle Fork of, 60 mi. from main Salmon River, Valley County; probably refers to Sheep Mountain on E side of river nearly opposite Pistol Creek; over 7000 ft.

Salmon River Mountains; a locality given by Merriam (1891) which refers to Lemhi Mountains, near Timber Creek, Lemhi County; directly S of Leadore, 7000 to 10,500 ft.

Salmon River Mountains, Custer County; a range of mountains W of Challis which rises to over 9000 ft.

Salmon Valley; near Alturas Lake, 7000 ft., in Blaine and Custer counties; river forms the boundary between the two counties.

Sawtooth City, Blaine County, 7346 ft.; on Beaver Creek, 2 mi. SE Alturas Lake; now abandoned.

Sawtooth Lake. See Alturas Lake.

Sawtooth Mountains, near Alturas Lake, Blaine County; these mountains rise from the floor of Salmon Valley, 7000 ft., to an average height of 9000 ft.; Snowyside, the highest peak in the vicinity of Alturas Lake, is 10,646 ft.

Sawtooth Mountains, 5 mi. NW Galena, Blaine County, 8000 ft.

Sawtooth National Forest; too general to locate precisely.

Schutt's Mine, 9 mi. E Pocatello, Bannock County, near 6300 ft.

Scout Mountain, Bannock County, 7000 ft.; in Bannock Mountains about 15 mi. SE Pocatello; T. 8 S., R. 35 E.

Seven Devils Mountains; range of mountains lying in Idaho and Adams counties on E side of Snake River in west-central Idaho; average elevation near 7000 ft.

Shelley, Bingham County, near 4600 ft.

Shelley, 5 mi. E of, in Bonneville County, near 4650 ft.

Shoshone, Lincoln County, near 4200 ft.

Shoshone, 2 mi. W of, Lincoln County, near 4200 ft.

Shoshone, 20 mi. N of, Lincoln County, near 4500 ft.

Shoshone Falls, N side Snake River, Jerome County, near 3500 ft.; collecting done in bottom of canyon and on adjacent rimrock.

Shoshone Falls, S side Snake River, Twin Falls County, near 3500 ft.; collecting done in bottom of canyon above falls.

Silver City, Owyhee County, 6200 ft.

Silver Creek, Owyhee County ?.

Sinyakwatun Depot; probably is the same as Sineaqueteen, the old crossing place of the Pend Oreille River in Boundary County. (Pend Oreille, or Pend d' Oreille, River is now known as Clarks Fork.)

Small, 8 mi. W Dubois, Clark County, near 6000 ft.; on Medicine Lodge Creek.

Smith Mountain, summit of, Adams County, 7500 ft.; located 34 mi. due N of Goodrich.

Snake River, 1 mi. W Heyburn, Minidoka County, near 4100 ft.

Snake River, S side of, 2 mi. W Reynolds Creek, Owyhee County, 2300 ft.

Snake River, North Fork of=Henrys Fork, N of Rexburg.

Snake River, N. fork of, 10 mi. SW Island Park, Fremont County, 6200 ft.

Snake River, Middle Fork of,=Teton River.

Snake River Desert, near Arco, Butte County, near 4800 ft.

Soda Springs, Caribou County, near 5500 ft.

Soldier Creek, 2 mi. NE Coolin; rises from 2431 ft. at Priest Lake, Bonner County, to 6000 ft. in the Selkirk Mountains in Boundary County.

South Fork Ranch. Could not locate.

Sparks Well, 23 mi. NE Minidoka; probably in western Power County, near 4600 ft.

Springfield, Bingham County, near 4500 ft.; on W. side Snake River, 17 mi. SW Blackfoot.

Springfield, 3 mi. S of, Bingham County, near 4480 ft.

St. Anthony, 5 mi. W of, Fremont County, near 5000 ft.

St. Maries, 10 mi. N of, in Kootenai County, near 2700 ft.; collecting done near U. S. Highway 95 A.

St. Marys=St. Maries, Benewah County, near 2700 ft.

Stanley Lake, Custer County, 6500 ft.; called Goat Lake on U. S. G. S. topo. sheet, 1893 ed.

Stanley Lake, mountains near, Custer County; refers to Sawtooth Mountains. See same.

Strawberry Creek [or Canyon], 20 mi. NE Preston (actually 16 mi. N and 13 mi. E), Franklin County, near 6700 ft.

Succor Creek, Owyhee County, near 4500 ft.; called Sucker Creek on U. S. G. S. map of Idaho, 1926 ed., in T. 3 S., R. 5 W.; not to be confused with Sucker Creek near Homedale.

Summit, Blaine County, 8795 ft.; is summit of pass over Sawtooth Mountains from Big Wood River Valley to Salmon Valley; commonly called Galena Summit.

Swan Lake, Bannock County, near 4769 ft.; in Sec. 15, T. 13 S., R. 38 E.

Swan Lake, 8 mi. W of, Bannock County, near 6300 ft.

Swan Valley, 3 mi. W of, on South Fork Snake River, Bonneville County, 5264 ft.; collecting done on both sides of river.

Taber, 2 mi. SE of, Bingham County, near 4800 ft.; on road to Arco, 23 mi. NW Blackfoot.

Tamarack, Adams County, near 4000 ft.; near head of Little Salmon River.

Targhee National Forest; in region near Yellowstone National Park.

Taylor Creek, 5 mi. S Montana line at Sheridan, Clark County, 7000
    ft.; located near junction of Taylor and Sheridan creeks 16 mi.
    W Trude, in Sec. 6, T. 13 N., R 1 E.
Teton Basin, Teton County, near 6000 ft.; basin in which Victor is
    situated.
Teton Canyon=Canyon on Teton River.
Teton River, N fork of; constitutes boundary between Fremont and
    Teton counties.
Thompson Pass, Shoshone County, 4862 ft.; located at head of Prich-
    ard Creek, tributary to Coeur d'Alene River, on Idaho-Montana
    line about 7 mi. SE Murray.
Three Creek, Owyhee County, near 5500 ft.; near head of E fork of
    Bruneau River.
Trail Creek, 1 mi. W Pocatello, Bannock County, near 4800 ft.
Trude, 4 mi. S of, Jefferson County, near 6500 ft.
Twin Falls, Twin Falls County, near 4000 ft.
Twin Falls, 13 mi. E of, Twin Falls County, near 4000 ft.; collecting
    done near U. S. Highway 30.
Twin Lakes, Minidoka County, near 4500 ft.; in Snake River desert,
    20 mi. N Minidoka.
Tygee Basin, Caribou County, 6400 ft.; in T. 32 N., R. 46 E.; Tygee
    Creek, tributary to Salt River in Wyoming, flows through the
    basin; about 5 mi. SW Auburn, Wyoming.
Van Wyck, Valley County, 4778 ft.; located 1 mi. W Cascade near
    N fork Payette River, at S end of Long Valley, which lies im-
    mediately S of Payette Lake.
Victor, 3 mi. S of, Teton County, near 6000 ft.; at upper end of
    Teton Basin; collecting done on Smith Canyon Creek.
Viola, Latah County, near 2600 ft.; 7 mi. N Moscow and 1 mi. E Idaho-
    Washington line.
Virginia, Bannock County, near 4500 ft.; 10 mi. S McCammon, on
    Marsh Creek.
Wapello, 3.5 mi. E of, Bingham County; small town on E side Snake
    River, 5 mi. NNE Blackfoot.
Warm Lake, 5 mi. E of, Valley County, 7000 ft.; near head of South
    Fork of Salmon River.
Warm River, Fremont County, near 5000 ft.; at junction of Warm
    River and Henrys Fork.
Warren, Idaho County, near 6500 ft.; in Sec. 12, T. 22 N., R. 6 E.
Weippe, 2 mi. NE of, Clearwater County, 3000 ft.
Weiser, Washington County, 2129 ft.
Wilder, 4 mi. S of, Canyon County, 2200 ft.; collecting done on N side
    Snake River opposite the town of Homedale.
Wildhorse Creek, head Big Lost River, Custer County, near 8000 ft.;
    the Devils Bedstead lies just to the west of this creek, which heads
    on and about Hyndman Peak.
Williams Canyon, head of, Wasatch Mountains, Bannock County,
    near 7000 ft.; in Sec. 19, T. 12 S., R. 42 E.

Wind River, 40 mi. S Grangeville, Idaho County, near 5000 ft.; located about 23 mi. due E of Lucile.

Wolverine Creek, Bingham County; heads in the Blackfoot Mountains at 7000 ft. and flows into Blackfoot River about 18 mi. ENE Blackfoot.

Yale, 6 mi. W of, Cassia County, near 4300 ft.; in Raft River Valley, 7 mi. S Snake River; at junction of Heglar Creek and Raft River.

MAMMALS OF IDAHO BY GROUPS

In each instance the generic name is followed by the number of kinds, that is, species and geographic races, that are known to occur in Idaho.

Sorex	4	Perognathus	5
Myotis	7	Dipodomys	2
Lasionycteris	1	Castor	2
Pipistrellus	1	Onychomys	2
Eptesicus	1	Reithrodontomys	2
Lasiurus	1	Peromyscus	4
Corynorhinus	1	Neotoma	3
Ursus	2	Phenacomys	1
Procyon	1	Clethrionomys	2
Martes	2	Microtus	5
Mustela	4	Lemmiscus	1
Gulo	1	Ondatra	1
Lutra	1	Rattus	1
Spilogale	1	Mus	1
Mephitis	2	Zapus	4
Taxidea	1	Erethizon	1
Vulpes	2	Ochotona	7
Canis	3	Lepus	3
Felis	1	Sylvilagus	3
Lynx	2	Cervus	1
Marmota	4	Odocoileus	2
Citellus	10	Alces	1
Callospermophilus	4	Rangifer	1
Ammospermophilus	1	Antilocapra	1
Eutamias	10	Bison	1
Tamiasciurus	2	Ovis	1
Glaucomys	2	Oreamnos	1
Thomomys	10		

Grouped by Order

Order	Kinds	Specimens examined
Insectivora	4	130
Chiroptera	12	102
Carnivora	23	157
Rodentia	80	2439
Lagomorpha	13	268
Artiodactyla	9	10
Total	141	3106

One hundred and forty-one kinds of mammals are here recorded from within the political limits of Idaho. These are divided among six orders, twenty families, and fifty-five genera. It is of interest to compare the present status of our knowledge of the mammals of Idaho with that of 1890. For convenience, full species and geographic races may be treated as of equal rank under the term "kinds."

1890		1937	
Orders	6	Orders	6
Families	20	Families	20
Genera	45	Genera	55
Kinds	67	Kinds	141

This comparison is merely indicative of the relative amount of attention that was given the mammals of Idaho prior to, and after, 1890. Additional collecting and study doubtless will reveal that several other "kinds," particularly among the shrews, bats, and rodents, occur in the state.

PLAN OF PROCEDURE IN SPECIES ACCOUNTS

The sequence of species and subspecies is essentially that employed by Miller (1924). Because emphasis here is placed on species and subspecies, accounts of the characteristics of orders, families, and genera often are omitted unless it is felt that their inclusion would contribute importantly to an understanding of the mammals of Idaho. For characterizations of these higher groups the reader may consult such general works as "Mammals Living and Extinct" by Flower and Lydekker (1891), "Die Säugetiere" by Max Weber (1927), field guides, as for example "Field Book of North American Mammals" by H. E. Anthony (1928), or textbooks treating of vertebrate zoology.

For each species or geographic race (subspecies) there appears first the accepted scientific name followed by the authority; under this is placed the vernacular name. Because of the great number of vernacular names which have been used to designate a single "kind," I have chosen the name which, to me, seemingly best applies.

This is followed by the scientific name as it appeared in the original description, name of the describer, citation to the publication in which the original description appeared, and statement of the locality whence the type specimen came. In stating the type locality I have followed Miller (1924) in nearly all instances except when the locality is in Idaho. For a complete list and discussion of the type localities in Idaho, see the section of this report headed *Type Localities in Idaho* (p. 65).

Scientific names (other than the one appearing in the original description) which have been applied in published accounts of the species or geographic race *as occurring in Idaho*, when different from the name in current use, are placed after the heading *Synonyms*. Each is followed by the authority and a citation to the published work.

The descriptive accounts have been drawn largely from specimens in hand; where these were lacking, recourse was made to published accounts. In most instances, the description includes first an account of external characters, including measurements (always given in millimeters, unless stated to be in feet or inches, in the following sequence: Total length, length of tail, length of hind foot, length or height of ear from notch). This is followed by a description of the skull.

Under *Remarks* are discussed relationships, migrational history when data permit, and other matters of interest; in some accounts, particularly in the Rodentia, a section on *Ecology* is added.

Under *Records of occurrence* is given first the number of specimens examined, followed by locality records grouped by counties, together with the number of specimens examined from each locality; unless otherwise stated, all specimens examined are in the California Museum of Vertebrate Zoology, Berkeley, California. The name of an institution or private collection in parentheses applies only to the locality and specimens as set off by semicolons. Example: *Minidoka County:* 4 mi. N Rupert, 1; Minidoka, 3 (Biol. Surv. coll.). Here, only the specimens from Minidoka are in the Biological Survey collection; the one from near Rupert is in the Museum of Vertebrate Zoology. Following the list of specimens examined is a list of additional records that have appeared in published accounts, together with authority and citation. If I have examined specimens from a locality from which specimens of the animal previously have been recorded in published form, I have not included that locality a second time in the list of additional records.

LIST OF COUNTIES IN IDAHO

The sequence in which counties are listed, approximately from north to south and from west to east, is as follows:

Boundary	Boise	Clark
Bonner	Canyon	Fremont
Kootenai	Ada	Butte
Shoshone	Elmore	Jefferson
Benewah	Owyhee	Madison
Latah	Lemhi	Teton
Clearwater	Custer	Bonneville
Nez Perce	Blaine	Bingham
Lewis	Camas	Power
Idaho	Gooding	Bannock
Adams	Lincoln	Caribou
Valley	Jerome	Oneida
Washington	Minidoka	Franklin
Payette	Twin Falls	Bear Lake
Gem	Cassia	

ACCOUNTS OF SPECIES

Class MAMMALIA Mammals

Order INSECTIVORA
Insectivorous Mammals

Family SORICIDAE
SHREWS

Members of this family are among the smallest of North American mammals. Externally they are characterized by small size; sharply pointed snout projecting anteriorly beyond oral opening; rudimentary eyes; small feet, all bearing five toes with claws; scantily haired tail; and short ears nearly concealed by the thick, soft pelage. They are distinguished readily from other small mammals by the presence of numerous, sharp-pointed teeth set close together, that is, no space or diastema exists beween the front (incisor) teeth and the cheek (molariform) teeth.

Four species of shrews occur in Idaho all of which are aquatic or semi-aquatic in habit. They commonly frequent stream sides, seepage places, and marshes where their tiny burrows and runways are encountered. I have had fair success in trapping them with small snap traps, baited with "chewed" rolled oats or bits of meat, placed crosswise in their runways under cut banks and at the sides of fallen logs.

Their food consists normally of insects, although they are known to feed on other kinds of animal life. Often they attack and partly devour small mammals caught in the collectors' traps.

Shrews are active the year round and in winter often travel considerable distances over or under the snow. Because of this, and the fact that many of them are semi-aquatic, they are widespread throughout Idaho and present few distributional problems. Deserts are barriers to their geographic movements only in summer because in winter sufficient snow is present to permit dispersal over them. Rivers, especially near the headwaters, do not restrict their movements because the animals are expert swimmers, and in winter when the wider portions are frozen over they can cross from side to side with ease. Another circumstance which may account in part for their wide distribution is that they appear to be solitary and nomadic in habit.

Genus **Sorex** Linnaeus
Shrews
Key to Adult Shrews of Idaho

1 Hind foot more than 20 mm., fimbriated; total length near 150 mm.
S. p. navigator, p. 104

1' Hind foot less than 15 mm., nonfimbriated; total length less than 120 mm.

  2 Third unicuspid tooth as large as, or larger than, fourth.
S. c. cinereus, p. 100

  2' Third unicuspid tooth smaller than fourth.

    3 Total length usually more than 110 mm.; tail usually more than 44; interorbital breadth 3.7 or more.
S. o. obscurus, p. 103

    3' Total length usually less than 110 mm.; tail usually less than 44; interorbital breadth less than 3.7.
S. v. monticola, p. 101

Sorex cinereus cinereus Kerr
GRAY SHREW

Sorex arcticus cinereus Kerr, Animal Kingdom, 1792:206. Type from Fort Severn, Ontario, Canada.

Synonyms.—Sorex idahoensis Merriam, 1891:32; *Sorex personatus,* Merriam, 1895:60.

In the field it is difficult to distinguish this shrew from the two following species. All three have nearly the same external proportions and color and one must rely upon cranial characters for certain determination. The rostrum is decidedly narrower in *cinereus* than in either the Wandering or the Dusky Shrew. In addition, the third unicuspid tooth in the upper jaw generally is as large as, or larger than, the fourth, and the molar teeth are narrower.

Two July-taken specimens, nos. 1865 and 8171 in the Ralph Ellis collection, from Adams County, measure, in millimeters, 115-44-12.5-3.5 and 105-41-12-4, respectively.

No. 8165, captured July 7, is still in the spring molt. A small patch of worn winter pelage, separated from the shorter summer fur by a distinct molt line, is present on the rump. There is little difference in coloration between summer and winter pelages. This knowledge is useful in distinguishing the nearly black winter-taken specimens of the Wandering Shrew from the brownish winter-taken specimens of this species.

The Gray Shrew occurs from Alaska east through Canada and the Great Lakes region to the Atlantic Coast and south in the Rocky Mountain region to northern New Mexico. Records of capture in Idaho indicate that *cinereus* is confined largely to the mountainous areas of the state where it occurs from 4000 feet up to at least 8200 feet.

Records of occurrence.—Specimens examined, 4, as follows: *Latah County:* Cedar Mountain, 2 (Chas. R. Conner Mus.). *Adams County:* 1 mi. N Bear Creek R. S., 1; ½ mi. E Black Lake, 1 (both in Ralph Ellis coll.). Additional records (Jackson, 1928:47): *Idaho County:* Bitterroot Mountains; Packers Meadow. *Blaine County:* Ketchum; Sawtooth City; Sawtooth (Alturas) Lake; Sawtooth National Forest. *Lemhi County:* Timber Creek, Lemhi Mountains, 8200 ft. (type locality of *Sorex idahoensis*). *Power County:* American Falls.

Sorex vagrans monticola Merriam
WANDERING SHREW

Sorex monticolus Merriam, N. Amer. Fauna, 3:43. September 11, 1890. Type from San Francisco Mountain, 11,500 feet, Coconino County, Arizona.

Synonym.—*Sorex dobsoni* Merriam, 1891:33.

The Wandering Shrew, as the name suggests, is encountered in a variety of situations. On Mt. Harrison a specimen was taken approximately fifty feet from the creek, in a runway of *Microtus mordax*, in a mixed growth of *Artemisia* and *Pentstemon*. At Victor it was found most commonly in the heavy, rank growth of herbage at considerable distances from water. Most often I have taken them in traps set in *Microtus* runways. A. E. Borell found them unusually abundant on Cuddy Mountain in June, 1930. He says (MS), "Shrews are more common here than they usually are in most localities. We have taken from two to six almost every day. Many of these are immature and the majority were taken under logs on moist hill sides rather than along the creek. Some were taken in wet bogs."

This species apparently is as active during the hours of daylight as at night. At Victor three of the four specimens collected were trapped during the forenoon, and at Alturas Lake one of three was taken during the day. Borell also took them in the daytime at Cuddy Mountain.

Most of the shrews I have taken appear to have been accidentally caught when they ran over the treadle of the trap. Nevertheless, when bacon grease or meat was used as bait, the animals often were caught in a position which suggested that they had been nibbling at the bait. Borell reports similar findings.

One female collected July 4 near Payette Lake contained six small embryos; another taken July 27 near Cocolalla contained one embryo 6 mm. in rump-crown length. Borell captured many immature animals at Cuddy Mountain in the latter part of June. These data indicate that two broods are reared yearly.

Three females from Alturas Lake average 106 - 44 - 13. A series of fourteen specimens in the Museum of Vertebrate Zoology, collected by Wayne B. Whitlow at localities in the vicinity of Pocatello, illustrate the stages of the autumnal molt. One specimen (no. 46923) collected September 21 retains the short brown summer pelage. Two specimens (nos. 46926-27), taken September 28, show the encroachment of the long, nearly black winter pelage on the rump and lower back. By October 5 (no. 46928) the molt had proceeded anteriorly and lateroventrally to such an extent that only the head, neck, and shoulders retained the short, brown summer pelage. By the middle of November the process of molt was completed (no. 46919), and apparently the ventral parts and the tail are the last to acquire new hair. In the vicinity of Pocatello some of these animals retain their winter pelage at least until April 19 (no. 46922) and by May 10 the change back to the summer coat is nearly complete (no. 46930).

This race occurs throughout the Rocky Mountain region, mainly south of latitude 49° N. In Idaho, records of its occurrence indicate a statewide distribution, save for the extreme southwestern portion, and an altitudinal range from 3000 feet up at least to 7400 feet.

Records of occurrence.—Specimens examined, 77, as follows: *Bonner County:* 5 mi. W Cocolalla, 9. *Shoshone County:* Glidden Lakes, 2. *Latah County:* Cedar Mountain, 5; Felton's Mill, 1; "Latah County," 1 (all 7 in Chas. R. Conner Mus.). *Clearwater County:* 2 mi. NE Weippe, 1. *Adams County:* 1 mi. N Bear Creek R. S., 2; ½ mi. E Black Lake, 5; summit Smith Mountain, 3 (all 10 in Ralph Ellis coll.); 3 mi. W Payette Lake, 3. *Valley County:* 5 mi. E Warm Lake, 2. *Washington County:* 1 mi. NE Heath, 13 (Ralph Ellis coll.). *Canyon County:* Nampa, 1. *Custer County:* head Pahsimeroi River, 1. *Blaine County:* Alturas Lake (type locality of *Sorex dobsoni*), 4. *Gooding County:* 2 mi. S Hagerman, 2. *Twin Falls County:* Salmon Creek, 8 mi. W Rogerson, 1. *Cassia County:* Mt. Harrison, 10 mi. S Albion, 1. *Teton County:* 3 mi. SW Victor, 5 (1 in Davis coll.). *Power County:* Bannock Creek, 4 mi S Portneuf River, 3 (1 in Ralph Ellis coll.). *Bannock County:* Indian Creek, 4 mi. S Pocatello, 1; 2½ mi. NW Pocatello, 2; 9½ mi. E Pocatello, 2; N. Fork Pocatello Creek, 6½ mi. E Pocatello, 2; Schutt's Mine, 4. *Franklin County:* Strawberry Creek, 20 mi. NE Preston, 1. Additional records (Jackson, 1928:112): *Kootenai County:* Coeur d'Alene. *Shoshone County:* 7 mi. E McKinnis; Mullan; Osborne. *Lewis County:* Nezperce. *Idaho County:* Seven Devils Mountains. *Adams County:* New Meadows; Tamarack. *Elmore County:* Bald Mountain R. S.; Cayuse Creek. *Blaine County:* Sawtooth City. *Cassia County:* Albion. *Bonneville County:* 10 mi. SE Irwin. *Bannock County:* Swan Lake; Pocatello.

Sorex obscurus obscurus Merriam
DUSKY SHREW

Sorex vagrans similis Merriam, N. Amer. Fauna, 5:34. July 31, 1891. Renamed *Sorex obscurus* by Merriam, N. Amer. Fauna, 10:72. December 31, 1895. Type from Timber Creek, 8200 feet altitude, Lemhi Mountains, Lemhi County, Idaho.

The single specimen from Idaho in the Museum of Vertebrate Zoology was collected April 15 by Wayne B. Whitlow in a field three miles north of Pocatello. This specimen, adult male, measures 112-47-13 and has not completed its spring molt.

Apparently the ranges of the Dusky Shrew and the Wandering Shrew are coextensive in Idaho, although, according to Jackson (1929:112), the Dusky Shrew largely is confined to the Boreal Zone while the Wandering Shrew occurs in the lower parts of the Boreal Zone and in upper Transition Zone. Although he cautions against too much dependence on habitat preferences in identification, he states *(loc. cit.)* that the Dusky Shrew is more often found along creek banks and in moist woods, whereas the Wandering Shrew more frequently occurs in meadows and marshes.

Records of occurrence.—Specimen examined, 1, from 3 mi. N Pocatello, Bannock County. Additional records (Jackson, 1928:121): *Boundary County:* Cabinet Mountains (east of Priest Lake). *Bonner County:* Priest Lake. *Elmore County:* Bald Mountain R. S. *Lemhi County:* Pahsimeroi Mountains, head of Pahsimeroi River. *Fremont County:* 4 mi. S Trude. *Caribou County:* Preuss Mountains.

Sorex palustris navigator (Baird)
WATER SHREW

Neosorex navigator Baird, Report Pacific R. R. Survey, Mammals, 8(1):11. 1857. Type from near head of Yakima River, Cascade Mountains, Washington.

Synonyms.—*Sorex palustris*, Merriam, 1891:35; *Sorex (Neosorex) palustris navigator*, Merriam, 1895:92.

This shrew can be distinguished readily from any of the other shrews in Idaho by its larger size, nearly black dorsal coloration, white ventral coloration, and large fimbriated hind feet. In external measurements five males and five females, all adults, from Cuddy Mountain average, respectively, 155-71-20.5, and 158-73-20.

In eastern Idaho, near Victor, I found them inhabiting small, slow-flowing creeks which were choked with dense stands of water cress *(Radicula nasturtium-aquaticum).* Unbaited traps placed in the water, so they were supported by the cress, across well-defined small channels or tunnels in the vegetation, yielded two specimens. In many of the smaller streams obstructions projected from both banks and forced the water through narrow channels. A shrew traveling down such streams apparently follows the course of least resistance and does not climb over obstacles, but goes around them. I have had fair success in trapping them by placing snap traps crosswise in these channels. Other specimens were captured at the edge of the water in places where the stream was more open and faster flowing.

The tendency of this shrew to rely upon water as a means of eluding danger is illustrated by the following incident. At Elba, Mr. Will Wickle and a group of men encountered an adult female in a small pool of water in an irrigation ditch which recently had been in use. Their attention was drawn to a "silver streak" moving rapidly through the water toward the far end of the pool. Hurrying to that end, one of the men attempted to catch the supposed "fish" and learned, to his astonishment, that he was after a "swimming mouse." The shrew eluded capture and swam rapidly under water toward the opposite end of the pool. After many unsuccessful attempts, it was finally captured, killed, and later presented to me. During the period of its pursuit, the shrew remained in the water and made no attempt to gain safety in the dense vegetation on land. Although it is adept at swimming, its power of locomotion on land is little, if at all, inferior to that of typical shrews. At Alturas Lake I caught three of them in traps set in runways of *Microtus mordax* a short distance from running water.

At Cuddy Mountain, Borell and Gilmore found them nearly as abundant individually as the small Wandering Shrew. They trapped many of them in little boggy springs or along boggy trickles which flowed into the main creeks. These bogs were overgrown with moss, grass, dogwood, currant, and willow. Some were taken along the edge of the main creek.

Unlike the Wandering Shrew, I have found the Water Shrew to be exclusively nocturnal. At Cuddy Mountain, however, Borell captured two, of eighteen specimens taken, between 9 A.M. and dusk.

None of the females I have examined from Idaho (collected during June, July, and August) contained embryos, but during this period a number of half-grown young were trapped. This indicates an early, definite breeding period. In California, however, this shrew apparently has an extensive breeding season. Females taken June 19, 23, 26, and August 1 contained from five to seven embryos, and a male taken August 11 had enlarged testes.

The geographic range of this species extends from Alaska south in the Rocky Mountains to New Mexico and

Arizona and south in the Cascade-Sierra Nevada ranges to Mount Whitney in California. Trapping records in Idaho indicate it is restricted to the vicinity of mountain streams; its altitudinal range there extends from 4000 feet to 7500 feet.

Records of occurrence.—Specimens examined, 48, as follows: *Latah County:* Cedar Mountain, 2 (Chas. R. Conner Mus.). *Adams County:* ½ mi. E Black Lake, 7 (5 in Ralph Ellis coll.); 1 mi. N Bear Creek R. S., 3 (Ralph Ellis coll.); summit Smith Mountain, 4 (3 in Ralph Ellis coll.). *Washington County:* 1 mi. NE Heath, 19 (18 in Ralph Ellis coll.). *Custer County:* head Pahsimeroi River, 2. *Blaine County:* Alturas Lake, 3. *Cassia County:* Elba, 1 (Davis coll.). *Teton County:* 3 mi. SW Victor, 3. *Bannock County:* Barrett's Ranch, 2; 6 mi. up Indian Creek, 1. *Franklin County:* Strawberry Creek, 20 mi. NE Preston, 1. Additional records (Jackson, 1928:188): *Shoshone County:* Thompson Pass. *Idaho County:* Bitterroot Mountains [E of Hamilton, Montana ?]; Warren. *Lemhi County:* Salmon River Mountains [= Timber Creek, Lemhi Mountains]. *Blaine County:* head Big Wood River; Sawtooth City. *Cassia County:* Albion. *Clark County:* Birch Creek. *Bonneville County:* 10 mi. SE Irwin. *Bingham County:* Fort Hall. *Caribou County:* Crow Creek (head of). *Oneida County:* Malad.

Order CHIROPTERA

Bats

Among living mammals, bats are unique in their power of sustained flight. The bones of the arms and fingers are greatly elongated and support the flying membrane, a thin, lateral extension of the body integument. The membrane is attached posteriorly to the hind legs and, in North American bats, to the tail. The thumb is free and clawed; the knee joint is directed outwards and backwards; each hind foot bears five toes equipped with sharp, curved claws; the ears in some species are greatly enlarged and curiously fluted; the tragus is prominent; the eyes are small. The dentition, like that of the Insectivora, is tuberculosectorial and well adapted to a diet of insects. Each molar has the cusps connected in such a way that a W-shaped set of ridges is formed; the upper incisors usually are separated by a wide, median space.

Bats are nocturnal or crepuscular in habit. Their food,

chiefly night-flying insects, is usually captured in mid-air, although, on occasion, they must resort to feeding on the ground as is evidenced by the remains of partly eaten flightless Jerusalem crickets *(Stenopelmatus)* in guano deposits under their roosts. Water seems to be a requisite for the well-being of most bats; often I have seen them swoop low over a quiet pool and apparently drink.

Many species are gregarious as regards their daytime roosts. Such roosts have been found in deserted mine tunnels, in natural caves, in crevices in rocks, in buildings; in fact, in any suitable place where protection and a degree of darkness are available. The Hoary Bat and a few others are solitary. Most bats hibernate during a part of the year, but, unlike some rodents which truly hibernate, the period is interrupted by more or less prolonged intervals of activity. According to Hahn (1903:152), a bat does not fly more than six hours out of twenty-four, and does even this for no more than eight months of the year. "At least five-sixths of its life is spent hanging head downward in the dark." The amount of time spent in a state of torpor is thought to be directly proportional to the amount of reserve fat stored in the animal's body and not upon time of year or temperature.

Like birds, many species of bats migrate seasonally. Some very interesting studies of this phenomenon, by the banding method, are in progress in the United States and in Germany. Griffin (1936:238-239) sums up the results of this work to date in the following words: "Marking studies have shown that bats generally return annually to the same caves to hibernate; there is also some tendency for the bats to return in successive summers to the same summer roosts. Several species of *Myotis* have been shown to possess a strong homing instinct and even these smaller species are capable of the long flights necessary for migration."

Functionally the most important of the special senses are those associated with the ear. For the perception of food, smell and taste are of little value. Sight may be of some aid, but hearing and the tactile sense are chiefly relied on to locate food. A definite correlation exists between the position of the external ear on the head and the method of foraging. Bats with the ears directed downward perceive sounds most readily from that direction and perform series of downward swoops in foraging; those with the ears directed forward fly an erratic zigzag course at a rather uniform altitude. Experimental studies (Hahn, *op. cit.)* show that neither sight nor the external ears and tragi are necessary for the perception of obstacles during flight. These are perceived chiefly through the sense organs located in the inner ear. Hahn assumes that perception probably is due to atmospheric condensation between the moving animal and the object it is approaching. A possible alternative explanation for this phenomenon is that of sympathetic vibrations. Because all objects vibrate to a greater or less degree, it seems possible to me that vibrations of the object the animal is approaching produce sympathetic vibrations in the inner ear of the bat and thus warn the animal of the nearness of the object. It is difficult to understand how the air between such a small object as a wire and a flying bat could be condensed sufficiently for the bat to perceive the presence of the object.

The young usually number one per litter, sometimes two, and in the solitary bats as many as four. For a time after birth, the young accompany the mother, clinging to the nipple and to the fur on the under side of her body, on her nightly excursions.

Of the eight families of bats occurring in North America only the family Vespertilionidae is found in Idaho.

Key to Adult Bats of Idaho

1 Interfemoral membrane furred dorsally.
    2 Total length near 100 mm.; hind foot near 10 mm.; **general coloration blackish, with dorsum frosted.**
                                Lasionycteris noctivagans, p. 118
    2' Total length near 140 mm.; hind foot near 16 mm.; general coloration brownish buff, heavily overcast with white.
                                Lasiurus cinereus, p. 122
1' Interfemoral membrane naked, or with scattered short hairs dorsally.
    3 Length of ear half, or more than half, the length of forearm.
        4 Height of ear above notch near 35 mm.; general coloration sooty brown.
                          Corynorhinus r. intermedius, p. 123

4' Height of ear above notch near 22 mm.; general coloration golden brown.

Myotis e. chrysonotus, p. 113

3' Length of ear much less than half the length of forearm.

5 Total length over 105 mm.; hind foot 11 mm., or more.

Eptesicus f. pallidus, p. 120

5' Total length less than 100 mm.; hind foot 11 mm., or less.

6 Hind foot 7.5 mm., or less.

7 Tragus straight and tapering; face furred, not leathery.

8 Face with black facial mask; tail free at tip; general dorsal color flaxen.

Myotis s. melanorhinus, p. 116

8' Face without black mask; tip of tail enclosed in flying membrane.

Myotis c. californicus, p. 115

7' Tragus blunt, tip bent forward; face with black leathery mask; general color grayish buff.

Pipistrellus h. hesperus, p. 119

6' Hind foot 8 mm., or more.

9 Hind foot near 8 mm.; **ears short and evenly rounded;** obvious extension of fur on ventral sides of flying membrane.

Myotis v. interior, p. 114

9' Hind foot 10 mm., or more; ears pointed, not evenly rounded; little, if any, fur on ventral sides of flying membrane.

10 Dorsal hairs dull tipped; hind foot near 10 mm.; forearm 32-37 mm.; skull with abruptly rising forehead; general color buffy.

Myotis y. sociabilis, p. 112

10' Dorsal hairs with bronzy tips; hind foot near 11 mm.; forearm 36-40 mm.; skull somewhat flattened; forehead rising gradually; general color golden or dark yellowish brown.

11   General color golden.
        Myotis l.
        carissima, p. 111
11 ' General   color   dark
     yellowish brown.
        Myotis l.
        alascensis, p. 110

Family VESPERTILIONIDAE
COMMON BATS

Genus **Myotis** Kaup
Mouse-eared Bats

Myotis lucifugus alascensis Miller
ALASKAN LITTLE BROWN BAT

Myotis lucifugus alascensis Miller, N. Amer. Fauna, 13:63. October 16, 1897. Type from Sitka, Alaska.

The species *lucifugus,* of which two races, *alascensis* and *carissima,* occur in Idaho, is characterized by medium size; ears of moderate length, when laid forward reaching to the nostril; foot moderately large (near 11 mm.), its length ranging from 53 to nearly 56 per cent of the length of the tibia; pelage long and, on the back, with conspicuous burnished tips.

The two races of *lucifugus* in Idaho differ chiefly in coloration. The Alaskan Little Brown Bat is so dark, especially its underfur, that the whole appearance is sooty with an inconspicuous dark bronzy gloss on the back. The extreme tips of the long hairs are glossy, reflecting the light in such a manner as to give the impression, especially when the hair is ruffled, of bronzy streaks.

These bats are gregarious, breeding and roosting in colonies. They occur usually in the vicinity of at least moderate tree growth and prefer to feed along small watercourses in the forest. According to Allen (1921:57), this bat has but a single young at birth; it may have two litters a season.

The species is wide ranging, occurring over most of the forested areas of North America. *Myotis l. alascensis* occurs along the coast from southern Alaska south to west-central California, and southward in the Rocky Mountains to Corvallis, Montana. A single adult male, skin and skull, no. 81 Chas. R. Conner Mus., collected July 3, 1923, by W. T. Shaw, measures 90-37-11. One I collected August 2, 1937, at Coeur d'Alene measures 87-35-12. As compared with *Myotis l. carissima* from Elba, they are much darker both dorsally and ventrally. There is no indication of the whitish ventral coloration of *carissima*.

Records of occurrence.—Specimens examined, 2, as follows: *Kootenai County:* Coeur d'Alene, 1. *Latah County:* Felton Mills, 1 (Chas. R. Conner Mus.).

Myotis lucifugus carissima Thomas
YELLOWSTONE LITTLE BROWN BAT

Myotis (Leuconoe) carissima Thomas, Ann. and Mag. Nat. Hist., Ser. 7, 13:383. May, 1904. Type from Yellowstone National Park, Wyoming.

Synonym.—*Vespertilio nitidus*, Merriam, 1891:36.

For a characterization of the species *lucifugus* see under *Myotis lucifugus alascensis*. The race *carissima* differs chiefly from *alascensis* in paler coloration ventrally and dorsally. The venter in *carissima* is whitish rather than sooty brown, and the upper parts are golden instead of bronzy or olive. The pelage of immature specimens is darker than that of adults.

I have observed individuals of this race feeding near Elba among willows bordering Cassia Creek and also above open water at Salmon Creek Reservoir. Specimens were obtained at both localities. At the latter place I had an opportunity to observe the evening flight of these bats on two consecutive evenings under different weather conditions. On May 14 I observed the first bats just after sundown, 8:30 P.M. (Mountain Time). They emerged from crevices in the canyon wall and flew up and over the dam and foraged above the open water. The sky was clear, the atmosphere warm, and visibility fair (to me). The next evening the sky was overcast and the thermometer had dropped several degrees. The bats appeared the second evening at 8:15 P.M. and foraged only for a short time. A month later at Elba these bats were not abroad until after

9:00 P.M. These observations tend to substantiate the theory that the nightly emergence of bats is correlated with light intensity.

A female collected June 16 at Elba contained a single 10 mm. foetus, and another collected at Granite Mountain, July 14, bore one nearly ready for birth.

This race inhabits the semi-arid parts of the western United States from Montana and Colorado west to the coast of southern California. In Idaho it is confined to the southern half of the state and probably intergrades with *M. l. alascensis* north of the Salmon River. The specimen from Black Lake is considerably darker than specimens from south of the Snake River.

Records of occurrence.—Specimens examined, 7, as follows: *Adams County:* W. slope Granite Mountain, 2; ½ mi. E Black Lake, 1 (all in Ralph Ellis coll.). *Twin Falls County:* Salmon Creek, 8 mi. W Rogerson, 2. *Cassia County:* Elba, 1. *Bannock County:* Pocatello, 1. Additional record (Miller and Allen, 1928:52): *Clark County:* Birch Creek.

Myotis yumanensis sociabilis H. W. Grinnell
YUMA LITTLE BROWN BAT

Myotis yumanensis sociabilis H. W. Grinnell, Univ. California Publ. Zool., 12:318. December 4, 1914. Type from Old Fort Tejon, Tehachapi Mountains, Kern County, California.

This species is structurally much like *Myotis lucifugus* but its size is uniformly less; the foot is smaller; the tail relatively longer; and the forearm shorter. The ears are thinner and narrower and usually less heavily pigmented. The forehead rises abruptly from the plane of the rostrum, and the skull is smaller and less flattened. The paler tips of the dorsal hairs are shorter and less glossy with the result that *Myotis yumanensis* appears dull colored in contrast to *Myotis lucifugus* with its deeper, more glossy fur. One usually can separate these two species by this character alone.

Little is recorded concerning the habits of this bat. It is probably less of a forest haunter than *Myotis lucifugus*, preferring more open country with scattered trees (Miller and Allen, 1928:65). I have encountered it foraging in the willow-cottonwood association near Oroville, California, and near this locality I collected nearly a hundred specimens from a summer colony in an old mill. Grinnell, Dixon, and Linsdale (1930:455) record two specimens from the Lassen area in California, both of which were captured in buildings. The specimens from southwestern Idaho were flying in the evening over willow thickets along the Owyhee River. The specimen from Pocatello was found in the attic of a house. A single young is born in early summer.

Geographically the species ranges over Montana, Wyoming, Idaho, eastern Washington, south through eastern Oregon into Nevada and central California.

For a discussion of the systematic status of the specimen from Payette Valley listed under this race by Miller and Allen *(op. cit.,* p. 69), see under *Eptesicus fuscus pallidus.*

Records of occurrence.—Specimens examined, 3, as follows: *Owyhee County:* South Fork Owyhee River, 12 mi. N Nevada line, 2. *Bannock County:* Pocatello, 1.

Myotis evotis chrysonotus (J. A. Allen)
GOLDEN LONG-EARED BAT

Vespertilio chrysonotus J. A. Allen, Bull. Amer. Mus. Nat. Hist., 8:240. November 21, 1896. Type from Kinney Ranch, Sweetwater County, Wyoming.

Among the moderate-sized bats, *Myotis evotis* is readily distinguished by a combination of greatly enlarged black ears and pale golden brown body color. When laid forward, the ears in freshly killed specimens extend about one fourth of an inch beyond the nose. Two adult females from near Pocatello average in external measurements 87-40-9-22.

The long-eared *Myotis* apparently are not gregarious and they are not common in collections. When Miller and Allen revised the genus in 1928 only one hundred and twenty-two specimens of this species were available to them. They are known to resort to human dwellings and also probably roost in hollow trees and crevices in rocky cliffs. At the summit of Smith Mountain, 7500 ft., Borell (MS) found them foraging among firs and spruces. Whitlow and Hall (1933:

241) report the finding of three individuals on June 11, 1932, in a deserted cabin near Pocatello. The bats were hanging side by side beneath the roofing paper on the gable. Two females were collected; each contained a single foetus, one 7 mm. in rump-crown length, the other 8 mm.

At the Great Owl Cavern in the Craters of the Moon National Monument I found dozens of these bats in company with a few larger ones of what I took to be *Corynorhinus* on the evenings of July 9 and 10, 1937. The cavern is an old lava tube about one hundred yards long and thirty feet in diameter with a large vent near one end. Ice was present in the cracks and crevices of the tube and water dripped continuously from the walls and ceiling. Probably the presence there of the only available water within a radius of several miles was attracting the bats. At any rate, just before dark dozens of bats emerged from the dry crevices near the vent and fluttered in and out of the cavern. The two we succeeded in collecting were *chrysonotus*. I know of no other record of this bat roosting in a cave.

This species, represented by two geographically varying races, occurs over a wide area chiefly west of the Rocky Mountains. In Idaho, the race *chrysonotus* occurs in the southern portion of the state and ranges north at least as far as latitude 45 degrees N. Although no specimens of the closely allied, darker, coastal race *M. e. evotis* have been recorded from Idaho, its occurrence in the northern part of the state is within the realm of geographical probability.

Records of occurrence.—Specimens examined, 5, as follows: *Adams County:* summit Smith Mountain, 1 (Ralph Ellis coll.). *Butte County:* Great Owl Cavern, 2 (1 in Davis coll.). *Bannock County:* Barrett's Ranch, 2. Additional records (Miller and Allen, 1928:117): *Adams County:* Tamarack. *Cassia County:* Albion.

Myotis volans interior Miller
INTERIOR LONG-LEGGED BAT

Myotis longicrus interior Miller, Proc. Biol. Soc. Washington, 27: 211. October 31, 1914. Type from Twining, Taos County, New Mexico.

This species, although superficially resembling *Myotis lucifugus,* has short, rounded ears; small hind foot; and an obvious extension of the fur on the ventral side of the membranes to a line joining the elbow and the knee. As compared with *lucifugus*, the rostrum is shorter and the brain case is larger and higher. The length of the foot is decidedly less than half the length of the tibia. A specimen from Black Lake measures 87-34-8-10 as compared with a specimen of *Myotis lucifugus* from the same locality which measures 80-33-10-13. In addition, in *volans* the fur of the ventral side is heavily washed with brown color.

Concerning its habits Miller and Allen (1928:138) record that "it seems to frequent open forest. . . . Apparently it is not social to any degree and in general it seems to avoid caves." I have no breeding records from Idaho.

The species, represented by four geographically varying races, is wide ranging over most of western North America. In Idaho, *M. v. interior* occurs in the semi-arid mountainous areas from Kootenai County south to Nevada and Utah. The closely allied *M. v. longicrus*, for geographical reasons, may be expected to occur in the more humid, northern portion of the state.

Record of occurrence.—Specimen examined, 1: *Adams County:* ½ mi. E Black Lake, 6800 ft. (Ralph Ellis coll.). Additional records (Miller and Allen, *op. cit.*, p. 143): *Kootenai County:* Mission. *Idaho County:* Warren. *Bannock County:* Inkom. *Oneida County:* Malad.

Myotis californicus californicus (Audubon and Bachman)
CALIFORNIA LITTLE BROWN BAT

Vespertilio californicus Audubon and Bachman, Jour. Acad. Nat. Sci. Philadelphia, ser. 1, 8:285. 1842. Type from "California" (See Miller and Allen, 1928:153).

This species, represented by four geographic races, of which one occurs in Idaho, is characterized by small size; small, slender hind foot; semitransparent external ears; and pelage without noticeable gloss. The hind foot is smaller than in any member of the genus except *Myotis subulatus*, from which it is readily distinguished by the following characters: ears semitransparent rather than heavily pigmented; thumb shorter; tip of tail not free from flying membrane; and lack of black facial markings. Two specimens of *californicus* from Idaho average in external measurements 82-36-7.5-11.5.

Little has been recorded concerning the habits of this species. H. W. Grinnell (1918:285) reports the finding of one individual in a rocky cavern in Yosemite Valley, California. A. E. Borell (MS), at Crane Creek and at Heath, observed them foraging close to the ground among willows along watercourses. They are thought to be noncolonial. The single young is born in early summer.

Myotis c. californicus has been collected at only two localities in Idaho; hence, little can be said concerning its general distribution in the state. For geographical reasons, however, it should occur from the Salmon River southward. In addition to this form, the paler Great Basin race *M. c. pallidus* may be expected to occur in the extreme southwestern part of the state.

Records of occurrence.—Specimens examined, 2, as follows: *Washington County:* Crane Creek, 15 mi. E Midvale, 1; 1 mi. N Heath, 1 (both in Ralph Ellis coll.).

Myotis subulatus melanorhinus (Merriam)

BLACK-NOSED BAT

Vespertilio melanorhinus Merriam, N. Amer. Fauna, 3:46. September 11, 1890. Type from Little Spring, north base of San Francisco Mountain, 8250 feet, Coconino County, Arizona.

In size and general proportions this bat is much like *Myotis californicus* but may be distinguished from it by black face and ears; tip of tail free from flying membrane; and tips of long hairs flaxen or yellowish rather than dull chestnut. In addition, the skull slopes gradually from the plane of the rostrum and lacks the abrupt rise found in *californicus*.

This bat resorts to caves where, during the winter, it hibernates. Whitlow and Hall (1933:242) record observations made on hibernating bats in mine tunnels near Pocatello. At no time were the animals completely dormant and, although they never were observed flying about during the winter, individuals changed roosting places many times during the period of observation.

Judged from my observations on this species in eastern Oregon and central Idaho, in summer it resorts to open desert areas to forage. On the evening of May 24, 1936, I found *melanorhinus* at the Alkali Lake Ranch, Lake County, Oregon. The first one was seen about an hour before dark, and from then until about two hours after dark numbers of them flew about camp uttering mouselike squeaks. For the most part, these individuals appeared to feed over the open pond west of the ranch house, but occasionally they foraged above and among the *Atriplex* in the surrounding desert. In foraging, they made numerous swoops close to the ground and seldom flew higher than twenty feet. The single specimen secured was foraging above *Atriplex*.

During the latter part of July, 1936, I found these bats in company with Big Brown Bats *(Eptesicus fuscus)* foraging over a small, open, quiet spring, and over the surrounding *Artemisia,* at Double Springs in Pahsimeroi Valley, Idaho. The Big Brown Bats appeared first, about half an hour before dark, and about fifteen minutes later the Black-nosed Bats appeared. Both kinds beat back and forth above the water, evidently catching insects, which were numerous, and on several occasions they actually touched the water, at which times they probably drank. The single specimen of Black-nosed Bat taken fell into the spring and was not discovered until the following morning. During the night most of the soft parts were devoured by flatworms *(Planaria).* This locality record marks a northward extension of known range in Idaho.

Breeding records from California and Nevada indicate that the single young is born in late June or early July.

This species, consisting of three geographic races, is widely distributed over the United States, northern Lower California, and northern Mexico. In Idaho the race *melanorhinus* has been taken at two localities in the semi-arid regions. For remarks concerning the systematic status of specimens from near Pocatello see Whitlow and Hall (1933: 241).

Records of occurrence.—Specimens examined, 15, as follows: *Custer County:* Double Springs, 1. *Bannock County:* 4 mi. E Pocatello, 9; Pocatello, 4; ½ mi. E Portneuf, 1.

Genus **Lasionycteris** Peters
Silver-haired Bats

Lasionycteris noctivagans (LeConte)
SILVER-HAIRED BAT

V[espertilio] noctivagans Le Conte, McMurtie's Cuvier, Animal Kingdom, 1:431. 1831. Type from eastern United States.

The Silver-haired Bat, as the name suggests, is to be known by its blackish coloration, overcast with a frosted appearance produced by the white terminal portions of the long hairs. The white tips are most numerous in the mid-dorsal region and are nearly absent from the face, crown, and throat. In addition, the interfemoral membrane is heavily furred dorsally; the ears are short and nearly as broad as high; the tragus is short, straight, and bluntly tipped. Three adult females from Idaho average, in external measurements, 99-38-9.

This species, like the Hoary and the Red bats, is a tree dweller, resorting to spaces under loosened bark or holes in the trees during the day. It is thought to be solitary most of the year, but during certain seasons numbers of them flock together much like certain of our birds and migrate. Thomas (1921) reports what was evidently a migrating flock that was observed some twenty miles off the North Carolina coast on September 3, 1920. The fact that individuals of this species have been recorded (Allen, G. M., 1923) from the Bermuda Islands, about 800 miles off our eastern coast, indicates that they are capable of long-sustained flight.

At Crane Creek, Idaho, and again at Black Lake, Borell (MS) found them flying, apparently foraging, over open meadows at dusk. A specimen from Pocatello was found hanging in a tree. In Idaho, specimens have been taken during the months of May, June, and July.

Two young, born in late June or early July, is the usual number in a litter. In California, nearly full-grown young have been taken in late July, a circumstance which indicates that extra-uterine development in this group apparently is quite rapid.

The species is widespread over North America and no geographic races have been named. In Idaho it probably occurs sparingly throughout the state. Specimens have been recorded, however, only from the southern half.

Records of occurence.—Specimens examined, 4, as follows: *Adams County:* ½ mi. E Black Lake, 1 (Ralph Ellis coll.). *Washington County:* Crane Creek, 15 mi. E Midvale, 2 (Ralph Ellis coll.). *Bannock County:* Pocatello, 1.

Genus **Pipistrellus** Kaup
Pipistrelles

Pipistrellus hesperus hesperus (H. Allen)
WESTERN CANYON BAT

Scotophilus hesperus H. Allen, Monogr. Bats N. Amer., Smithsonian Misc. coll., 165:43. June, 1864. Type from Old Fort Yuma, Imperial County, California; on right bank of Colorado River, opposite present town of Yuma, Arizona.

Members of this genus are the smallest of North American bats. In addition to small size, the western species is characterized by black, leathery facial mask and ears; blunt tragus with the tip bent forward; and small feet. They can be distinguished by the black facial mask and blunt tragus from *Myotis californicus* and *Myotis subulatus,* which most closely approach them in size. The single specimen examined from Idaho measures 65-23-5-10.

As compared with other bats, *Pipistrellus* is abroad earlier in the evening, often shortly after sundown. At the Salmon Creek reservoir *Pipistrellus* appeared about fifteen minutes before *Myotis.* Both kinds seemed to be foraging above the open water of the reservoir, and in comparison with *Myotis* the pipistrelle appeared to be slow and very erratic in flight.

At this same locality hundreds of Cliff Swallows *(Petrochelidon albifrons)* were nesting. The swallows actively foraged after sundown until about five minutes before the first bat appeared. This same relative sequence of behavior was observed nightly during our stay there. There was no overlap in the forage times of the birds and the bats, both of which foraged in the same area. The activities of each seemed to be initiated and terminated by complementary intensities of light. Due to positive phototropic tendencies in some insects and negative tendencies in others, the swallows and bats, both of which feed on insects, are not competitors for a common food supply, but, on the contrary, act as natural checks upon two different groups of insects.

The pipistrelle is known to resort to rocky crevices during the day. Breeding records from California and Nevada indicate that two young, born in late June or early July, is the usual number in a litter.

Pipistrellus hesperus, consisting of five geographic races, is widely distributed over the southwestern United States, Lower California, and western Mexico. In his revision of this group Hatfield (1936) examined no specimens from Idaho and apparently the single individual, MVZ no. 67252, which I collected May 14, 1935, is the only record for the state. Comparison with specimens from Nevada shows that it is referable to the Great Basin race *P. h. hesperus.* Since no *Pipistrellus* has been recorded from northeastern Nevada, it seems probable, on geographical grounds, that the Idaho record marks an eastern extension of range, along the Snake River, from Oregon rather than a direct northward extension from Nevada.

Record of occurrence.—Specimen examined, 1, from Salmon Creek, 8 mi. W Rogerson, Twin Falls County.

Genus **Eptesicus** Rafinesque
Serotine Bats

Eptesicus fuscus pallidus Young
PALLID BIG BROWN BAT

Eptesicus pallidus Young, Proc. Acad. Nat. Sci. Philadelphia, 1908: 408. October 2, 1908. Type from Boulder, Boulder County, Colorado. *Synonym.*—*Vespertilio fuscus,* Miller, 1897:98.

The Big Brown Bat is the largest of the brown-colored bats occurring in this region. It is characterized by short, thick, leathery, black ears, which are furred above on the basal third; large hind feet; black, naked membranes; and sepia brown dorsal, and somewhat lighter brown ventral, coloration. External measurements of four adult males from Double Springs, Idaho, average 115-44-11.5.

This bat is colonial, often living in buildings, crevices in rocky cliffs, and in natural caves. It is not a true "cave dweller," however. It comes out of its daytime roosting place shortly after sundown. At Double Springs it appeared before *Myotis subulatus* and like the latter foraged over the spring and the surrounding desert. In forested areas, it usually cruises about open places. At Alturas Lake it appeared about half an hour before dark. The clearing over the road and the area above the creek at the outlet of the lake were used as flyways. Here it kept near the tops of the lodgepole pines *(Pinus murrayana)*, darting here and there apparently after insects. Unlike the smaller brown bats *(Myotis)*, this bat flies slowly, a feature which may be correlated with its relatively shorter, broader wings. It often pursues a straight course for several yards, in contrast to the many twists and turns made by many of the other kinds of bats.

The single young is born in July. Females taken in the Monitor Range, Nye County, Nevada, in mid-July were parturient. A female wounded the evening of July 14 was placed in a cage. During the night a single young was born and next morning it was found clinging to the mother's teat. She clung to the top of the cage and her interfemoral membrane was curved forward in such a manner that it covered her offspring. On several occasions the mother "washed" the young one with her tongue.

The species *fuscus*, comprised of five geographic races, occurs over most of the temperate portions of North America. The race *pallidus*, which Engels (1936) assigns to the general area from east of the Cascade-Sierra Nevada mountain chain, ranges east to the Great Plains, and has an altitudinal range in Idaho from 2150 feet at Coeur d'Alene to 8000 feet at Double Springs.

A single mummified specimen, no. 24411, Mus. Vert. Zool., from Payette Valley was referred to *Myotis yumanensis sociabilis* by Miller and Allen (1928:69). Whitlow and Hall (1933:241) remark that Dr. Seth B. Benson regards it as *Myotis lucifugus carissima*. Upon re-examination (the skull being removed and studied) I find it to be a young *Eptesicus fuscus pallidus*. Characters which identify it as such are size of the skull; width of rostrum; one premolar in each upper jaw (permanent dentition appearing) ; outline and thickness of ear; and large hind foot (larger than in any *Myotis* occurring in the region).

Records of occurrence.—Specimens examined, 8, as follows: *Adams County:* 1 mi. N Bear Creek R. S., 1; ½ mi. E Black Lake, 1 (both in Ralph Ellis coll.). *Payette County:* Payette Valley, 1. *Custer County:* Double Springs, 4 (1 in Davis coll.). *Bannock County:* Pocatello, 1. Additional record (Miller, 1897:98): *Kootenai County:* Fort Sherman.

Genus Lasiurus Gray
Red Bats and Hoary Bats

Lasiurus cinereus (Beauvois)
HOARY BAT

Vespertilio cinereus (misspelled *linereus)* Beauvois, Catalog Raisonné Mus. Peale, Philadelphia, 1796:18 (p. 15 of English edition by Peale and Beauvois). Type from Philadelphia, Pennsylvania.

The Hoary Bat is the largest member of the order Chiroptera in Idaho. In addition to large size, it is characterized by having the dorsal portion of interfemoral membrane and feet furred; ears furred and bordered by a black rim; distinct patch of fur at base of forearm and base of thumb; general coloration umber brown heavily overcast with white. A specimen from Pocatello, Idaho, measures 140-55-13-17.

Like the Silvery-haired Bat, this species dwells in trees where often it is found hanging head down from a branch. In the field it is recognized by its strong, swift flight. Near Albion, in mid-June, a single individual thought to be of this species was observed flying above the treetops beyond range of a 16-gauge shotgun. It pursued a course down canyon and was soon out of sight.

Two appears to be the usual number of young in each litter. A female collected May 9, 1919, in California contained two embryos. The young probably are born in June or July.

During the summer season, this species is thought to be Boreal in distribution, while during the winter it resorts to more southerly regions. Most of the specimens from California in the Museum of Vertebrate Zoology were taken from October to March. Allen (1923) records its occurrence in the Bermuda Islands some 800 miles off our eastern coast, a fact which attests to its strong powers of flight. It is widespread throughout temperate North America.

A single specimen, MVZ no. 46945, collected October 20, 1930, by Miss Helen Newton at her father's ranch two miles northeast of Inkom, constitutes the only definite record I have of the occurrence of this bat in Idaho.

Record of occurrence.—Specimen examined, 1, from Newton's Ranch, 2 mi. NE Inkom, Bannock County.

Genus Corynorhinus H. Allen
Lump-nosed Bats

Corynorhinus rafinesquii intermedius H. W. Grinnell
INTERMEDIATE LUMP-NOSED BAT

Corynorhinus macrotis intermedius H. W. Grinnell, Univ. California Publ. Zool., 12:320. December 4, 1914. Type from Auburn, 1300 feet, Placer County, California.

The Lump-nosed Bat may be distinguished from all other bats occurring in Idaho by its extremely large ears (more than half the length of the forearm) ; tragus wholly free from auricle; and general brownish monotone coloration. Forty-five males from near Pocatello, Idaho, average in external measurements 97.6-46.1-9.3-35.3 (forearm 43.5).

Bats of this genus are essentially cave-dwellers, often occupying mine shafts and tunnels. A specimen from Blackfoot was found in a barn. There is no evidence that they are migratory. According to Allen (1916:336), "they appear to rest singly, scattered along the rock walls, rather than in clusters." In discussing their roosting habits in mine tunnels near Pocatello during the winter months, Whitlow and Hall (1933:245) state that "on the uneven ceilings of these tunnels, the dormant *Corynorhinus* cling singly, head downward, to the inclined faces of the rocks." Evidence that they do cluster is found in my field notes of May 27, 1933. "Springdale, N end Oasis Valley, Nye Co., Nevada. (Ward) Russell and I went up to an abandoned mine tunnel about ½ mi. to the E where bats were said to be. The tunnel was about 125 feet long and about 30 feet from the entrance a cluster of *Corynorhinus* was hanging from the ceiling. I clapped my butterfly net over them and caught 29. Six more were caught individually while on the wing." All these specimens were females, many of which contained a single foetus. The young is born in June or July.

The species is widespread over the Austral portions of North America. In Idaho, the race *intermedius* occurs; probably it is restricted to the southern part of the state. Concerning the use of the name *intermedius* for specimens from Idaho, see Whitlow and Hall *(op. cit.,* pp. 245-246).

Records of occurrence.—Specimens examined, 53, as follows: *Bingham County:* Blackfoot, 1. *Bannock County:* 3 to 4 mi. E Pocatello, 14 (5 in Ralph Ellis coll.); Portneuf, 29 (1 in Ralph Ellis coll.); ½ mi. E Portneuf, 4; Schutt's mine, 5 (2 in Ralph Ellis coll.).

Order CARNIVORA
Flesh-eating Mammals

Family URSIDAE
BEARS

Large, terrestrial, plantigrade carnivores; eyes and ears relatively small; tail rudimentary; feet large and broad, five-toed; digits almost equal in length, claws large. Skull heavy, angular, with distinct postorbital process; tympanic bullae small, dorsoventrally flattened, auditory tube long; paroccipital process broad, but independent of bulla; carotid canal on inner side of bullae; alisphenoidal canal present; molars $\frac{2}{3}$, bunodont, elongated; Pm⁴ not developed as a carnassial; os penis cylindrical; intestine without caecum; prostate rudimentary.

Some paleontologists (see Matthew, 1915) regard the bears as an offshoot from the Canidae, but, on structural evidence, they appear to be related to the weasels. Their distribution indicates a Palaearctic origin. The most primitive bears first appear in the Miocene of Europe; in the New World they appear first in the Pleistocene. This situation suggests a rather late migration across the Alaska-Siberian land bridge to North America. The family today is chiefly Holarctic; forms related to *Ursus* occur in South America and in the Oriental region. Gazin (1935) records fossil ursids from Pleistocene deposits at American Falls, Idaho.

In the early part of the 19th century, bears were abundant in Idaho, but due to their persecution and to the encroachment of "civilization" both the black and the grizzly bears have been greatly reduced in numbers. In fact, in Idaho the grizzly bear is on the verge of extinction and it may not be long until it, too, is added to the list of "vanished species." All the early explorers in Idaho encountered both the black and grizzly bears. Alexander Ross (1855), among other observations on bears, records seeing, in 1824, nine black and grizzly bears in a four-acre tract in Salmon River Valley near what is now Yankee Fork. Townsend (1839) records an amusing, but at the time serious, encounter he had with a large grizzly in 1834 on the headwaters of the Blackfoot River and remarks that Richardson and two others in the company killed three grizzlies in the course of the afternoon and saw several others on the trip from Soda Springs to the Blackfoot River. Several grizzlies were killed by Townsend's associates in the vicinity of Fort Hall. Today, the grizzly is restricted to the more inaccessible portions of the state; the black bear is said to be still occupying an extensive range. Dr. Fayre Kenagy, of Rupert, Idaho, told me that the grizzly is still to be found in fair numbers in the Selway National Forest.

Bears are omnivorous in food habits, consuming nearly everything containing food value that is available. Berries, insects, rodents, birds, fish, and green vegetation constitute part of the normal diet. In regions where livestock are grazed, certain individuals may turn to mutton or beef. This circumstance has given *all* bears a bad name and consequently most herders are equipped with high-powered rifles and are instructed to kill all bears on sight. This same circumstance is responsible for the bears' being unprotected by law in that part of the state where grazing is an important industry. A more general realization that not all bears are killers should help to prevent their needless slaughter.

In colder regions bears den up for the winter, but their winter sleep is not as deep as it is in most hibernating mammals. The young, one or two in number and weighing less than a pound each at birth, are born during late winter while the female is denned up. In comparison with the smaller carnivores, the young develop slowly; they do not reach maturity until about three years old.

Genus Ursus Linnaeus
Bears

Ursus americanus cinnamomum Audubon and Bachman
ROCKY MOUNTAIN BLACK BEAR

Ursus americanus var. *cinnamomum* Audubon and Bachman, Quad. N. Amer., 3:125. 1854. Type from Northern Rocky Mountains.

Distribution.—Occurs widely, although sparingly, throughout the mountainous portions of the state.

Comparison.—Differs from the grizzly bear in smaller size, lack of ruff or mane; claws considerably shorter, more curved, and darker; skull less massive; Pm_4 conical, lacking the sulcate heel of the grizzly.

Remarks.—Occasionally black bears are taken in the lava beds in the Snake River Plains. I saw one that was roped in July, 1918, by cowboys on the desert about 20 miles northeast of Minidoka. Each year sheepmen report black bears from Laidlaw Park and Sparks Well where they are said to do some damage to the sheep in lambing season.

Records of occurrence.—*Adams County:* Reported as quite common on the heavily timbered slopes of Smith Mountain. "Mr. Eldon Walker who runs sheep north of Smith Mountain told us that he killed one on June 30, 1930, at the head of Deep Creek. Fresh tracks were noted at Black Lake." (Borell, MS). *Lemhi County:* Timber Creek, Lemhi Mountains (Merriam, 1891:87). *Custer County:* Loon Creek (Kenagy, *in litt.*). *Blaine County:* Sawtooth Mountains near Alturas Lake (Merriam, *ibid.*). *Clark County:* Lost River Mountains (Merriam, *ibid.*). *Fremont County:* Henrys Lake (Merriam, 1873: 663).

Ursus idahoensis Merriam
IDAHO GRIZZLY

Ursus idahoensis Merriam, N. Amer. Fauna, 41:54. February 9, 1918. Type from North Fork Teton River, Fremont County?, Idaho.
Synonym.—Ursus horribilis, Merriam, 1891:86.
Distribution.—Formerly widespread, now greatly reduced in numbers and confined to the central portion of the state.

Remarks.—The name *idahoensis* is here employed with full cognizance of the inadequacy of our knowledge of the relationships and distribution of the different named forms of grizzly bear. Until such information is available, the above name appears to be as applicable to the grizzlies of Idaho as any one of many others that might be used.

The only specimen I have examined from Idaho, an adult of unknown sex, consisting of the skull and parts of the skeleton, picked up in 1933 by R. R. Lee in a lava tube north of Shoshone and temporarily deposited in the Museum of Vertebrate Zoology, does not agree in all respects with the published description of *idahoensis*. The frontal shield is not convex, and the size of the skull is smaller. Some cranial measurments, in millimeters, of this specimen are as follows: Basilar length of Hensel, 278; occipitonasal length, 292; palatal length, 160; zygomatic breadth, 175; interorbital breadth, 70.

Records of occurrence.—Specimen examined: *Lincoln County:* 20 mi. N Shoshone, 1. Additional records: *Lemhi County:* Timber Creek (Merriam, 1891:87). *Custer County:* Stanley Lake (Anthony, 1923: 150). *Fremont County ? :* Teton Canyon (Merriam, 1873:662); N. Fork Teton River (Merriam, 1918:54).

Family PROCYONIDAE
RACCOONS AND ALLIES

Medium-sized, semiplantigrade, arboreal carnivores; eyes and ears of medium size; face with black mask (in *Procyon*); tail about one third the length of head and body, usually with alternate rings of dark and light color; feet relatively large and long, soles naked; third digit longest, claws short. Skull relatively smooth, rounded; tympanic bullae small; paroccipital processes broad, but independent of bullae; alisphenoidal canal generally lacking; carotid canal on inner side of bulla; molars $\frac{2}{2}$, brachydont, rooted, nearly bunodont, carnassial undifferentiated; intestine without caecum; os penis cylindrical.

This family is considered an offshoot of the Miocene Miacidae which gave rise to the Canidae, Ursidae, and Mustelidae as well. In structural characters the family Procyonidae is more closely related to the Ursidae and Mustelidae than to the Canidae, and in mode of life, type of dentition, and structure of the feet it is primitive. Its range now is restricted to the New World, the center of distribution lying in South America; in North America it occurs north probably as far as Canada. Its present distribution and the paleontological record suggest an early migration of the ancestral stock southward from the Nearctic region. Two distantly related forms, the pandas, occur in the Himalaya Mountains of Asia.

Genus **Procyon** Storr
Racoons

Procyon lotor excelsus Nelson and Goldman
SNAKE RIVER VALLEY RACCOON

Procyon lotor excelsus Nelson and Goldman, Jour. Mammalogy, 11:458. November 11, 1930. Type from Owyhee River, Malheur County, Oregon (10 miles west of Fairylawn, Idaho).
   Synonym.—*Procyon lotor*, Merriam, 1891:86.
   Distribution.—In Idaho, apparently confined to the vicinity of watercourses in the Great Basin area.

Remarks.—Raccoons are uncommon in Idaho, a circumstance which suggests that here, at this longitude, they reach the northern limit of their distribution. The two specimens I have examined were collected in November, 1935, by Ned Emery, of Oakley, Idaho. They were caught in coyote sets fully one quarter of a mile from the stream in Goose Creek Valley. Due to the scarcity of large deciduous trees in southern Idaho, raccoons often are found occupying dens in basaltic cliffs and outcroppings. Few trappers in southern Idaho with whom I talked had seen raccoons there, and most of them did not know they occurred in the state.

Records of occurrence.—Specimens examined, 2, as follows: *Cassia County:* Goose Creek, 25 mi. SW Oakley, 2. Additional records: *Bannock County:* Junction of Ross Fork Creek and Portneuf River (Whitlow and Hall, 1935:246). "Raccoons are common in the cañons of Snake River, where they feed largely on crayfish ... " (Merriam, 1891: 86).

Family MUSTELIDAE
WEASELS AND ALLIES

Small to medium-sized, terrestrial, aquatic, or arboreal carnivores; tail long or short; digitigrade or semiplantigrade. Skull usually smooth, braincase rounded, elongated, rostrum short; tympanic bullae usually small; paroccipital processes expanded, but usually independent of bullae; alisphenoidal canal lacking; M $\frac{1}{2}$; carnassial well differentiated; os penis cylindrical; intestine without caecum; prostate rudimentary.

Although apparently arising from a stock also ancestral to the Canidae, Ursidae, and Procyonidae, the Mustelidae are more primitive in many respects than the other families; they tend to be comparatively small in size, with short, stocky limbs and the full complement of five toes. Also, most of the typical forms are forest-dwelling and largely arboreal; the specialized forms, however, are largely terrestrial or aquatic.

Key to Genera of Mustelidae in Idaho

1 Feet short, rounded, toes fully webbed; upper molar large and quadrate. **Lutra, p. 139**

1' Feet rounded or elongate, toes not fully webbed; upper molar variable.

    2 Feet elongate; toes straight; claws nonretractile, slightly curved, blunt, longer on front feet than on hind.

        3 Claws of forefeet 30 mm. or more in length; occipitonasal length more than 100 mm.; opening of posterior nares considerably back of last molar; general coloration grayish. **Taxidea, p. 142**

3' Claws of forefeet 20 mm. or less in length; occipitonasal length less than 80 mm.; opening of posterior nares near posterior border of last molars; general coloration black and white.

   4 Larger, total length near 600 mm.; dorsum with continuous longitudinal white stripes.   **Mephitis, p. 141**

   4' Smaller, total length usually less than 400 mm.; dorsum "spotted," stripes not continuous.

   Spilogale, p. 140

2' Feet rounded, toes short, partially webbed; claws short, acute, curved, often semiretractile, equal or nearly so on front and hind feet.

   5 Size larger, occipitonasal length more than 65 mm.; tail decidedly bushy.

      6 Tail short, thick, bushy.   **Gulo, p. 138**

      6' Tail long, at least half the length of head and body.   **Martes, p. 130**

   5' Size smaller, occipitonasal length less than 60 mm.; tail not bushy, or only slightly so.

   Mustela, p. 133

Genus **Martes** Pinel
Martens and Fishers

Martes caurina caurina (Merriam)
WESTERN MARTEN

Mustela caurina Merriam, N. Amer. Fauna, 4:27. October 8, 1890. Type from near Grays Harbor, Grays Harbor County, Washington.

Synonym.—Mustela americana, Merriam, 1891:84.

Distribution.—In Idaho, probably from Canada south through the mountainous parts of the state to Wyoming and Utah. May intergrade with *M. c. origenes* in southeastern Idaho and southern Wyoming.

Description.—A long, slender-bodied, arboreal, sexually dimorphic carnivore; limbs short, digitigrade; soles furred, pads naked; claws compressed, sharp, semiretractile; tail moderately long, bushy; ears large, white on rim and inner side of concha; head roughly triangular with sharp nose; color above wood brown, shading to clove brown on tail and feet; ventral coloration light wood brown with dark orange-buff throat and breast patches which taper into a median ventral stripe (often indistinct or interrupted) that reaches posteriorly to anus. External measurements of an adult male from Baker Creek are 612-228-85-44; females are smaller. Skull: Rostrum short and relatively broad; postorbital processes distinct; zygoma bowed dorsally; width of rostrum considerably more than anteroposterior length of auditory bullae; M^1 with widely expanded inner moiety; basilar length of three adult males and three adult females from central Idaho average, respectively, 72.3 mm. and 65.3 mm.

Remarks.—I have compared the specimens from Idaho with specimens of *M. americana abietinoides, M. caurina caurina, M. c. sierrae,* and with the published description (Rhoads, 1902) of *M. c. origenes.* On the basis of relatively short, broad rostrum; small bullae (rostral width much greater, rather than less, than anteroposterior length of auditory bullae); large internal moiety of M^1; bright orange-buff gular and chest patches; and relatively longer tail, they must be regarded as *M. caurina,* rather than as *M. americana.* One specimen (no. 69696), however, resembles *M. americana* in having a decidedly grayish-colored head. All the specimens (three skins available) differ from *origenes* and are like *caurina* in having the inner surface and the rim of the concha distinctly white. The skulls are indistinguishable from specimens collected at Anahim Lake, British Columbia, which are referred to *caurina.*

When Rhoads revised the martens in 1902, he described *origenes* from Colorado as a subspecies of *M. caurina,* which was known then only from the Pacific Coast. Because *M. americana* occurred in the northern Rocky Mountain region, he inferred, logically I think, that it occurred also in the central Rocky Mountains south as far as Utah and west to eastern Oregon and Washington. The presence of *caurina* in Idaho clears up a distributional problem which puzzled him because the "link" connecting the Rocky Mountain and the coastal populations of M. *caurina* is here established with fair certainty. Also, these specimens give a clue to the migrational history of the martens in North America.

When the ancestral stock split into the two groups, the one that gave rise to *americana* may have pushed eastward across Canada to the Atlantic Coast; the other, giving rise to *caurina,* may have migrated southward along the Sierra Nevada-Cascade and Rocky mountains. Perhaps the Great

Ice Sheet was instrumental in pushing *americana* eastward and separating it geographically from *caurina*. The occurrence now of *americana* in Alaska and in the northern Rocky Mountain region may be explained by assuming that it re-invaded that region since the Pleistocene. Evidence corroborating this assumption is found in the composition of the fauna of that area today. Swarth (1936) has assembled convincing evidence that many species of both birds and mammals in the Sitkan district of southeastern Alaska today are relatively late immigrants from the east. This circumstance strongly suggests early migrations from west to east in North America and later migrations in the reverse direction. The fact that *caurina* structurally resembles the Asiatic forms more than it does its American neighbor *americana* suggests that it may have migrated to the New World after *americana* was established here and that the northern part of the former range of *caurina* was later invaded and usurped by *americana*.

Ecology.—Martens are largely arboreal in habit and their distribution coincides closely with the distribution of coniferous forests. They are active the year round and travel considerable distances overland or through the treetops. According to Mr. A. Linderman, who traps them regularly in the Sawtooth Mountains, in winter each family group of from five to seven individuals establishes a forage beat varying from ten to twenty-five miles in diameter which is covered systematically and regularly. They prey upon a number of kinds of birds and small mammals, but pine squirrels *(Tamiasciurus)* constitute an important part of their diet. An interesting feature that I have never seen recorded is their tendency to travel through tunnels under the snow. Mr. W. Kuebli, of Stanley, Idaho, tells me that when the snow is five or six feet deep he has experienced difficulty in trapping them. This he attributes to their habit of traveling and foraging under the snow. Also, he has found that pelts from individuals trapped after the snow is deep and crusted are of poor quality due to abrasion induced by continued contact with the walls of the tunnels.

Records of occurrence.—Specimens examined, 10, as follows: *Custer County:* Five Mile Creek, 25 mi. NE Stanley, 5. *Blaine County:*

Baker Creek, 12 mi. N Ketchum, 5. Additional records: *Lemhi County*: Salmon River (Lemhi) Mountains (Merriam, 1891:84); near Fort Boise (Baird, 1857:158). Although I have not examined the specimen from the Lemhi Mountains which Merriam (1891) records under the name *Mustela americana*, this locality is only fifty miles due east of Five Mile Creek whence I have specimens of *caurina* and I assume that those in the Lemhi Mountains, too, are *caurina*.

Martes pennanti columbiana Goldman
BRITISH COLUMBIA FISHER

Martes pennanti columbiana Goldman, Proc. Biol. Soc. Washington, 48:176. November 15, 1935. Type from Stuart Lake, near headwaters of Fraser River, British Columbia, Canada.

Synonym.—Mustela pennanti, Merriam, 1891:84.

Distribution.—In Idaho, probably restricted to the mountainous central part of the state.

Description.—Similar in structure to the marten, but larger. Sexually dimorphic, males larger than females; body long, lithe, and powerful; weight up to 18 pounds; legs short; muzzle pointed; ears prominent; tail moderately bushy; dorsal coloration brownish black, lighter on sides and belly. Skull: Basilar length of males near 100 mm.; anteroposterior length of auditory bullae less than rostral breadth; zygoma bowed dorsally; postorbital processes rudimentary.

Remarks.—Although probably never abundant in Idaho, the fisher is now one of the rarest carnivores in the state. Mr. A. Linderman saw tracks of one in the winter of 1934-35 in Big Wood River Valley above Ketchum. In several years of trapping in that region, this was the only evidence he saw of the presence of fisher. He is of the opinion that they are more common in the relatively inaccessible central portion of the state. Merriam (1891:84) records a single specimen that was trapped October 1, 1890, by Basil Hicks Dutcher at Alturas Lake.

Genus **Mustela** Linnaeus
Weasels, Ferrets, and Minks

Long, slender-bodied carnivores; tail not distinctly bushy (semibushy in mink); head but little larger than neck; skull usually smooth, braincase elongated; tympanic bullae cancellous, especially mastoidal portion, with paroccipital processes closely appressed; palate terminating considerably posterior to last molar; inner moiety of M^1 larger than outer one; in M_1 trigonid longer than talonid, metaconid absent.

Key to Mustela of Idaho

1 Total length over 325 mm.; length of hind foot 36 mm. or more; greatest length of mandible more than postglenoidal length of skull.

    2 Ventral color yellowish (summer) or white (winter); tail bicolored, black-tipped; tympanic bullae large, swollen.

                                                  M. f. nevadensis, p. 135

    2' Ventral color wood brown or clove brown both summer and winter; tail unicolored, not distinctly tipped; tympanic bullae flattened.   **M. v. energumenos**, p. 137

1' Total length usually less than 300 mm.; length of hind foot 36 mm. or less; greatest length of mandible less than postglenoidal length of skull.

      3 Size larger; total length 230 to 300 mm.; hind foot 30 mm. or more.   **M. c. cicognanii**, p. 134

      3' Size smaller, total length less than 230 mm.; hind foot near 26 mm.   **M. c. lepta**, p. 135

Mustela cicognanii cicognanii Bonaparte
BONAPARTE SHORT-TAILED WEASEL

M [*ustela*] *cigognanii* [*sic*] Bonaparte, Charlesworth's Mag. Nat. Hist., 2:37. January, 1838. Type from northeastern North America.

Distribution.—In Idaho, apparently confined to the northern part of the state.

Description.—Typical weasel form, general size small; tail about *one third the length of head and body;* anterior portion of auditory bullae flattened and merging smoothly, or nearly so, with squamosal; greatest length of mandible less than postglenoidal length of skull. External measurements of three males and two females from northern Idaho average, respectively, 286-81-36 and 245-60-30.

Remarks.—Individuals of this species often are mistaken for the larger long-tailed weasel *Mustela frenata*. In all *cicognanii* examined, the greatest length of the mandible is less than the postglenoidal length of the skull whereas in *frenata* the reverse is true. Also, in *frenata* the anterior portion of the auditory bulla is truncate and ventrally bulged while in *cicognanii* from Idaho the bullae merge smoothly with the squamosal. Perhaps the best field character of *cicognanii* is its short tail; in *frenata* the tail equals about half, in *cicognanii* about a third, of the length of head and body. In cranial characters and proportions of external parts, *cicognanii* is similar to *lepta*. The two differ mostly in size, *lepta* being much smaller (see measurements under *lepta*).

Records of occurrence.—Specimens examined, 6, as follows: *Bonner County:* Coolin, 5 (Biol. Surv. coll.). *Benewah County:* Benewah, 1 (W. T. Shaw coll.).

Mustela streatori lepta (Merriam)
DWARF WEASEL

Putorius streatori leptus Merriam, Proc. Biol. Soc. Washington, 16:76. May 29, 1903. Type from Silverton, San Juan County, Colorado.
Synonym.—*Mustela streatori leptus*, Whitlow and Hall, 1933:246.
Distribution.—In Idaho, known only from near Pocatello, but probably widespread, although sparingly, throughout the central Rocky Mountain area.
Description.—Structurally similar to *cicognanii*, but smaller. Measurements of an adult female from Idaho are 197-50-25. Males of *lepta* are about the size of females of *cicognanii*.

Remarks.—This weasel, as the name suggests, is one of the smallest of North American carnivores. Trappers usually do not recognize its distinction as a separate species and consider it as the "kitten" of larger species.

Record of occurrence.—Specimen examined, 1, from Barrett's Ranch, Bannock County.

Mustela frenata nevadensis Hall
NEVADA LONG-TAILED WEASEL

Mustela frenata nevadensis Hall, Carnegie Inst. Wash., Publ. 473:91. November 20, 1936. Type from three miles east of Baker, White Pine County, Nevada.
Synonyms.—*Putorius pusillus*, Merriam, 1873:661; *Putorius longicauda*, Merriam, 1891:83; *Mustela arizonensis*, Whitlow and Hall, 1933:247.
Distribution.—Occurring throughout the state.

Description.—Largest of the weasels of Idaho; total length more than 330 mm.; tail about half the length of head and body; sexually dimorphic, females smaller than males; seasonally dichromatic, white in winter, brown in summer; skull with distinct postorbital processes; greatest length of mandible more than postglenoidal length of skull; tympanic bullae truncate anteriorly and swollen at juncture with squamosals. According to Hall (1936), external measurements of adult males average 400-150-46; adult females, 349-127-36. Three adult males from southern Idaho average 377-138-43.

Remarks.—For comparisons, see under account of *M. cicognanii.* The long-tailed weasel is by far the commonest weasel in Idaho. The species ranges from southern Canada south into South America and in North America from the Pacific to the Atlantic. Weasels are active throughout the year and are somewhat nomadic in habit. They are not limited by altitude, and in winter they can cross the larger rivers on the ice and snow.

Ecology.—Although I have made no special attempt to trap weasels in Idaho, four of the five I have collected were taken in traps set at entrances to burrows of ground squirrels, which animals, at least in southern Idaho, the weasels seemed to be seeking as food. At Double Springs one was observed trying to capture what I took to be a ground squirrel in a burrow (for particulars, see under account of *Citellus elegans aureus).* Near American Falls I saw another in a basaltic outcropping where it probably was hunting mice. Here I witnessed its keenness of hearing and sense of curiosity. I had been hunting marmots in a near-by rocky outcropping when I noticed the weasel dart into a crevice in the rocks. I hid behind a boulder and gave a few high-pitched "squeaks." Although the animal was fully fifty feet away and down in the rocks, it almost immediately thrust its head out of the crevice and looked in my direction. When I "squeaked" again, it ducked back into the rocks and soon reappeared at a spot about fifteen feet closer. At Yellowstone Lake I observed one watching me with only its head projecting from the burrow of a pocket gopher. When I approached, it withdrew into the burrow and soon re- appeared at another opening about twenty feet farther on. My closer approach again caused it to retreat and reappear at a third opening. We played this game of "hide-and-seek" for about ten minutes, and each time I was able to get no closer than fifteen feet before it disappeared. To me, the strange part of its behavior was that it insisted on exposing itself and watching me. It appeared to be unafraid, and I attribute its actions to curiosity.

Records of occurrence.—Specimens examined, 58, as follows: *Latah County:* Cedar Mountain, 1 (W. T. Shaw coll.). *Idaho County:* Lochsa River, 1 (Biol. Surv. coll.). *Adams County:* summit Smith Mountain, 1 (Ralph Ellis coll.). *Washington County:* Midvale, 2 (Biol. Surv. coll.). *Payette County:* 2 mi. S Payette, 1. *Canyon County:* Nampa, 3 (Biol. Surv. coll.). *Owyhee County:* 5 mi. SE Riddle, 1; Three Creek, 2 (all in Biol. Surv. coll.). *Lemhi County:* Leadore, 3; Timber Creek, Lemhi Mts., 5 (all in Biol. Surv. coll.). *Custer County:* Mackay, 1; Pahsimeroi Mountains, 1; Stanley Lake, 1 (all in Biol. Surv. coll.); Double Springs, 1. *Blaine County:* Ketchum, 5 (W. E. Snyder coll.); Sawtooth City, 1 (Biol. Surv. coll.). *Lincoln County:* Shoshone, 1 (Biol. Surv. coll.). *Cassia County:* Elba, 1. *Clark County:* Birch Creek, 2 (Biol. Surv. coll.); Dry Creek, 1 (Amer. Mus. Nat. Hist.). *Jefferson County:* 20 mi. W Camas, 1 (Biol. Surv. coll.). *County questionable:* North Fork Teton River, 1 (Biol. Surv. coll.). *Teton County:* 3 mi. SW Victor, 1. *Bingham County:* Alridge, 2; Shelley, 1; Springfield, 1 (all in Biol. Surv. coll.). *Power County:* 4 mi. NW American Falls, 1. *Bannock County:* Mink Creek, 2 mi. from Portneuf River, 2 (1 in Ralph Ellis coll.); 3 mi. N Pocatello, 1; 3 mi. S Pocatello, 1; 1 mi. E Portneuf, 1; Pocatello (near), 1; Ross Fork Creek, 11 mi. NE Pocatello, 1; Inkom, 2; Swan Lake, 1 (last three in Biol. Surv. coll.). *Bear Lake County:* Geneva, 1; Montpelier, 1; Pegram, 2 (last three in Biol. Surv. coll.); Paris, 1 (Brigham Young Univ., Zool. Dept. coll.). Additional record: *Butte County:* Big Butte (Merriam, 1891:84).

Mustela vison energumenos (Bangs)
MINK

Putorius vison energumenos Bangs, Proc. Boston Soc. Nat. Hist., 27:5. March, 1896. Type from Sumas, British Columbia, Canada.

Synonym.—*Lutreola vison*, Merriam, 1891:83.

Distribution.—In Idaho, doubtless widespread throughout the state along streams and lake margins.

Description.—Large, aquatic, weasellike carnivore; tail semi-bushy; general coloration wood brown or clove brown dorsally, slightly lighter below; auditory bullae small, flattened; greatest length of mandible greater than postglenoidal length of skull. External measurements of an adult male from near Acequia are 520-142-69; an adult female from near Ketchum measured 515-162-47.

Remarks.—The subspecific name *energumenos* is here applied tentatively to the mink from Idaho. I have compared the specimens from Idaho with specimens from the Puget Sound region assigned to *energumenos,* and find the former to be much darker, that is, less reddish. Specimens from Indian Point Lake, British Columbia, referred to *energumenos* (Hall, 1934), are less reddish than Puget Sound specimens and, in this respect, compare favorably with the Idaho mink.

One skin from Bellevue, no. 69693, is peculiar in that it is completely *white* save for two small brown patches on the rump. The posterior patch continues on the tail, both dorsally and ventrally, and terminates about 37 mm. from the end, leaving a white tip. In addition, the hair on the tail is short (15 mm.) for a November-taken individual, and reminds one of the tail of a weasel. Mr. Gene Glahn, the trapper from whom I purchased the skin, told me that he, his brother, and several residents of Bellevue observed this animal on four different days feeding in the storage reservoir above the power plant. As far as he was able to determine, its behavior was normal.

Records of occurence.—Specimens examined, 7, as follows: *Blaine County:* Bellevue, 1; Big Wood River, 1-12 mi. N Ketchum, 3. *Cassia County:* Snake River, 3 mi. SE Acequia, 1. *Bannock County:* junction of Ross Creek and Portneuf River, 2. Additional record: *Clark County:* Birch Creek (Merriam, 1891:83).

Genus **Gulo** Pallas
Wolverines

Gulo luscus luscus (Linnaeus)
WOLVERINE

Ursus luscus Linnaeus, Syst. Nat., ed. 12, 1:71. 1766. Type from Hudson Bay.

Distribution.—Probably extinct in Idaho; if not, restricted to the more inaccessible mountainous central portion of the state.

Description.—Large, powerful, bearlike mustelid; tail short, bushy; feet large, powerful, claws modified for climbing, semiretractile; ears short; fur moderately long; color blackish brown with lighter areas on face and rump; sexes alike; weight up to 25 pounds. A large male may have a total length of 3 feet or more. Skull large, basilar length ranging from 110 to 140 mm.; facial angle steep; palate terminates considerably behind molars; dental formula $\frac{3\ 1\ 4\ 1}{3\ 1\ 4\ 2}$; inner moiety of M^1 larger than outer one; talonid of M_1 longer than trigonid, metaconid absent.

Remarks.—Apparently the wolverine never was common in Idaho. Trappers in the Sawtooth and Salmon River mountains claim that none has been seen or reported in those areas in the last twenty years. Its range in Recent time is from the Arctic south into the Rocky Mountain and Sierra Nevadan ranges of the United States.

Records of occurrence (Merriam, 1891:85).—*Lemhi County:* Salmon River Mountains. *Blaine County:* Sawtooth Mountains. *Bingham County:* Wolverine Creek, Blackfoot Mountains.

Genus **Lutra** Brisson
River Otters

Lutra canadensis nexa Goldman
NEVADA OTTER

Lutra canadensis nexa Goldman, Proc. Biol. Soc. Washington, 48:182. November 15, 1935. Type from Deeth, Humboldt River, Elko County, Nevada.

Synonym.—*Lutra hudsonica*, Merriam, 1891:82.

Distribution.—The larger streams and lakes of the state.

Description.—Large, aquatic mustelid; body long, lithe; legs short; toes webbed; tail long and rounded, tapering from a thick base; general color brownish; total length near 36 inches. Skull flattened dorsally; tympanic bullae flattened and not in contact with paroccipital processes; palate terminates considerably posterior to molars; dental formula $\frac{3\ 1\ 4\ 1}{3\ 1\ 3\ 2}$; M^1 large, quadrate; M_1 with trigonid and talonid nearly equal in length, metaconid large.

Remarks.—This interesting and valuable mammal now is greatly reduced in numbers. Merriam (1891) reported it as "common along most of the streams and lakes in Idaho" in 1890. Mr. W. A. Curtis told me that in his twelve years of trapping for aquatic fur bearers along the Snake River near Rupert he had never seen sign of otter. He believes that Shoshone Falls prevents them from ascending the Snake River beyond that point. Mr. A. W. Linderman who has trapped in the vicinity of Hailey since 1923 has no record of

the occurrence of otter in Big Wood River and its tributaries. Trappers at Grand View, Owyhee County, told me
that only one otter, taken in the winter of 1934-35, had been
trapped in that vicinity in the past fifteen years.

Records of occurrence.—Owyhee County: 40 mi. S Bruneau; Riddle
(Biol. Surv. coll.). *Custer County:* Loon Creek (sight record by Dr.
F. Kenagy, *in litt.*). *Blaine County:* Hagerman (Goldman, 1935:183).
Clark County: Birch Creek (Merriam, 1891:82). *Teton County:* Teton
Basin (Biol. Surv. coll.).

Genus Spilogale Gray
Spotted Skunks

Spilogale gracilis saxatilis Merriam
LITTLE SPOTTED SKUNK

Spilogale saxatilis Merriam, N. Amer. Fauna, 4:13. October 8,
1890. Type from Provo, Utah County, Utah.
Synonyms.—Mephitis bicolor, Merriam, 1873:662.
*Distribution.—*In Idaho, apparently restricted to the southern half
of the state.
*Description.—*Small "spotted" black and white mustelid; form
moderately thickset; tail long, bushy, with long, drooping hairs; anal
scent glands well developed; pads four on each foot, naked. Skull
slightly arched dorsally in longitudinal section; palate terminating
adjacent to last molars; mastoidal bullae highly inflated; dental
formula $\frac{3131}{3132}$; M¹ roughly quadrangular; in M_1 trigonid longer than
talonid, metaconid large; basilar length near 50 mm. An adult male
from near American Falls measures 420-150-45-26.

Remarks.—For the use of the name *saxatilis*, see Whitlow and Hall (1933:248). These little skunks are found most
commonly along streams, especially in the vicinity of basaltic
outcroppings and rock piles. They are reported by fur
trappers as being common in southern Idaho. Mr. M. B.
Ebbertson, of Hagerman, Idaho, told me that he and his sons
caught several "civet cats" near Hagerman in the winter
of 1934-35. Mr. Leo Davis, of Acequia, Idaho, reported they
were "common in the rocks near Minidoka Dam." Mr.
Ebbertson showed me the decayed bodies of two spotted
skunks that he had caught and left in the traps. According
to him, the traps had been set side by side in about three
inches of water at the entrance to a burrow which he sup-

posed was occupied by a muskrat. Apparently the burrow had been occupied by the skunks, and, if so, the only way they could have entered or left it was by entering the water. Due to the low commercial value of their pelts and the strong odor of their musk, trappers in southern Idaho make no effort to catch these animals and, in most instances, discard them when they accidentally are caught.

Records of occurrence.—Specimens examined, 6, as follows: *Blaine County:* Wood River, 1 mi. N Ketchum, 1. *Gooding County:* 2 mi. S Hagerman, 2. *Cassia County:* Howells Canyon, 6 mi. S Albion, 1. *Power County:* 3½ mi. SW American Falls, 1. *Bannock County:* Justice Park, 1. Additional record (Merriam, 1873:662): *Bannock County:* Marsh Valley.

Genus **Mephitis** Geoffroy and Cuvier
Common Skunks

Mephitis mephitis major (Howell)
GREAT BASIN STRIPED SKUNK

Chincha occidentalis major Howell, N. Amer. Fauna, 20:37. August 31, 1901. Type from Fort Klamath, Klamath County, Oregon.
Synonym.—*Mephitis* sp. ?, Merriam, 1891:85.
Distribution.—Probably restricted to the southern, more arid, portions of the state.
Description.—Large, robust mustelid with long bushy tail, the terminal hairs of which are drooping; body thickset; general color black with two clear white dorsal stripes that extend from shoulders to and upon tail; legs short, soles naked; claws longer on front feet than on hind feet; anal musk glands well developed; no seasonal dichromatism. Skull arched dorsally, deepest in frontal region; auditory bullae small, mastoidal portion but little inflated; paroccipital processes independent of bullae; palate terminates slightly behind molars; dental formula $\frac{3\ 1\ 3\ 1}{3\ 1\ 3\ 2}$; M^1 roughly quadrangular, the inner moiety with two distinct cusps; in M_1 trigonid longer than talonid, metaconid distinct. An adult male from near Hailey measures 690-285-75-34; a female from near Hagerman, 655-330-60-30.

Remarks.—*M. m. major* is said to differ from *M. m. hudsonica* (see Howell, 1901) in larger size, longer tail; bifurcation of stripes between shoulders, rather than on neck; broader premaxillae; and more nearly parallel zygomata. Except for external measurements, the specimens I have seen from Idaho are most like *major*. The hind foot is smaller, however, than measurements given (Howell, *ibid.*) for both *hudsonica* and *major*. Even so, it seems best to refer them tentatively to *major*.

Striped skunks are reported by trappers to be common in southern Idaho. Mr. M. B. Ebbertson, of Hagerman, caught 21 in the winter of 1934-35 in the vicinity of his home. Mr. Leo Davis, of Acequia, caught 15 the same winter and he is of the opinion that they constitute a large portion of the fur catch made in that area. Mr. Walter Nelson, of Rupert, who is engaged in predator control activities, told me that striped skunks occasionally were found dead at his poison stations.

Records of occurrence.—Specimens examined, 8, as follows: *Blaine County:* Hailey, 1. *Minidoka County:* 2 mi. E Acequia, 1. *Twin Falls County:* 2 mi. S Hagerman, 2. *Bannock County:* junction of Ross Fork Creek and Portneuf River, 4. Additional records (Merriam, 1891:85) : *Lemhi County:* Salmon River Mountains. *Blaine County:* Sawtooth Lake.

Mephitis mephitis hudsonica Richardson
NORTHERN PLAINS SKUNK

Mephitis americana var. *hudsonica* Richardson, Fauna Boreali-Americana, 1:55. 1829. Type from plains of the Saskatchewan, Canada.

Synonym.—*Chincha hudsonica*, Howell, 1901:24.

Distribution.—In Idaho, apparently confined to the northern and central Rocky Mountain areas.

Description.—Similar to *major*, but smaller, with shorter tail; divergence of white stripes on neck, rather than on shoulders; zygomata conspicuously bowed laterally.

Records of occurrence (Howell, 1901:24).—*Kootenai County:* Coeur d'Alene. *Bear Lake County:* Bear Lake (east side).

Genus Taxidea Waterhouse
American Badgers

Taxidea taxus taxus (Schreber)
BADGER

Ursus taxus Schreber, Saugthiere, 3:520, pl. 142B. 1778. Type locality, Labrador and Hudson Bay.

Synonym.—*Taxidea americana*, Merriam, 1891:85.

Distribution.—In Idaho, widely distributed throughout at least the southern half of the state.

Description.—Form thickset, body muscular; tail short, bushy; legs short, front feet powerful, with long claws (one inch or more) modified for digging; ears short; head broadly triangular, nose pointed; hair long and falling from sides like a mantle; general color silver-gray, face black with white stripe from nose to back and another running through or under each eye. Skull with abruptly rising forehead, deepest through occiput; auditory bullae large, with paroccipital processes closely appressed; palate terminating considerably behind molars; dental formula $\frac{3\ 1\ 3\ 1}{3\ 1\ 3\ 2}$; M¹ triangular, with apex laterad; in M_1 trigonid nearly twice as long as talonid, metaconid well developed; talonid with two or more well-developed cusps. Both sexes are similiar in color and size; adults may weigh as much as 24 pounds. One adult female from Mink Creek measures 750-130-112-55.

Remarks.—The badger now is greatly reduced in numbers in southern Idaho. This reduction is due primarily, I believe, to the poison campaigns instituted against the coyote. One reliable trapper who is engaged in predator control told me that on one trip from the Snake River across the desert to Little Lost River he found 21 coyotes, 21 badgers, and nearly an equal number of bobcats. He said that on several trips he found nearly as many poisoned badgers near his stations as he did coyotes. The badger is the most effective natural control agent of the ground squirrel we have, yet it is sacrificed that a few coyotes may be killed for the sheepmen.

Records of occurrence.—Specimens examined, 20, as follows: *Owyhee County:* 1 mi. S Riddle, 1. *Blaine County:* Bellevue, 1; Baker Cr., 12 mi. N Ketchum, 1. *Twin Falls County:* Salmon Cr., 8 mi. W Rogerson, 1 (Davis coll.). *Cassia County:* 6 mi. SE Albion, 3; Elba, 1; Goose Cr., 15 mi. SW Oakley, 1. *Clark County:* 2 mi. SE Kaufman, 1. *Bannock County:* Mink Creek, near Justice Park, 1; "Bannock County," 9. Additional records (Merriam, 1891:85): *Lemhi County:* Salmon River Mountains. *Custer County:* Head of Pahsimeroi River. *Clark County:* Birch Creek. *Butte County:* Lost River Mountains.

Family CANIDAE
DOGS, FOXES, WOLVES

Small to large, cursorial, digitigrade carnivores; eyes and ears relatively large, usually pointed; tail medium to long, often bushy; feet rounded, with four functional toes on each foot, pollex rudimentary; digits 3 and 4 longest; claws blunt, nonretractile. Skull elongate, rostrum narrow; tympanic bullae large, paroccipital processes closely appressed and partly fused with them; alisphenoidal canal present; anterior opening of infraorbital canal between Pm³ and Pm⁴; carnassial well differentiated; os penis grooved; intestine with caecum.

In the order Carnivora the Canidae is geologically an old family, and today it is nearly world wide in distribution, being absent only from Madagascar and the oceanic islands. The lengthening of the limbs, the perfection of the shearing and crushing teeth, and the increase in size of brain mark the chief lines of evolutionary progress. The members of the family Canidae are closely related phylogenetically to the bears, raccoons, and mustelids, all of which can be traced back to the Eocene creodonts of the family Miacidae from which all living carnivores are thought to have descended. Canids were present in Idaho in the Pleistocene (see Gazin, 1935 and 1936), as is evidenced by fossil remains of the four genera *Canis, Urocyon?, Aenocyon,* and *Hyaenognathus.* The two genera last mentioned are extinct, and *Urocyon* is absent from the region today.

Genus **Vulpes** Oken
Foxes

Vulpes fulva macroura Baird
WESTERN RED FOX

Vulpes macrourus Baird, Stansbury's Report, Expl. . . . of the Valley of the Great Salt Lake of Utah. . . . June, 1852:309. Type from Wasatch Mountains bordering Great Salt Lake, Utah.

Synonyms.—*Vulpes macrourus,* Merriam, 1891:82; *Vulpes macroura,* Whitlow and Hall, 1933:249.

Distribution.—In Idaho, the mountainous parts of the state; absent from the Snake River Plains and unknown from the mountains to the south and west.

Description.—Fur soft, long; tail long and bushy, white-tipped; ears long, erect, pointed, black on posterior side; nose pointed, elongate; feet blackish, claws long, blunt; general dorsal coloration yellowish red, whitish ventrally. Skull: Rostrum slender, width less than length of auditory bullae; postorbital processes prominent; dental formula $\frac{3\ 1\ 4\ 2}{3\ 1\ 4\ 3}$; in M_1 trigonid more than twice the length of talonid, metaconid well developed. An adult female from near Stanley measures (dry) 970-385-156-75.

Remarks.—Although red foxes from Idaho are rare in collections, they are not uncommon in the mountainous central part of the state.

Records of occurrence.—Specimens examined, 3, as follows: *Custer County:* 15 mi. NE Stanley, 1; Five Mile Cr., 25 mi. NE Stanley, 2. Additional records: *Blaine County:* Sawtooth Mountains (Merriam, 1891:82). *Clark County:* Birch Creek (Merriam, *ibid.*). *Bannock County:* near Pocatello (Whitlow and Hall, 1933:249).

Vulpes macrotis nevadensis Goldman
NEVADA LONG-EARED DESERT FOX

Vulpes macrotis nevadensis Goldman, Jour. Washington Acad. Sci., 21:250. June 4, 1931. Type from Willow Creek Ranch, near Jungo, Humboldt County, Nevada.
Distribution.—In Idaho, desert regions south of the Snake River.
Description.—Similar to, but much smaller than, the red fox; general color paler, less redish; tail tipped with black, rather than with white.

Remarks.—This fox is typical of the Great Basin desert country; it reaches its northern limit of distribution in southern Idaho, where it is known from one skull.

Record of occurrence (Goldman, *ibid.*).—*Owyhee County:* 20 mi. S Grand View.

Genus Canis Linnaeus
Dogs, Wolves, Coyotes, and Jackals

Canis latrans lestes Merriam
GREAT BASIN COYOTE

Canis lestes Merriam, Proc. Biol. Soc. Washington, 11:25. March 15, 1897. Type from Toyabe Mountains, near Cloverdale, Nye County, Nevada.
Synonym.—*Canis latrans*, Merriam, 1891:82.
Distribution.—Widely distributed throughout most of at least the southern half of the state.
Description.—Doglike, nose sharp and slender; ears large, furred, erect, pointed; tail moderately long, bushy; hair long and thick, buffy gray and black above, whitish below; sexes about alike in size and color. Skull: Rostrum slender, its breadth but little more than length

of auditory bullae; postorbital processes present, but not well developed; sagittal crest distinct, with prominent posteriorly projecting inion; dental formula $\frac{3\ 1\ 4\ 2}{3\ 1\ 4\ 3}$; carnassial large; in M_1 trigonid more than twice as long as talonid, metaconid small but distinct; hypoconid nearly twice the size of entoconid. Average external measurements of dried carcasses of 3 adult males from near Minidoka are 1106-359-182; of 4 adult females from the same locality, 1115-369-181.

Remarks.—In Idaho, the coyote is most common on the sage-covered plains in the southern part of the state. Even though it is persistently hunted, trapped, and poisoned, it is still common. In the winter of 1934-35 I saw the coyote catches made by three trappers, each of whom had taken well over 100 pelts. In addition to these three large catches, many trappers I visited had taken from 5 to 30 coyotes during the fall and early winter.

The coyotes from the Little Lost River area are larger than those taken on the Snake River desert, and coyotes from north of the Snake River average grayer in color than those from the south side of the river. Possibly two races occur in Idaho, as many trappers in that area suggest, but the subspecific name *lestes* may be applied at least until the distribution and relationships of the various named races in the West are better known.

Records of occurrence.—Specimens examined, 30, as follows: *Owyhee County:* Castle Cr., 8 mi. S Oreana, 1; Riddle, 1. *Custer County:* head Little Lost River Valley, 1. *Blaine County:* 12 mi. NE Minidoka, 9. *Minidoka County:* 2 mi. E Acequia, 1. *Twin Falls County:* 3 mi. S Rogerson, 2. *Cassia County:* 6 mi. S Albion, 1. *Butte County:* Little Lost River Valley, near Howe, 11. *Power County:* 9 mi. SW Pocatello, 1. *Bannock County:* 8½ mi. NE Pocatello, 2. Additional records: *Jerome County:* Shoshone Falls (Merriam, 1891:82). *Clark County:* Birch Creek (Merriam, 1891:82). *Bannock County:* 4 mi. E Pocatello (Whitlow and Hall, 1933:250).

Canis lupus youngi Goldman
SOUTHERN ROCKY MOUNTAIN WOLF

Canis lupus youngi Goldman, Jour. Mammalogy, 18:40. February 14, 1937. Type from Harts Draw, north slope of Blue Mountains, 20 miles northwest of Monticello, San Juan County, Utah.

Synonym.—*Canis nubilus*, Merriam, 1891:82, part.

Distribution.—In Idaho, formerly in the southeastern part of the state, where it now probably is extinct.

Description.—Size large; nose elongate and pointed; ears moderately large, erect, pointed; tail of medium length, bushy; legs long, powerful; feet large; hair long and heavy; dorsum from nape to rump warm buff overlaid with black; sides purer buff; under parts buffy white. Skull similar to that of coyote but nearly twice the bulk; auditory bullae actually and relatively smaller than in coyote, less inflated; width of rostrum twice the anteroposterior length of bullae; in M_1 trigonid about three times the length of talonid. The type measures 1800-470-255 (Goldman, *ibid.*). A large adult may weigh nearly 80 pounds.

Remarks.—Wolves now are practically extinct in Idaho. Mr. Walter Nelson, of Rupert, Idaho, who traps regularly for predators, told me that he had seen no sign of wolves in southern Idaho for the past several years. Other trappers with whom I have talked made similar statements. They probably never were as abundant as the smaller coyotes, and their disappearance from much of their former range can be attributed for the most part directly to the extermination policy of the Bureau of Biological Survey. Although I have no definite records of wolves from the northern part of the state, Merriam (1891:82) states that it is "said to be common in northern Idaho. A trapper named N. C. Linsley states that he and his partner killed forty wolves near Pend d'Oreille River during the winter of 1888-89."

The following records, as well as those listed under *C. l. irremotus*, were furnished by A. H. Howell from specimens not seen by me in the Bureau of Biological Survey collections. Unfortunately, in the original description of the two races of wolves found in Idaho, Goldman *(ibid.)* failed to list localities whence he examined specimens. Consequently, the allocation of the localities herein to the two subspecies is highly tentative.

Records of occurrence.—Twin Falls County: Castleford. *Blaine County:* Bear Park, 35 mi. NE Minidoka. *Bingham County:* Alridge. *Power County:* Sparks Well, 23 mi. NE Minidoka. *Bannock County:* Black Rock; Pocatello. *Caribou County:* Dry Valley; Soda Springs; Tygee Basin. *Bear Lake County:* Montpelier.

Canis lupus irremotus Goldman
NORTHERN ROCKY MOUNTAIN WOLF

Canis lupus irremotus Goldman, Jour. Mammalogy, 18:41. February 14, 1937. Type from Red Lodge, Carbon County, Montana.

Synonym.—Canis nubilus, Merriam, 1891:82, part.

Distribution.—In Idaho, formerly from near the Yellowstone region northward through the mountainous areas; now probably extinct in the state.

Description.—Similar to *youngi,* but whiter, the upper parts less heavily overlaid with black; skull differs especially in the narrowness of the frontal region.

Records of occurrence.—Elmore County: Atlanta; S. fork Boise River; Hammett. *Lemhi County:* Leadore. *Clark County:* Argora. (All records furnished by A. H. Howell from specimens in the Bureau of Biological Survey collections.)

Family FELIDAE
CATS AND ALLIES

Small to large, semi-arboreal, digitigrade carnivores; eyes large; ears medium in size, often tufted; tail short to long, seldom bushy; feet large, rounded, digits 4-5, claws sharp, recurved, retractile. Skull highly arched in frontal region; rostrum short; carotid canal short or lacking; alisphenoidal canal absent; tympanic bullae large, internally subdivided into two chambers; palate terminates posterior to molars; dental formula $\frac{3\ 1\ 2\text{-}3\ 1}{3\ 1\ 2\text{-}3\ 1}$; M^1 rudimentary; carnassial well developed, with distinct deuterocone; M_1 lacking talonid and metaconid; glans and os penis rudimentary; intestine with caecum.

Among the living carnivores, the cats are most closely related to the true civets and the hyenas of the Old World. Some paleontologists (see Romer, 1933) consider the family as having arisen directly from the miacid creodonts, the now extinct family from which all modern carnivores are thought to have evolved. The cats are almost as widely spread as the Canidae and even more uniform in type. The finding of fossil remains of forms related to the present-day mountain lion and the extinct saber-toothed tiger in the Pleistocene beds near American Falls (see Gazin, 1935) and in Upper

Pliocene or Lower Pleistocene deposits near Hagerman (see Gazin, 1933) indicates that the family has been present in Idaho for a considerable length of time.

Genus **Felis** Linnaeus
True Cats

Felis concolor hippolestes Merriam
MOUNTAIN LION

Felis hippolestes Merriam, Proc. Biol. Soc. Washington, 11:219. July 15, 1897. Type from Wind River Mountains, Fremont County, Wyoming.

Synonym.—*Felis concolor*, Merriam, 1891:81.

Distribution.—Probably widely, although locally, distributed throughout the mountainous parts of the state.

Description.—Very large, catlike carnivore; body long and lithe; tail more than half the length of head and body, rounded, black-tipped; claws long, sharp, recurved; soles haired, pads naked; general color pale tawny brown above, lighter below; ears prominent, without tufts; total length of adult males near 7 feet, females slightly smaller; weight of adults 150 to 200 pounds. Skull large, heavy, greatest length near 200 mm.; sagittal crest and inion well developed; width of mandibular condyle much more than anteroposterior length of auditory bullae.

Remarks.—The mountain lion, locally known by such names as cougar, panther, and puma, is still fairly common in Idaho in spite of the concerted efforts of fish and game officials, the predatory animal control agents of the Federal Bureau of Biological Survey, and the stockmen to exterminate it. It is holding its own best in the large Primitive Area in Idaho and Lemhi counties and in the numerous game refuges wherein the use of firearms is prohibited. Mr. Will Wickel, a rancher living near Elba, informed me that mountain lions have been reported regularly during the past few years from the game refuge in the Minidoka National Forest south of Albion. He is of the opinion that there they are increasing in number, a condition which seems to be correlated with a marked increase in deer and the prohibition of shooting. Dr. Fayre Kenagy, of Rupert, Idaho, reports *(in litt.)* that they are fairly common in western Lemhi County.

Records of occurrence.—Specimens examined, 2, as follows: *Power County:* 8 mi. SW Pocatello, 1. *Bannock County:* 9 mi. NW Pocatello,

1. Additional records: *Lemhi County:* Forney (Kenagy, 1934, *in litt.);* Lemhi Valley (Merriam, 1891:81). *Cassia County:* Mt. Harrison (sight record, Davis, 1935).

Genus Lynx Kerr
Lynxes and Bobcats
Lynx canadensis canadensis Kerr
CANADIAN LYNX

Lynx canadensis Kerr, Animal Kingdom, 1, systematic catalogue inserted between pages 32 and 33 (description, p. 157). 1792. Type from eastern Canada.

Distribution.—In Idaho, occurs in the mountainous regions north and east of the Snake River Plains.

Description.—A stout-bodied, long-legged cat; ears prominent, tufts usually more than an inch and a half long; fur long and dense; feet very large; claws sharp, strong; tail shorter than length of hind foot; ruff of long hairs on sides of head; male slightly larger than female, total length near 36 inches; general color light gray, more or less grizzled with brown. Skull with lyrate temporal ridges, inion prominent; width of mandibular condyle less than anteroposterior length of auditory bullae.

Records of occurrence (records furnished by Mr. A. H. Howell from specimens in Biol. Surv. coll.).—*Bonner County:* Coolin. *Kootenai County:* 10 mi. S Coeur d'Alene. *Latah County:* Viola. *Idaho County:* Clearwater River; 40 mi. SE Elk City; Lochsa River; Green Mountains. *Elmore County:* 22 mi. N Hill City. *Lemhi County:* Leadore; Leesburg. *Blaine County:* Sawtooth City.

Lynx rufus pallescens Merriam
PALLID BOBCAT

Lynx fasciatus pallescens Merriam, N. Amer. Fauna, 16:104. October 28, 1899. Type from south side of Mount Adams, near Trout Lake, Skamania County, Washington.

Synonym.—*Lynx baileyi* Merriam, 1891:81.

Distribution.—In Idaho, probably occurs locally throughout the state; most common in southern half.

Description.—Similar to *Lynx canadensis,* but smaller; spotted; form thickset, legs long; tail as long as hind foot; ears prominent but not conspicuously tufted; total length near 36 inches. Skull similar to *L. canadensis,* but differs as follows: smaller; relatively larger auditory bullae; postpalatine foramina situated farther from orbital rim of palate; presphenoid anteroposteriorly elongate, narrow, rather than transversely broad; postorbital processes larger (see Merriam and Stock, 1932).

Remarks.—The bobcat or wildcat is reported to be abundant in the lava fields north of the Snake River. Mr. Walter Nelson, of Rupert, informed me that he traps them regularly in the area, and in one week he took eighteen. Mr. Ned Emery, of Oakley, finds them to be most common in the "rimrock country" in the vicinity of Oakley. Merriam (1891) reported them as being particularly abundant in the lava canyons of the Snake River.

For the use of the subspecific name *pallescens* rather than *uinta,* see Grinnell and Dixon (1924:350).

Records of occurrence.—Specimens examined, 3, as follows: *Cassia County:* Goose Creek, 15 mi. SW Oakley, 2. *Power County:* 9 mi. SW Pocatello, 1. Additional records: *Owyhee County:* Grand View. (In May, 1935, I saw the skin of one that had been taken in the vicinity.) *Jerome County:* Shoshone Falls (Merriam, 1891:82). *Cassia County:* N. slope Mt. Harrison, 8 mi. S Albion. (In December, 1935, I saw the skin of one that had been trapped there by Archie Launsbury, of Albion.) *Clark County:* Birch Creek (Merriam, 1891:82). *Bingham County:* near Fort Hall (Whitlow and Hall, 1933:250). *Bannock County* (Whitlow and Hall, *ibid.*): 5 mi. SW Pocatello (tracks seen); 4 mi. SE Pocatello (skin seen).

Order RODENTIA
Gnawing Mammals

The rodents, of which some 2,800 species (not counting subspecies) are known, comprise nearly a third of the known living land-dwelling mammals of the world. They are world wide in distribution, occurring on all the major land masses, and from the lowest to nearly the highest elevations. The group illustrates well the principal of adaptive radiation; some rodents are fossorial, others are cursorial, aquatic, arboreal, or volant. None has developed true flight.

Rodents are unguiculate, mostly small, five-toed, plantigrade or semi-plantigrade, herbivorous mammals. In addition, they possess in common the following characters: (1) one pair of curved, chisel-shaped incisors in upper and lower jaws, (2) no canine teeth, (3) premolars reduced in number or lacking, (4) wide diastema separating the incisors from the cheek teeth, (5) mandibular condyle elongated and articulating with an anteroposteriorly elongated glenoid fossa, (6) orbit not separated from temporal opening by a postorbital bar, (7) testes usually abdominal, except in breeding season when they may be extra-abdominal, (8) uterus duplex.

Most rodents feed on plant materials and in turn comprise the principal food of carnivorous mammals and birds of prey. Thus, they play an important part in the economy of nature by transforming plant material into a form available as food to flesh-eating animals. The fur-bearing mammals, for example, rely mainly upon rodents for their food.

Depending for the most part on plants for food, rodents inevitably influence man's agricultural interests; hence they are of great economic importance. Because they eat wild forage plants and cultivated crops, man has recognized them as his competitors. The farmer is not only justified in applying control measures against such mammals as ground squirrels and pocket gophers, but may even be compelled to do so on intensely cultivated lands.

On uncultivated lands, rodents are regarded by many as beneficial. They point out that the burrowing activities of rodents result in cultivation and aeration of the soil, incorporation of humus in the soil, and allow more rapid penetration of water. By reason of promoting plant growth, and probably lessening the surface run-off after rains, rodents are obviously sometimes of benefit to agriculture.

Key to Families and Genera of Rodents in Idaho

1 Infraorbital canal round or ovoid, never slitlike; if anterior opening in or near maxillary plate of zygoma, its least diameter less than width of molar teeth; if far forward on side of rostrum, much larger than any tooth; cheek teeth always more than three in each jaw.

  2 Fur-lined cheek pouches never present; cheek teeth cusped or with numerous transverse ridges; anterior opening of infraorbital canal in or near maxillary plate.

   3 Postorbital processes present; cheek teeth rooted, low-crowned; auditory bullae internally subdivided into three incomplete chambers.   **SCIURIDAE, p. 156**

    4 Width of Pm^4 always more than half the width of M^2.

     5 Adults large, 2 feet or more in total length; skull flat dorsally.   **Marmota, p. 156**

5' Adults smaller, usually less than 18 inches in total length; skull arched.

    6 Dorsum never distinctly marked with longitudinal stripes. **Citellus, p. 163**

    6' Dorsum conspicuously marked with longitudinal stripes. **Callospermophilus, p. 197**

4' Width of Pm^4 always less than half the width of M^2.

    7 Flying membrane between front and hind legs. **Glaucomys, p. 229**

    7' Flying membrane absent.

        8 Hind foot less than 40 mm.; total length less than 260 mm.; distinctly striped.

            9 Dorsum conspicuously marked with **two** longitudinal white stripes; under surface of tail white. **Ammospermophilus, p. 204**

            9' Dorsum marked with as many as nine longitudinal stripes; under surface of tail grayish or reddish, never white. **Eutamias, p. 206**

        8' Hind foot more than 45 mm.; total length near 300 mm.; never distinctly striped. **Tamiasciurus, p. 225**

3' Postorbital processes absent; cheek teeth rootless (except in very old age), high-crowned, with 8 to 10 transverse enamel ridges; auditory bullae consisting of a single chamber. **CASTORIDAE (Castor), p. 271**

2' External fur-lined cheek pouches present; cheek teeth with anterior and posterior enamel plates, never cusped except in very young; anterior opening of infraorbital foramen on side of rostrum.

        10 Tail short, never as long as head and body; front feet larger than hind feet, with longer claws; upper incisors not distinctly grooved. **GEOMYIDAE (Thomomys), p. 234**

        10' Tail as long as, or longer than, head and body; hind feet larger than front feet; upper incisors distinctly grooved. **HETEROMYIDAE, p. 261**

11 Hind legs much longer than front legs; tail nearly twice the the length of head and body, striped with black and white.
Dipodomys, p. 266

11' Hind legs but little longer than front legs; tail but little longer than head and body, never striped with black and white.
Perognathus, p. 261

1' Infraorbital canal a large vertical slit; or, if circular, restricted to maxillary plate of zygoma and much larger than any molar tooth.

12 Cheek teeth never more than three; infraorbital canal a large, vertical slit.

13 Upper molars with **three** longitudinal rows of cusps; cheek teeth always short-crowned and rooted.
MURIDAE, p. 331

14 Mouse size; upper incisors with distinct, terminal, internal notch.
Mus, p. 331

14' Rat size; upper incisors never distinctly notched.
Rattus, p. 331

13' Upper molars with **two** longitundinal rows of cusps or consisting of numerous triangles and transverse enamel folds.
CRICETIDAE, p. 276

15 Upper and lower molars short-crowned, upper ones with two longitudinal rows of cusps; mouse size.

16 Upper incisors grooved; hind foot near 17 mm.
Reithrodontomys, p. 278

16' Upper incisors ungrooved; hind foot more than 18 mm.

17 Coronoid process of mandible rudimentary; tail more than three times the length of hind foot.
Peromyscus, p. 284

17' Coronoid process of mandible well developed; tail about twice the length of hind foot.
Onychomys, p. 276

15' Upper and lower molars with series of triangles and transverse loops.

18 Rat size; occipitonasal length over 35 mm.; incisive foramina longer than width of rostrum.

19 Tail laterally compressed; aquatic. **Ondatra, p. 328**

19' Tail terete or dorsoventrally flattened; terrestrial.
Neotoma, p. 294

18' Mouse size; occipitonasal length usually less than 30 mm.; incisive foramina shorter than width of rostrum; ears nearly concealed by pelage.

20 Inner re-entrant angles of molars deeper than outer ones; no cement in re-entrant angles; stapedial artery naked. **Phenacomys, p. 302**

20' Inner and outer re-entrant angles of molars nearly equal; cement present or absent; stapedial canal enclosed in at least a partial osseous tube.

21 Back distinctly reddish; molars rooted in adults; cement lacking in re-entrant angles **Clethrionomys, p. 305**

21' Back never distinctly reddish; molars ever growing; cement present in re-entrant angles.

22 Color light gray; auditory bullae large, of foamlike cancellous bone; M_3 with four prisms. **Lemmiscus, p. 325**

22' Color brownish or blackish, but never light gray; bullae never of foamlike cancellous bone; M_3 with three transverse loops. **Microtus, p. 312**

12' Cheek teeth always more than three (usually four or five) in each jaw; infraorbital canal in maxillary plate, nearly circular, much larger than any molar tooth.

23 Mouse size; tail much longer than head and body; hind legs elongated for saltation; general coloration yellowish brown, white ventrally; tail unicolor.
ZAPODIDAE (Zapus), p. 333

23' Larger, total length near 2 feet; tail short, heavy, equipped with quills; hind legs short, feet large.
ERETHIZONTIDAE
(Erethizon), p. 334

Family SCIURIDAE
SQUIRRELS, MARMOTS, SPERMOPHILES, and CHIPMUNKS

According to Romer (1933), the squirrels and their allies are but little changed from the primitive Eocene and Oligocene types *Paramys* and *Ischyromys*. The skull is somewhat arched, the brain case larger; a postorbital process is present, and also a well-developed groove on the front of the zygomatic process in front of the orbit for an important division of the masseter muscle. Otherwise, the skulls of living forms are much like those of their primitive ancestors; the teeth are almost always low-crowned, rooted, and of the modified tritubercular type; the third upper premolar usually is retained. The main group is comprised of arboreal forms; others, as ground squirrels and chipmunks, are primarily terrestrial, while a third group includes the somewhat more fossorial marmot and prairie dog. Both Gazin (1935) and Wilson (1933) record fossil *Citellus* from Pleistocene deposits in southern Idaho. Although fossil remains of the other genera of the family now occurring in Idaho have not as yet been found there, they are known from Pleistocene deposits in other regions.

Genus **Marmota** Blumenbach
Marmots

Large, heavy-bodied, fossorial, squirrellike rodents; tail less than twice the length of hind foot; pollex rudimentary, with flat nail; internal cheek pouches rudimentary; mammae in four or five pairs; pelage coarse, with fine underfur; ears short, lacking tragus and antitragus; eyes moderately large. Skull massive, angular, ridged, dorsoventrally flattened; postorbital processes triangular, projecting laterally except in young, where they project posterolaterally; rostrum short and broad with nasals projecting posteriorly beyond premaxillary tongues; auditory bullae rounded, subdivided internally into three incomplete chambers, cancellous material lacking; stapedial artery enclosed in a complete osseous tube; pterygoid fossae large with distinct lateral walls; dentition as in most other squirrels with two premolars above and one below; cheek teeth rooted, triangular above, quadrangular below, brachyodont, modified bunolophodont; incisors heavy with enamel plates of upper pair covering all of anterior and half of lateral surfaces.

Marmots, known also as rockchucks, woodchucks, whistlers, ground hogs, and by various other names, are closely related to ground squirrels *(Citellus)*. In fact, except for large size and certain modifications of the skull which appear to be correlated with size, structural characters separating the two genera are few. Each character listed above is duplicated in *Citellus* with the exceptions of posterior extension of nasals considerably beyond premaxillary tongues, dorsoventral flattening of the skull, direction assumed by the postorbital processes, and amount of enamel on the lateral surfaces of the upper incisors. The differences which separate the two appear to be no greater than ones distinguishing two species of the same genus in other groups of mammals, for instance, the weasel from the mink, the house cat from the mountain lion, and the snowshoe rabbit from the jack rabbit. A detailed comparative study of the osteology and anatomy of the soft parts of *Citellus* and *Marmota* may reveal that the two should be considered as congeneric.

Marmots are widespread in the Holarctic regions of both the Old World and the New World. As far as I am aware, no revision of the entire genus has been attempted; the American forms were reported on by Howell (1915). In North America three distinct groups, each of which occurs in Idaho, are recognized: the *monax* group, occurring from Alaska south through the Rocky Mountains to Idaho, eastward across boreal Canada and southward over much of the United States east of the 97th meridian; the *flaviventer* group, confined largely to the boreal areas of the western United States and southern British Columbia; and the *caligata* group, restricted to the territory westward from the Rocky Mountains, and from Alaska southward to Idaho and Washington.

The life history of the eastern woodchuck, *Marmota monax rufescens,* has been studied in detail (Hamilton,

1934); unfortunately, our western forms have not been similarly studied. A single litter, averaging four or five young, is born early in the spring. The young grow rapidly and remain in the vicinity of the home den most of the summer during which time, in young and old alike, fat accumulates in large masses under the skin and in the visceral cavity. This material is utilized in the metabolism of the animals during the long period of hibernation. This sleep really begins in late summer, and at that time is more properly called æstivation. Marmots are voracious eaters and, when established in the vicinity of cultivated areas, a colony can do considerable damage to farmers' crops.

At least the eastern species, *Marmota monax*, swims well and does not hesitate to enter water (Hamilton, *op. cit.*, p. 100). Near Hagerman, Idaho, in the summer of 1935, I saw a few individuals on a small rocky island in the middle of the river which could have been reached only by swimming. Probably this ability explains the presence of individuals of the same race on both sides of the Snake River in the region west of Blackfoot where the river acts as an absolute barrier to ground squirrels and pocket gophers.

Key to Marmots of Idaho

1   Postorbital processes terminating on plane anterior to M^3; mammae in four pairs.

M. monax petrensis, p. 159

1' Postorbital processes terminating on plane posterior to M^3; mammae in five pairs.

   2   Upper parts mainly grizzled black and white, white predominating over shoulders; side of neck without conspicuous buffy patch.

M. caligata nivaria, p. 162

   2' Upper parts grizzled brownish; side of neck with conspicuous buffy patch.

      3   Ventral coloration cinnamon red.

M. flaviventer nosophora, p. 159

      3' Ventral coloration buffy or yellowish.

M. flaviventer avara, p. 159

Marmota monax petrensis Howell
BRITISH COLUMBIA MARMOT

Marmota monax petrensis Howell, N. Amer. Fauna, 37:33. April 7, 1915. Type from Revelstoke, British Columbia.

Distribution.—Extreme northeastern portion of the state (see map, fig. 7).

Record of occurrence.—This species is known from Idaho by a single specimen from Thompson Pass, Shoshone County (Howell, 1915:33).

Marmota flaviventer avara (Bangs)
YELLOW-BELLIED MARMOT

Arctomys flaviventer avarus Bangs, Proc. New England Zool. Club, 1:68. July 31, 1899. Type from Okanogan, British Columbia, Canada.

Synonym.—*Marmota flaviventris engelhardti,* Howell, 1915:46, part.

Distribution.—In Idaho, occurs in extreme western part of state from Kootenai County south to Nevada (see map, fig. 7).

Description.—Dorsal coloration grizzled brownish; distinct black and white markings on face; side of neck with buff patch; ventral coloration yellowish brown. External measurements of an adult male from Washington County are 595-180-80; of an adult female from the same county, 532-150-78.

Remarks.—See *Remarks* under *M. f. nosophora.*

Records of occurrence.—Specimens examined, 12, as follows: *Kootenai County:* 10 mi. N St. Maries, 1. *Idaho County:* Rapid River, near Riggins, 2 (David MacKaye coll.). *Washington County:* Crane Creek, 15 mi. E Midvale, 4 (Ralph Ellis coll.) ; 2 mi. S Cambridge, 2 (Ralph Ellis coll.). *Canyon County:* 2 mi. S Melba, 1. *Owyhee County:* 1 mi. S Riddle, 2 (skulls only). Additional record (Howell, 1915:46): *Washington County:* Midvale.

Marmota flaviventer nosophora Howell
CHESTNUT-BELLIED MARMOT

Marmota flaviventer nosophora Howell, Proc. Biol. Soc. Washington, 27:15. February 2, 1914. Type from Willow Creek, 7 miles east of Corvallis, 4000 feet, Ravalli County, Montana.

Synonyms.—*Arctomys flaviventer,* Merriam, 1873:664; *Arctomys* sp?, Merriam, 1891:36.

Distribution.—In Idaho, eastern and southeastern parts of state, west in Snake River Valley as far as Hagerman (see map, fig. 7).

Description.—Similar to *M. f. avara,* but with ventral parts distinctly cinnamon red. External measurements of two large males from near Pocatello average 618-180-85. Two adult males from near

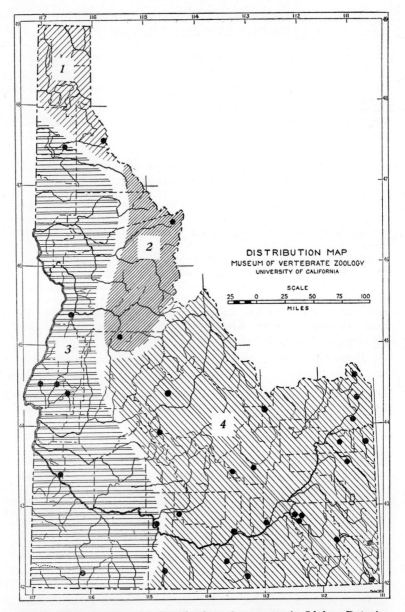

FIG. 7. Map showing the distribution of marmots in Idaho. Dots indicate localities whence specimens have been examined or recorded.
1. *Marmota monax petrensis*, 2. *Marmota caligata nivaria*, 3. *Marmota
flaviventer avara*, 4. *Marmota flaviventer nosophora*.

Acequia average 597-137-83. One adult male from near Hagerman measures 570-165-78. Females average slightly smaller; one adult from near Acequia measures 565-130-75, and one from near Hagerman, 545-140-75.

Remarks.—In Idaho this species ranges altitudinally from 2000 feet along the Snake River to above 8000 feet in the mountains. Thus, it is found in association with xerophytic types of plants at one extreme of its range and with alpine types at the other. It is exceedingly abundant in the lava fields and basaltic outcroppings in the Snake River desert. This distribution is difficult to correlate with any given set of climatic conditions, or with the occurrence of any particular food plants. The presence or absence of suitable rocky refuge sites is thought to be more important as a range-determining factor. Of course, food, in the nature of green herbs, must be present, but where food of a kind acceptable to them is present and rock piles or outcroppings are absent, no marmots occur.

Nearly every large colony of *flaviventer* that I have observed in summer consists of three size-groups, which I take to be adults, yearlings, and young. Third-grown young were observed in late May at the Salmon Creek reservoir. A female, accompanied by five third-grown young, was collected in early June near Hagerman. Young collected in the Salmon River Mountains between Mill Creek and Custer in late July were half grown. Doubtless all these small individuals were young of the year. However, two-thirds-grown individuals observed in early summer are thought to be yearlings. This situation suggests that marmots, like their close relatives the ground squirrels, do not reach adult size until the second year.

From the material available, it appears that south-central Idaho is an area of intergradation between *avara* and *nosophora*. Specimens from the western part of the state, Crane Creek and Cambridge, appear to be typical of *avara* in that the ventral coloration is light yellowish brown, the animals average slightly smaller than those farther east, and the rostrum is narrow. Specimens from localities east of Hagerman are typical *nosophora*, but specimens from Hagerman and farther west (Melba) exhibit cranial characters of *avara* and the ventral coloration of *nosophora* and, thus, appear to be intergrades. The single specimen from south of Albion (Mt. Harrison) is light brown ventrally and appears to be comparable with specimens from the Ruby Mountains, Nevada, which Borell and Ellis (1934:24) provisionally referred to *avara*. However, in cranial characters it is nearer *nosophora* and herein is referred to that race. I am unable to say how the single specimen from Midvale, Washington County, which Howell (1915:46) referred to *M. f. engelhardti* Allen, differs from specimens from Crane Creek and Cambridge which are most like *avara*, to which race I have tentatively assigned the record of occurrence.

Records of occurrence.—Specimens examined, 19, as follows: *Blaine County:* Alturas Lake, 1. *Lincoln County:* 2 mi. W Shoshone, 1. *Gooding County:* 2 mi. S Hagerman, 3. *Minidoka County:* 2 mi. E Acequia, 3. *Twin Falls County:* Salmon Creek, 8 mi. W Rogerson, 2. *Cassia County:* Mt. Harrison, 12 mi. S Albion, 1. *Butte County:* 3 mi. SE Arco, 1 (skull only); mouth of Little Cottonwood Creek Canyon, Craters of the Moon, 2 (1 skull only). *Power County:* 4 mi. NW American Falls, 1. *Bannock County:* Pocatello, 2; 4 mi. S Pocatello, 1 (Ralph Ellis coll.); 1 mi. E Portneuf, 1 (Ralph Ellis coll.). Additional records (Howell, 1915:48): *Blaine County:* Sawtooth National Forest. *Cassia County:* Bridge. *Fremont County:* Conant Creek; Island Park; Henry Fork of Snake River. *Madison County:* Moody Creek. *Teton County:* Teton Basin. *Bonneville County:* 20 mi. NW Irwin. *Bannock County:* Grace. *Caribou County:* Preuss Mountains. *Bear Lake County:* Bear Lake (east side).

Marmota caligata nivaria Howell
MONTANA HOARY MARMOT

Marmota caligata nivaria Howell, Proc. Biol. Soc. Washington, 27:17. February 2, 1914. Type from mountains near Upper St. Mary Lake, 6100 feet, Glacier National Park, Montana.

Distribution.—In Idaho, known only from the Bitterroot and Salmon River mountains in the central eastern portion of state (see map, fig. 7).

Description.—Largest of the marmots; dorsal coloration grizzled black and white, white predominating on shoulders; top of head black, mixed with white, with large white patch across face in front of eyes. Large individuals may weigh as much as sixteen pounds. Measurements of a young adult male from the type locality are 755-250-110 (Howell, 1915:67).

Records of occurrence (Howell, 1915:67).—*Clearwater County:*
Bitterroot Mountains (head of Clearwater River). *Valley County:*
Elk Summit, Salmon River Mountains.

Genus **Citellus** Oken
Ground Squirrels*

Structurally, the ground squirrels occurring in Idaho
may be divided into four groups, each fairly homogeneous
within itself, and with similar habitats. These are: (1)
mantled ground squirrels (genus *Callospermophilus),* (2)
big-eared ground squirrels (all *Citellus* except the species
C. mollis), (3) short-eared ground squirrels *(Citellus mollis*
and its races), and (4) antelope ground squirrels (genus
Ammospermophilus).

The mantled ground squirrels (often called big chipmunks) are predominantly dwellers in the mountains where
they occur in open forests or, more commonly, on rocky
talus areas. They are characterized by reddish or chestnut
coloration of head and neck; three dorsolateral stripes, a
white one bordered by two black ones, extending from hip
to shoulder on each side. Occasionally the white stripe
extends anteriorly to the base of the ear, but never continues
on the side of the head as in true chipmunks *(Eutamias).*
Also, these animals are larger than any chipmunk and less
adept at climbing. Four geographic races of mantled ground
squirrels occur in Idaho.

The big-eared group includes *Citellus beldingi oregonus,*

---

* A. H. Howell's (1938) "Revision of the North American ground
squirrels...." appeared after the following accounts were written.
Changes in nomenclature made necessary by his findings include the
following: Use of the specific name *Citellus townsendii* in place of
Citellus mollis, so that *C. mollis artemesiae* of the present paper, for
example, will correctly stand as *C. townsendii artemesiae.* Also Howell, I think correctly, has employed the subspecific name *Citellus lateralis tescorum* for the animals to which I have applied the name
Callospermophilus lateralis cinerascens. Howell's suppression of the
generic names *Callospermophilus* and *Ammospermophilus* in favor of
Citellus also should be noted. His arrangement of *Citellus elegans* as
a geographic race of *Citellus richardsonii* may be correct though the
limited material available to me, from the area where intergradation
is to be expected, was easily referable to one or the other and hence
led me to regard the two as distinct species. I am still inclined to
regard *Citellus idahoensis* Merriam as only subspecifically distinct
from *Citellus townsendii artemesiae,* in spite of Howell's having
treated it as a distinct species. Otherwise our findings agree.

Citellus armatus, Citellus columbianus columbianus, Citellus brunneus, Citellus elegans nevadensis, and *Citellus elegans aureus.* None of them does much, if any, climbing, and all except *C. brunneus* inhabit meadows and submarginal land in the vicinity of water. Seemingly correlated with their habitat preference, is the fact that they usually hibernate later in summer than do the desert-dwelling, short-eared ground squirrels. All of them except *C. brunneus,* are relatively large animals. They have large hind feet, a well-haired tail that is approximately one fourth the length of head and body, and a color pattern in which varying degrees of reddish brown are found along the dorsum and on the nose, legs, and tail. On the basis of color pattern of the tail, the big-eared squirrels may be divided into two groups: (1) Those with reddish on the lateral hairs of tail (includes *Citellus beldingi oregonus* and *Citellus beldingi beldingi;* the latter occurs in California) and (2) those with grayish, rusty brown, or yellowish ventral tail coloration and with from five to eight color bands on the lateral hairs of the tail. Phylogenetically, all these squirrels appear to be closely related to one another and, through *Citellus columbianus,* to the large, spotted ground squirrels of northern Canada, Alaska, and Siberia.

The short-eared ground squirrels *(mollis)* are typically of the Great Basin fauna. They are characterized by soft, grayish or avellaneous pelage; short, stubby tails, and lack of distinct dorsolateral stripes. As judged from their present distribution and differentiation they have occupied portions of their present range at least since the Pliocene. This view is supported by the fact that they now occupy territory on both sides of the Snake River. Additional support is given by the presence of a geographically isolated race, *C. m. yakimensis,* on the north side of the Columbia River in Washington.

The antelope ground squirrel appears to be a Recent emigrant, from the south, to Idaho where it is restricted to the desert areas along the Snake River in the western part of the state. There is one distinct, white, dorsolateral stripe from rump to shoulder on each side; the ventral coloration, including the under surface of the tail, is pure white.

Artificial Key to Adult Ground Squirrels of Idaho

1 Ears large or conspicuous; dorsum with six stripes, or with mottled reddish brown coloration.

    2 Distinct dorsolateral stripes (two black and one white) from hip to shoulder on each side; head and shoulders reddish (this part known as mantle).

        3 Under surface of tail grizzled grayish yellow, sometimes yellowish; mantle deep rusty chestnut; inner black stripe distinct and as broad as outer, or nearly so.
                Callospermophilus l. cinerascens, p. 197

        3' Under surface of tail fulvous, or deep chestnut.

            4 Under surface of tail fulvous (never deep chestnut).

                5 Mantle rich chestnut; inner black stripe as wide as outer.   **C. l. connectens**, p. 201

                5' Mantle pale yellowish chestnut; inner black stripe as wide as outer.   **C. l. trepidus**, p. 202

            4' Under surface of tail deep chestnut.
                C. l. castanurus, p. 203

  2' No distinct black or white dorsal stripes; general dorsal coloration grayish with admixture of brownish; hind foot more than 40 mm. (except in **brunneus**).

            6 Ventral coloration of tail distinctly reddish; lateral hairs of tail with from three to four alternately dark and light color bands.
                Citellus b. oregonus, p. 168

            6' Ventral coloration of tail gray, yellowish, or rusty brown; lateral hairs of tail with from five to eight (usually seven) alternately dark and light color bands.

                7 Under surface of tail gray or rusty gray.

                  8 Dorsum distinctly dappled; legs rusty brown or brick red.

                    9 Large; total length near 350 mm.; hind foot more than 50 mm.; legs brick red.
                        C. c. columbianus, p. 173

                    9' Small; total length less than 275 mm.; hind foot less than 38 mm.; legs rusty brown.
                        C. brunneus, p. 182

8′ Dorsum grizzled, not dappled; legs yellowish brown; total length near 300 mm.; hind foot more than 40 mm. and less than 50 mm. **C. armatus, p. 170**

7′ Under surface of tail yellowish; general coloration yellowish brown.

10 Hind foot near 44 mm.; tail usually less than 90 mm.; width of M², 3.0 mm.

C. e. aureus, p. 177

10′ Hind foot near 46 mm.; tail usually more than 90 mm.; width of M², 3.5 mm.

C. e. nevadensis, p. 177

1′ Ears small, inconspicuous; dorsum with white, but no black stripes, or with mottled vinaceous grayish coloration, occasionally dappled.

11 One distinct white stripe from hip to shoulder on each side; under surface of tail white; abdomen pure white.

Ammospermophilus l. lecurus, p. 204

11′ No stripes on dorsum; under surface of tail reddish or buffy; abdomen never clear white.

12 Under surface of tail reddish; dorsum dappled; length of hind foot near 37 mm. **Citellus m. idahoensis, p. 184**

12′ Under surface of tail buffy (not reddish); dorsum grizzled grayish or indistinctly dappled; hind foot usually less than 35 mm.

13 Auditory bullae small, usually less than 8.0 mm. in width; width of M² averaging 2.3 mm.; length of upper tooth row averaging 7.6 mm.; ratio of palatal to postpalatal length averaging 75.5%.

C. m. artemesiae, p. 194

13′ Auditory bullae large, usually 8.5 mm. in width; ratio of palatal to postpalatal length near 72.5%.

14 Width of M² near 2.3; length of upper tooth row near 8.0 mm.; general dorsal coloration avellaneous. **C. m. vigilis, p. 188**

14′ Width of M² near 2.6 mm.; length of upper tooth row near 8.6 mm.; general dorsal coloration grayish.

C. m. mollis, p. 190

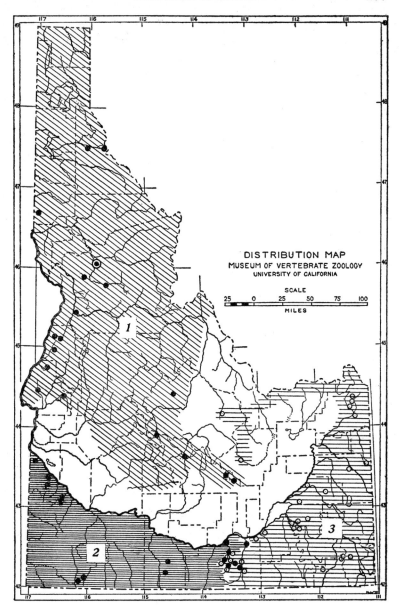

FIG. 8. Map showing the distributions of some ground squirrels in Idaho. Dots and circles indicate localities whence specimens have been examined or recorded. 1. *Citellus columbianus columbianus*, 2. *Citellus beldingi oregonus*, 3. *Citellus armatus*.

Citellus beldingi oregonus (Merriam)
RED-TAILED GROUND SQUIRREL

Spermophilus oregonus Merriam, Proc. Biol. Soc. Washington, 12:69. March 24, 1898. Type from Swan Lake Valley, Klamath Basin, Klamath County, Oregon.

Distribution.—In Idaho, south of the Snake River from Oregon east to Raft River, Cassia County (see map, fig. 8).

Description.—Adults: General coloration gray with usually a broad, reddish-brown dorsal stripe extending from tip of nose to dorsal surface of tail; stripe indistinct in neck region; shoulder area and under parts grayish, faintly tinged with yellow; *under surface of tail reddish,* individual hairs white-tipped; hairs toward tip of tail with three color bands, reddish, black, and white; upper surfaces of feet whitish. Young: Similar to adults but sides and under parts more heavily tinged with yellow; basal portion of tail less heavily haired. External measurements of adults from Reynolds Creek average (two males) 296-71-47-18, (three females) 287-65-42-16. An old female from the same locality measures 303-67-47-18. Skull: Adult males and females differ but little in size; rostrum broad and short (breadth of rostrum, measured between anterior tips of maxillary arms of zygomatic arches, averages 61.3% of length of nasals).

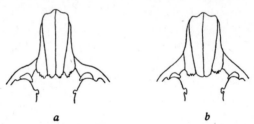

a   *b*

Fig. 9. Outline drawings, dorsal view, x 1, of the facial portions of the skulls of (a) *Citellus armatus* and (b) *Citellus beldingi oregonus.* Note the relatively short and wide rostrum of *oregonus* as compared with *armatus.* The expanded posterior portion of the premaxilla is typical of *armatus.*

Remarks.—In studying the relationships of these "red-tailed" ground squirrels of southern Idaho, comparisons were made with their near relatives *Citellus b. beldingi* in California. Externally, *beldingi* differs from *oregonus* in having the dorsal reddish stripe accentuated. A specimen of *oregonus* from Beckwith, California, however, is nearly as red as selected specimens of *beldingi* from Yosemite National Park, and indistinguishable from one taken at Bridgeport on the Great Basin side of the Sierra Nevada. The skull of *beldingi* averages smaller than that of *oregonus,* but in other cranial characters the two are similar; in fact, certain individuals are indistinguishable. In each the rostrum is relatively broad and in five proportional measurements of the skull they are almost identical. On the basis of these findings, it seems justifiable to consider *oregonus* as a subspecies of the earlier described *beldingi.*

In Idaho, *oregonus* is confined to the region south of the Snake River where usually it inhabits meadows and seldom, if ever, occurs in large numbers far from water. Altitudinally it ranges from slightly over 2000 feet at Reynolds Creek up to 8000 feet on the top of Mt. Harrison. From Albion east to the Raft River its range interdigitates with that of *armatus;* often individuals of both species occur in the same general area. Where this condition is found, each colony usually consists of individuals of but a single species and there appears to be but little intermingling of the two. That cross-breeding does occur is evidenced by a single male specimen (no. 67468, Mus. Vert. Zool.) from the Wickel Ranch at Elba where both species occur in the meadow along Cassia Creek. This individual resembles *oregonus* in having the lower surface of the tail reddish, and the individual hairs of the tail banded with red, black, and white. In general dorsal coloration and in most of the cranial characters it is like *armatus.* Hybridization appears to be infrequent because evidence of it was found in only one of thirty-nine specimens of both species collected from the area where the two are known to occur together. I was unable to detect any differences between the two in habits or habitat preference and, where they occur together, I infer that they compete.

Ecology.—At Sinker Creek, Aldrich (MS) observed individuals of *oregonus* to enter water voluntarily. Here a colony of these squirrels lived on a hillside separated by an irrigation ditch about four feet wide from an alfalfa field in which they foraged. The animals, of necessity, swam the ditch in going to and from their forage grounds.

Their burrows usually are located in fairly dry situations above the level where surface water or a high water table would reach them. In cultivated fields, ditch banks and hillocks seem to be favored places; they do not occur in fields that are regularly and abundantly irrigated. Occasionally they resort to rock fences for refuge, and on Mt. Harrison a few appeared to have established quarters in rocky crevices, simulating in this respect the marmots.

In June and July they forage mainly in early morning and late afternoon. During these months the old ones become excessively fat in preparation for the long period of quiescence. On several occasions in late June, I observed fat, old males basking at the mouths of their burrows in the warm late-afternoon sun. By July 15, most of the old ones had begun to æstivate, but at this season young of the year were less fat, and they were active and abroad until the latter part of August.

Apparently each female has but a single litter of young, early in the season. None of the old females collected in May, June, and July was pregnant, but most of them had bare areas around their nipples which indicated that young had been nursed earlier in the season. By June 1, most of the young are half grown.

Records of occurrence.—Specimens examined, 44, as follows: *Owyhee County:* 1-6 mi. S Riddle, 5; 2 mi. SE Riddle, 2; S. bank Snake River, Homedale, 1; Reynolds Creek, 12 mi. S Snake River, 4; S. side Snake River, 2 mi. W Reynolds Creek, 1; Sinker Creek, 7 mi. SE Murphy, 3. *Twin Falls County:* 3 mi. N Hollister, 1; 2 mi. W Rogerson, 4. *Cassia County:* 1-4 mi. S Albion, 9; 4 mi. W Elba, 4; Mt. Harrison, 12 mi. S Albion, 1; 2 mi. S Malta, 4; Raft River, 2 mi. S Snake River, 1; S. bank Snake River, 6 mi. S Rupert, 3; Wickel Ranch, Elba, 1.

Citellus armatus (Kennicott)
GRAY-TAILED GROUND SQUIRREL

Spermophilus armatus Kennicott, Proc. Acad. Nat. Sci. Philadelphia, 1863:158. Type from foot of the Uinta Mountains, near Fort Bridger, Uinta County, Wyoming.

Synonym.—*Spermophilus armatus*, Merriam, 1891:38.

Distribution.—In Idaho, from Albion east along south side of Snake River, from Utah into Montana, thence west, at higher elevations, across headwaters of the Snake River to Big Lost River and Pahsimeroi valleys (see map, fig. 8).

Description.—Adults: General dorsal coloration dappled gray with suffusion of brownish along back from tip of nose to basal third of tail; upper parts of legs yellowish brown; ventral parts grayish, changing to whitish on chin, flanks, and axilla; *under surface of tail gray,* the terminal hairs of which bear *seven* distinct color bands in the following order, from base to tip: white, gray, white, gray, white, black, white; ears rounded. Skull: No appreciable difference in size of skulls in the two sexes; rostrum relatively long and narrow (ratio of breadth of rostrum, measured between the anterodorsal tips of maxillary arms of zygomatic arches, to length of nasals averages 54); posterior extensions of premaxillae usually expanded. External measurements of three adult females and three adult males from near Albion average, respectively, 304-76-46-17 and 288-81-45-17. Young: Externally similar to adults, but with less admixture of brown, that is, more grayish.

Comparisons.—Differs externally from *Citellus b. oregonus* chiefly in gray, rather than reddish, coloration on under surface of tail; presence of seven, rather than three, distinct color bands on terminal hairs of tail; dorsal, reddish brown coloration less intense. Differs externally from *Citellus elegans* chiefly in having under surface of tail gray, rather than ochraceous buff.

Remarks.—*Citellus armatus* appears to be more closely related to *Citellus elegans* than to *Citellus b. oregonus* or *Citellus richardsonii.* Both *armatus* and *elegans* have seven distinct color bands on the terminal hairs of the tail; in each the rostrum is relatively narrow. They seem to react to each other as full species and in range complement each other.

The ranges of *armatus* and *oregonus* meet and interdigitate in the vicinity of Elba and Albion, where both species occur in the same fields, although in separate colonies. One individual from Elba has structural characters which indicate hybridization between the two. For more complete details concerning this individual see *Remarks* under *Citellus beldingi oregonus.*

Along much of its course, the Snake River is a barrier to the northward and westward extension of range of *armatus,* but in the region toward the headwaters where the river is smaller the species occurs on both sides of the stream. Although I have no definite knowledge that *armatus* voluntarily enters water as does its near relative *C. b. oregonus,* it is a strong swimmer. Each of several individuals, only slightly injured by traps, that were thrown into the river swam to shore with apparent ease. One swam fully two hundred feet in rapid water and reached shore safely.

In the Big Lost River and Pahsimeroi valleys both *armatus* and *elegans* occur in the same type of habitat, but their ranges are complementary. In the Pahsimeroi Valley, *armatus* was found only near the head of the Pahsimeroi River; *elegans* was found farther down the valley at Double Springs and Patterson. The same situation is found in Big Lost River Valley; *armatus* occurs at Arco, *elegans* at Dickey. The present distribution of these two species, and their close structural resemblance, suggest a relatively recent common ancestral population, which at some time in the past was split geographically, thus giving rise to the two species. Considering the present discontinuous distribution of *elegans,* it seems probable that *armatus* migrated into the Great Basin from some more easterly region, whereas *oregonus* came from some region to the westward, and that each usurped much of the former territory occupied by *elegans* which now occurs in isolated localities in northeastern Nevada, in the Lost River country in Idaho, and in the western part of Wyoming.

Ecology.—*Citellus armatus* usually is found in meadows or at the edges of cultivated fields and seldom far from water. Altitudinally, it ranges from about 4000 feet along the Snake River to approximately 8000 feet on the top of Mt. Harrison, where it was more numerous than *oregonus*. In one instance on Mt. Harrison, a colony of *armatus* was located on a hillside about a mile from water. Here, deep snowbanks, which persist at that altitude until mid-July, supply the necessary moisture for the growth of green vegetation. Evidently the presence of these squirrels in the vicinity of water depends directly on the presence of green vegetation rather than on the presence of water itself.

Data on breeding habits of *armatus* indicate that each breeding female gives birth to but a single litter of young each year, in April. Females collected from March 23 to April 8 in the vicinity of Pocatello were pregnant; the average number of embryos was five, with extremes of four and six. The presence of eight mammae suggests, however, that larger litters are born. No embryos were found in females collected after May 1, but females collected in that month usually had enlarged, active mammae. By June 11, young of the year are nearly half grown and by August 15, they have attained nearly adult size.

Records of occurrence.—Specimens examined, 69, as follows: *Custer County:* head Pahsimeroi River, 1. *Cassia County:* 4 mi. S Albion, 2; Bridge, 1; Conner Canyon, 4 mi. N Elba, 1; Howells Canyon, 10 mi. S Albion, 4; Mt. Harrison, 12 mi. S Albion, 1; Raft River, 1 mi. E Malta, 3; Wickel Ranch, Elba, 4. *Fremont County:* N. Fork Snake River, 10 mi. SW Island Park, 11 (Amer. Mus.); 5 mi. S Island Park, 1 (Amer. Mus.); near Island Park, 1 (Amer. Mus.); Warm River, 1. *Butte County:* Arco, 5. *Teton County:* summit Big Hole Mountains, 7 mi. SW Victor, 1. *Bonneville County:* S. Side South Fork, 3 mi. W Swan Valley, 2. *Bingham County:* Fort Hall Indian School, 10 mi. N Pocatello, 1; 3½ mi. E Wapello, 4. *Power County:* S. Side Snake River, 5 mi. SW American Falls, 1; S. Side Snake River, 19 mi. SW American Falls, 2. *Bannock County:* Mink Creek, 2 mi. S Portneuf, 1; Trail Creek, 1 mi. W Pocatello, 13 (3 in Ralph Ellis coll.); head of Williams Canyon, Wasatch Mountains, 1; ¼ mi. W Copenhagen Basin, 1. *Franklin County:* Strawberry Canyon, 20 mi. NE Preston, 1; 16 mi. E Malad, 1. *Bear Lake County:* mouth of North Canyon, 4. Additional records: *Bannock County:* (Whitlow and Hall, 1933): 4 mi. N Inkom; 1 mi. E Pocatello; 4 mi. S Pocatello. *Bingham County:* Blackfoot Mountains (Merriam, 1891).

Citellus columbianus columbianus (Ord)
COLUMBIAN GROUND SQUIRREL

Arctomys columbianus Ord, Guthrie's Geography, 2nd Amer. ed., 2:292, 303. 1815. Type from about two miles north of Kamiah, Idaho County, Idaho.

Synonyms.—*Anisonyx brachiura* Rafinesque, 1817:45; *Arctomys brachyura*, Harlan, 1825:304; *Spermophilus columbianus*, Merriam, 1891:39.

Distribution.—In Idaho, north of the Snake River Plains from Craters of the Moon National Monument and Weiser north to the Canadian border; east from the Oregon boundary as far as the main fork of the Salmon River in Custer County; complements the ranges of *Citellus elegans* and *Citellus armatus* in the Salmon River country (see map, fig. 8).

Description.—Largest of the ground squirrels occurring in Idaho. Adults: General coloration dappled gray with admixture of brown along dorsum; forehead, upper surfaces of feet, legs, throat, belly, and inguinal region suffused with reddish; under surface of tail gray, terminal hairs of tail with six or seven alternating black and white color bands; ears rounded. Young similar in external appearance to adults. Skull: Relatively large; rostrum relatively long and narrow (ratio of breadth of rostrum, measured between anterodorsal portions of the maxillary plates of the zygomatic arches, to length of nasals about 56) ; length of maxillary tooth row in adults averages 12 mm.; teeth relatively large. External measurements of a large, adult female from Mann Creek are 368-96-53-19.

Comparisons.—*Citellus c. columbianus* differs externally from all other species of *Citellus* occurring in Idaho in having the legs and abdomen brick red in color. The skull is larger and the dentition heavier.

Remarks.—As judged from the general shape of the skull and the arrangement of the bands of color on the hairs of the tail, *columbianus* is more closely related to *Citellus armatus* and *Citellus elegans* than to *Citellus oregonus* or *Citellus richardsonii*. Also, it has affinities with *Citellus plesius, C. parryii, C. beringensis, C. lyratus,* and *C. eversmannii,* which inhabit northern Canada, Alaska, the northern Islands, and Siberia. All of them have the following characteristics in common with *columbianus:* Large size; relatively long rostrum; tendency toward redness on abdomen and legs; general mottled dorsal coloration; and, in some specimens of *lyratus* (no. 55009, Mus. Vert. Zool., in particular) and *plesius,* the terminal hairs of the tail tend to be banded with alternating dark and light colors. These structural similarities, and the present distribution of these squirrels, suggest that this whole complex originated in the north and probably occupied a range during the Pliocene that was geographically continuous. Their present distribution and differentiation can be explained by assuming that later geographic changes completely isolated portions of the original stock and permitted divergence. Perhaps the great ice sheet which covered Canada, but not northwestern Alaska, was instrumental in separating the range of *columbianus* from that of the *plesius-parryii* group. The species *C. columbianus,* having three geographic races, now occurs from the Blue Mountains in Oregon north through eastern Washington, Idaho, western Montana, and western Alberta at least as far as Barkerville, British Columbia. The *plesius-parryii* group occurs across arctic North America from Alaska to Hudson Bay.

The presence of the race *Citellus columbianus ruficaudus* south and west of the Snake River in the Blue Mountains of Oregon suggests that the species *C. columbianus* was present in Idaho at an early time. The range of *ruficaudus* is separated from that of *C. c. columbianus* by the Snake River which, along most of its lower course, averages six hundred feet in width and apparently prevents the movement of ground squirrels across it in either direction. Perhaps the population of *ruficaudus* became established on the south and west side of the river at the time when the Snake River was blocked in the region where it forms the boundary between Oregon and Idaho.

If my interpretation of the relationships of the species *C. columbianus* to *C. plesius, C. beringensis, C. elegans,* and *C. armatus* be correct, Bergman's Law is here well illustrated. The largest of these squirrels, *beringensis,* occurs farthest north, the smallest, *elegans,* farthest south, while *plesius, columbianus,* and *armatus,* in the order named, occupy the intermediate territory from north to south. These squirrels are strictly diurnal in habit, and, during the period of nonhibernation, their activities are controlled by the sum total of daylight hours. In the north this total is greatest, in the south least. Given two animals similar in food habits, the larger one must consume a proportionately larger amount of food to supply bodily needs and, if other factors be equal, the larger one will require a longer period in which to forage. Perhaps the difference in size between *columbianus* and *beringensis* is more closely correlated with the difference in the total number of daylight hours available to each for foraging in its respective range than with temperature, a factor on which Bergman based his hypothesis. Shaw (1925 a) has shown, however, that in early spring the activities of the Columbian Ground Squirrel are controlled to a large extent by temperature alone.

Ecology.—This squirrel prefers meadows or the peripheries of cultivated lands and forested areas. Here their paths through the vegetation and the entrances to their underground burrow systems are conspicuous. In mountainous areas they occur along streams where the forest is open; never have I found them far from water or in heavily forested areas. Altitudinally they occur from about 700 feet at Lewiston up to over 8000 feet in the Salmon River Mountains.

According to Shaw (1924, 1925 a, b, c, d, e, f, g, h) who

studied *columbianus* in Washington, the male leaves the hibernation den in February or March, depending on the weather; the female appears about two weeks later and breeding activities begin soon thereafter. The young, born after a gestation period of approximately twenty-four days, average 4 per litter with extremes of 2 and 7. But a single litter is reared each year. The young grow rapidly and at the age of one month are able to shift for themselves.

Each squirrel eats a large amount of food daily; in one known instance (Shaw, 1925 e) this was calculated to be 17.2 per cent of the weight of the individual. Early in the season green vegetation is preferred, but later, as the period of plant maturing approaches, the squirrel turns its attention to seeds. During this period of voracious eating, fat accumulates in layers under the skin and around the viscera. This reserve food supply nourishes the animal during its long period of quiescence which in this species averages 204 days for males and 220 days for females. The longest known period of æstivation and hibernation is 238 days for a young female (Shaw, 1925 b); she spent 64 per cent of the year with only the nourishment obtainable from the fat accumulated in her body during the brief period in summer. The squirrels are active only in daylight, and in summer in Idaho this amounts at most to sixteen hours per day. Figuring daylight hours, the female squirrel just mentioned had available no more than 23 per cent of the year in which to eat enough food to maintain life during the remaining 77 per cent of the year when she was inactive! Aestivation begins early in July, and by August few squirrels are seen above ground.

Records of occurrence.—Specimens examined, 42 as follows: *Shoshone County:* Glidden Lakes, 1; 7 mi. E McKinnis, 1. *Idaho County:* Castle Creek R. S., 2; Riggins, 2 (David McKaye coll.). *Adams County:* 1 mi. N Bear R. S., 6 (5 in Ralph Ellis coll.); ½ mi. E Black Lake, 2 (Ralph Ellis coll.); summit Smith Mountain, 3 (Ralph Ellis coll.). *Washington County:* Crane Creek, 15 mi. E Midvale, 11 (10 in Ralph Ellis coll.); S. W. slope Cuddy Mountain, 7 (5 in Ralph Ellis coll.); Mann Creek, 20 mi. N Weiser, 1. *Custer County:* Mill Creek, 14 mi. W Challis, 1. *Blaine County:* Alturas Lake, 2; Ketchum, 1; Craters of the Moon, 1. *Butte County:* Cottonwood Creek, 2 mi. W Craters of the Moon National Monument, 1. Additional records (Merriam, 1891:39): *Latah County:* Moscow. *Idaho County:* Grangeville.

Citellus elegans nevadensis Howell
NEVADA YELLOW-TAILED GROUND SQUIRREL

Citellus elegans nevadensis A. H. Howell, Proc. Biol. Soc. Washington, 41:211. December 18, 1928. Type from Paradise, Humboldt County, Nevada.

Distribution.—In Idaho, known only from Riddle, Owyhee County (see map, fig. 10).

Description.—Adults: General coloration dappled gray with admixture of brownish along dorsum; shoulders, legs, upper surface of feet, sides, and abdomen washed with ochraceous buff; *undersurface of tail ochraceous buff*, terminal hairs of same with from five to seven bands of alternately dark and light colors. Skull: Rostrum relatively long and narrow; nasals long, averaging 17.7 mm. External measurements of the type specimen are 337-100-47 (Howell, *loc. cit.*). Young are much like adults in external appearance, but more brownish on dorsum and abdomen.

Comparisons.—Differs from *Citellus beldingi oregonus*, which occurs in the same general region, as follows: Undersurface of tail ochraceous buff, rather than reddish; terminal hairs of tail with from five to seven color bands, rather than with three or four; rostrum relatively longer and narrower; cheek teeth average 16 per cent wider (3.5 mm. as opposed to 3.0 mm.). Differs from *Citellus elegans elegans* from Wyoming as follows: Larger; general coloration grayer; tail longer; hind foot averages 15 per cent longer; skull larger, postorbital region relatively longer and less rounded; auditory bullae larger; cheek teeth larger. See also *Comparisons* under *Citellus elegans aureus* from which it differs chiefly in larger cheek teeth and longer hind foot.

Remarks.—The single specimen from Idaho was taken in the same general area and type of habitat as *Citellus beldingi oregonus*. Hitherto, *nevadensis* had not been recorded from Idaho; its occurrence at Riddle extends the known range of this race about thirty miles to the northward.

Record of occurrence.—Specimen examined, 1, from 1 mi. S Riddle, Owyhee County.

Citellus elegans aureus, new subspecies
IDAHO YELLOW-TAILED GROUND SQUIRREL

Type.—Male, subadult, skin and skull; no. 71965, Mus. Vert. Zool.; Double Springs, 16 miles northeast of Dickey, Custer County, Idaho; collected July 20, 1936, by J. A. Donohoe; original no. 71.

Distribution.—In Idaho, the Lost River country, including **Big**

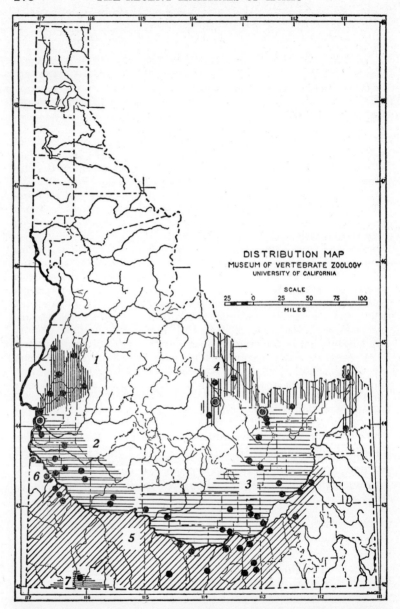

Fig. 10. Map showing the distribution of some ground squirrels in Idaho. Dots indicate localities whence specimens have been examined or recorded. 1. *Citellus brunneus*, 2. *Citellus mollis idahoensis*, 3. *Citellus mollis artemesiae*, 4. *Citellus elegans aureus*, 5. *Citellus mollis mollis*, 6. *Citellus mollis vigilis*, 7. *Citellus elegans nevadensis*.

Lost River, Pahsimeroi, Lemhi, and Birch Creek valleys, and east probably to Henry Lake (see map, fig. 10); occurs also in southwestern Montana.

Description.—A relatively large ground squirrel (see measurements). Adults (summer): General coloration dappled gray with suffusion of Ochraceous Buff (Capitalized color names are from Ridgway: Color Standards and Color Nomenclature, Washington, D. C., 1912) along dorsum; shoulders, legs, abdomen, and undersurface of tail Ochraceous Buff; chin white; rostral area Ochraceous Tawny; hairs of tail banded in sequence from base to tip with Light Buff, black, Light Buff, black, Light Ochraceous Buff, black, white. (Winter): Ochraceous Buff more pronounced, especially on hind legs, rump, and top of tail. Cheeks, crown, and nape clear bluish gray. Skull: Rostrum relatively slender; nasals long. Hind foot large, averaging 44 mm. in length. Young similar to adults in external appearance but grayer.

Comparisons.—Compared with *Citellus elegans elegans* (eight adult topotypes available): Dorsal coloration averaging grayer, that is, less brownish; larger; hind foot 10 per cent longer; more ochraceous ventrally. Skull: Larger; occiput longer, less rounded; auditory bullae larger. Compared with *Citellus elegans nevadensis*: Similar in size and color, but cheek teeth from 10 to 16 per cent narrower; maxillary tooth rows divergent anteriorly, rather than nearly parallel; hind foot shorter.

Measurements.—Average and extreme measurements, in millimeters, of ten adults and near adults from Double Springs, Dickey, Patterson, and Birch Creek: Total length, 293 (279-301); length of tail, 78.4 (71-93); length of hind foot, 43.8 (41-45); greatest length of skull, 45.9 (45.0-47.0); zygomatic breadth, 29.6 (28.4-30.7); breadth of cranium, 20.0 (19.9-20.3); least interorbital breadth, 9.8 (9.5-10.3); least postorbital breadth, 11.2 (10.8-12.2); length of nasals, 16.2 (15.5-17.1); alveolar length of maxillary tooth row, 10.2 (9.8-10.4).

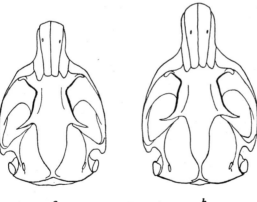

a   *b*

FIG. 11. Outline drawings, x 1, dorsal view, of skulls of (a) *Citellus elegans elegans*, and (b) *Citellus elegans aureus*.

Remarks.—Of the three races of this species, *C. e. elegans* is smallest, darkest, and has the smallest hind foot. *C. e. nevadensis,* whose center of distribution is in northern Nevada, is largest, lightest colored, has the longest hind foot, and the widest cheek teeth; in many respects individuals of *aureus* are structurally, although not geographically, intermediate between *elegans* and *nevadensis.* They are large and light colored as is *nevadensis,* but the cheek teeth are narrow as in *elegans.* The range of *aureus* is separated from that of *elegans* by the range of *Citellus armatus* which extends from Utah north through eastern Idaho into Montana in the region of Yellowstone National Park and the Bitterroot Mountains. The ranges of these two are complimentary, not coincident. The range of *nevadensis* is fully two hundred miles to the southwest and separated from the range of *aureus* by territory which now is occupied by *Citellus mollis* and *Citellus beldingi oregonus.*

Structurally, individuals of the species *elegans* appear to be most closely related to *C. armatus,* but each reacts to the other as a full species wherever their ranges meet. For further comments see under *Remarks* in the account of *C. armatus.*

Ecology.—The yellow-tailed ground squirrel occurs in the vicinity of water where it probably is attracted by the presence of green vegetation rather than by the water itself. At Double Springs this was the only kind of ground squirrel present, while farther southeast, at the head of the Pahsimeroi River, only *armatus* was found. Apparently these two compete for the same food; at any rate, I have detected no differences in their food habits.

Individuals of *aureus* are not as shy and retiring as *Citellus columbianus.* At the head of Double Springs we camped in the midst of a colony of *aureus* and observed that they were active in the morning from sunup until about nine o'clock at which time they retired to their burrows. They reappeared again in late afternoon. At this time of year, July 21, green vegetation was lacking except in the vicinity of the springs where it was cropped short and the squirrels were observed to eat the matured flower-heads of small annual herbs. Their burrows were in gravelly soil amidst low *Artemisia* and each burrow system had two or more openings.

Perhaps one of their most persistent enemies is the long-tailed weasel *(Mustela frenata nevadensis)*. One of these carnivores was observed in its attempts to capture a ground squirrel at Double Springs. When first noticed, the weasel was crouched at the mouth of a burrow apparently listening. Suddenly it ran to another opening of the same burrow system and, finding nothing there, quickly returned to its original position. During a period of approximately five minutes, it made several trips between the two openings. We wondered if a squirrel in the burrow was alertly watching the weasel and ready to escape through whichever burrow was left unguarded should the predator come underground after it. The weasel's actions could be explained by assuming that it recognized the chance of the squirrel escaping in the manner suggested.

Two subadult males of *aureus* that were kept in a small wire cage tolerated each other fairly well except when fresh meat, of which they were very fond, was given them. Then a battle for possession of the food began. They fought mainly with their front paws, standing on their hind legs facing each other. When one was overthrown, he assumed a position flat on his back and dealt his opponent vicious blows with his hind feet. They seldom attempted to bite each other. When a live, adult chipmunk *(Eutamias amoenus)* was put in the cage both squirrels attacked it immediately and in less than a minute had killed it by severing the spinal cord at the base of the skull. The chipmunk then was devoured, one squirrel beginning to feast on the brain, the other at the perineal region. At the end of ten minutes nothing of the chipmunk remained but the feet, a few larger bones, and the hide.

None of the females collected in June and July was pregnant. Half-grown young were collected in June at Birch Creek and at Small. Although young of the year reach nearly adult size before they hibernate in July or August, they do not breed until the following year and are not fully adult until two years old.

Merriam (1891:39) records four specimens of *C. elegans*

from Henrys Lake and from near Teton Canyon. I have not examined them, but, on geographical grounds, I would expect them to be *aureus*. A single subadult female from the Lemhi Valley west of Junction is not typical of *aureus;* it tends toward *elegans,* but probably should be considered as an individual variant of *aureus.*

Records of occurrence.—Specimens examined, 18, as follows: *Lemhi County:* Lemhi Valley (near Timber Creek), 1 (Biol. Surv. coll.); Patterson, 3 (Biol. Surv. coll.). *Custer County:* Dickey, 3 (Biol. Surv. coll.); Double Springs, 16 mi. NE Dickey, 6 (1 in Davis coll.). *Clark County:* Birch Creek, 2 mi. NW Kaufman, 2; Small, 8 mi. W Dubois, 3. Additional records (Merriam, 1891:39): *Fremont County:* Henrys Lake. *Teton County ?:* near Teton Canyon.

Citellus brunneus Howell
IDAHO SPOTTED GROUND SQUIRREL

Citellus townsendii brunneus A. H. Howell, Proc. Biol. Soc. Washington, 41:211. December 18, 1928. Type from New Meadows, Adams County, Idaho.

Distribution.—Known only from Weiser and Payette valleys in western Idaho (see map, fig. 10).

Description.—Smallest of the big-eared ground squirrels occurring in Idaho. Adults: General dorsal coloration dappled grayish brown, the brown predominating on lower portion of back; nose, outer portions of hind legs, and ventral surface of tail rusty brown; shoulders and forelegs ochraceous buff; ventral portions grayish fulvous, chin white; terminal hairs of tail with from five to eight alternating black and white (or fulvous) color bands. In external measurements, five adult females from Bear Creek average 211-46-33-8; four adult males from Bear Creek and Crane Creek average 220-50-35-9. Young: Individuals in light color phase similar to adults as described above, but grayer dorsally; those in brown color phase much darker than adults. Skull: Smallest of the big-eared group; similar in size to that of the short-eared *Citellus mollis,* but differing from it in having a broader rostrum, shorter nasals, less highly inflated auditory bullae, and wider cheek teeth.

Remarks.—In the original description, Howell (1928) considered *brunneus* as a subspecies of *Citellus townsendii.* At that time he pointed out that *brunneus* differs in having large conspicuous ears; brown, rather than grayish dorsal coloration; and small dorsal spots. Specimens at hand reveal that *brunneus* differs additionally as follows: Pelage shorter and coarser; absence of distinct, white, ventrolateral stripe; auditory bullae smaller; premaxillary tongues wider; rostrum shorter and broader (ratio of palatal to postpalatal length 82 as opposed to 70.5) and sphenopalatine fissures smaller.

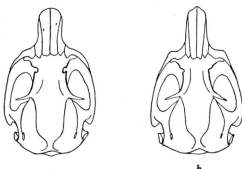

a   *b*

FIG. 12. Outline drawings, x 1, dorsal view, of skulls of (a) *Citellus brunneus*, and (b) *Citellus townsendii*. Note particularly differences in the rostrum.

Many of these differences are of a quantitative nature such as one would expect to find in two subspecies, but some are trenchant and of a qualitative nature. For example the distinct external ear, complete lack of white, ventrolateral stripe, short, coarse pelage, and small auditory bullae (probably correlated with degree of development of external ear), to me, set *brunneus* apart from *C. townsendii* as a distinct species. The affinities of *brunneus* are with the big-eared group comprised of *C. columbianus*, *C. armatus*, and *C. elegans*, whereas those of *townsendii* are with *Citellus mollis*. The few changes necessary to transform such a squirrel as *Citellus mollis idahoensis* into a *townsendii* are ones merely of degree, that is to say, these two differ quantitatively rather than qualitatively. In fact, their similarities are so many and their differences so few that one might justifiably consider them as conspecific.

Ecology.—At Bear Creek, Borell (MS) found a colony of *brunneus* occupying an area about five acres in extent on a dry, flat-topped, rocky ridge which was covered with sparse grass, wild onion, and low herbs. Entrances to their underground burrows were under logs and rocks. If this type of habitat be typical for this species, it differs in habits markedly from other squirrels of the big-eared group. It must be borne in mind, however, that the much larger Columbian Ground Squirrel occupies the meadows within the general range of *brunneus,* and, as judged from the known behavior and distribution of other species of this group, these two probably are mutually exclusive. Perhaps *brunneus,* too would occupy the meadows were competition removed.

According to Borell, at Bear Creek both adults and young of the year were still active in early July. The old ones, however, were fat and probably ready to hibernate. He found evidence here that the squirrels had been digging up and eating the bulbs of the wild onion. One individual was observed to jump into the air and, with its teeth and fore-feet, pull down the seed head of an unidentified herb which was about a foot above the ground.

At Crane Creek, in late May, many of the young were in juvenile pelage, but most of them had acquired their first summer coat. By mid-July the young are nearly the size of adults.

Records of occurrence.—Specimens examined, 22, all from the Ralph Ellis collection, as follows: *Adams County:* 1 mi. N Bear Creek R. S., 15. *Washington County:* Crane Cr., 15 mi. E Midvale, 7. Additional records (Howell, 1928:211): *Adams County:* Goodrich; New Meadows. *Washington County:* Midvale; Weiser. *Boise County:* Van Wyck.

Citellus mollis idahoensis Merriam
PAYETTE GROUND SQUIRREL

Citellus idahoensis Merriam, Proc. Biol. Soc. Washington, 26:135. May 21, 1913. Type from Payette, at junction of Payette and Snake rivers, Payette County, Idaho.

Distribution.—North of the Snake River in Idaho from Payette east at least to Mountain Home (see map, fig. 10).

Description.—Adults: General dorsal coloration dappled gray, faintly tinged with avellaneous; sides and abdomen smoke grey; nose, postauricular patches, outer surfaces of lower hind legs, and under surface of tail near sayal brown; terminal hairs of tail with from five to seven alternately light and dark color bands, the last dark band wide and producing a subterminal black spot; external ears extremely short. External measurements of 10 adult and near adult males from the type locality average 239-57-37; 9 adult and near adult females from the same locality average 219-51-35. Skull: Largest of the *mollis* group. Rostrum relatively long and narrow; occipitonasal length of males averages 40.4 mm., of females, 38.3 mm.; auditory bullae large (9.0 mm. in males, 8.8 mm. in females, as measured between jugular and postglenoidal foramina); dentition heavy, maxillary tooth row averages 8.8 mm.; ratio of palatal to postpalatal length averages 72.5. Young: Two color phases, one dappled gray, the other with dapplings less pronounced and with dorsal surface overcast with avellaneous. Sides darker than in adults.

Remarks.—This ground squirrel, described as a separate species of the *mollis* group by Merriam in 1913, is, so far as I have been able to determine from a study of one hundred and forty-four specimens of the *mollis* group from localities north of the Snake River in Idaho, conspecific with *Citellus mollis*. Field observations show the *mollis* group of ground squirrels to be fairly uniformly, though not continuously, distributed throughout the drier areas north of the Snake River from Payette east to near Blackfoot. They live in colonies and the areas suitable for them often are not contiguous. A distribution similarly discontinuous is characteristic of most of the land-dwelling mammals which exhibit geographic variation in that same area.

    Citellus mollis idahoensis appears to integrade with *Citellus mollis artemesiae* in the region from Bliss east to western Bingham County. As one proceeds from Payette eastward to the Lost River country, there is a gradual transition from the larger *idahoensis* to the smaller *artemesiae*. The following table (average measurements, in millimeters, of adult and near adult males) shows this.

	Payette	Mountain Home	Gooding	Pingree	Berenice
Length of hind foot	37	37	34.5	33	33
Width of incisors*	2.8	2.9	2.6	2.5	2.4
Length of maxillary tooth row	8.8	8.8	8.4	7.8	7.6
Width of bullae†	9.0	8.7	8.2	8.0	7.8
Width of rostrum	6.5	6.4	6.0	6.0	5.8
Ratio of palatal to postpalatal length	72.5	73.5	74.5	75.5	75.5
Specimens averaged	10	4	2	5	6

* Measured across tips of both incisors.
† Measured between jugular and postglenoidal foramina.

So far as I am aware, there are at present no physical barriers along the north side of the Snake River, save perhaps the extensive lava fields in the vicinity of the Craters of the Moon National Monument, which would prevent the dispersal of this group of squirrels in an east-west direction. To the south, the Snake River is thought to be a barrier impassable to ground squirrels of all species, while to the north the lack of proper habitat requirements in the mountainous areas limits the distribution of *mollis* in that direction.

The differentiation and present distribution of *idahoensis* and *artemesiae* may be explained by assuming that at an earlier time the active lava fields, in what are now Lincoln, Minidoka, Blaine, Butte, and Power counties, separated an originally geographically continuous population into two portions. Any genetic difference which appeared in either or both of the then separated population, if having selective value, would tend to be preserved. Subsequent geologic changes, including the cessation of volcanism, are thought to have permitted the squirrels to reoccupy portions of their previous range. This last inference is supported by the presence today of small colonies of *mollis* in suitable localities among the old lava fields.

If such was their history, one would expect in the course of time to find these populations first differentiating, and then, after the barrier in part was removed, spreading, meeting, and intermingling in the intermediate territory. Here blending would occur provided the differences were not too great, while at the two extremes of the range the individuals would remain recognizably distinct. That such is the nature of the differences between *idahoensis* and *artemesiae* is suggested by the gradual transition exhibited by the specimens (see above table). In color pattern, texture of pelage, size of ear, and habits, these two are essentially alike. The only difference of a qualitative nature that I have detected is that of voice. The warning call of *idahoensis* usually consists of four notes, "*dee, dee, dee, dee,*" that of *artemesiae* usually of one or two notes of a higher pitch.

Seven specimens (Biol. Surv. coll.) labeled as from Wei-

ser and one as from Payette, collected in June, 1913, by
L. E. Wyman, differ markedly from *idahoensis*. Mr. A. H.
Howell, who is revising the ground squirrels of North America, refers these specimens, I think incorrectly, to *Citellus
mollis mollis*. In coloration and width of M² they differ
from *mollis* and resemble *vigilis* from the Oregon side of
the river. Because of the similarity to *vigilis*, it seems probable that either the specimens came from the Oregon side
of the river, rather than from the Idaho side, or that they
were introduced into Idaho by man. At any rate, the only
kind of ground squirrel that I have found on the Idaho side
of the river at Payette is *idahoensis*.

Ecology.—The habitat occupied by the Payette Ground
Squirrel is varied, but consistent as regards preference for
dry ground. At Payette they were numerous in pasture
lands along the river. Here their burrows, 80 mm. in diameter, and entering the ground usually at an angle of
forty degrees, were on dry ground above the marshy areas.
South of Fruitland, and near Mountain Home, they were
concentrated in areas which once had been dry-farmed, but
later abandoned by man. Near Emmett they were common
in open areas, amongst *Artemisia*, in which June grass
(Koeleria) was abundant. At Melba they lived along a large
irrigation ditch on the side of Walters Butte. Occasionally
they inhabit areas overgrown with *Artemisia*, but I gained
the impression that such places are second choice.

Their food varies with locality and perhaps with season.
At Payette they foraged chiefly on grass *(Poa* sp.) and pep-
pergrass *(Lepidium)*, although shepherd's purse *(Capsella)*
and white clover were taken readily. The stomachs of specimens collected near Emmett were gorged with June grass.

These squirrels usually are shy and at the first indication of danger retreat to the openings of their burrows.
Here, if not hard pressed, they generally sit up "picket-pin
fashion" and watch the intruder. If approached too closely,
they drop onto all four feet, crouch close to the ground
facing the entrance to the burrow, and, if further threat-
ened, disappear below ground.

Hibernation in *idahoensis* begins in early summer. An
extremely fat old male, which was captured alive May 31,

1935, and kept in captivity, went into hibernation June 9. The time when this phenomenon occurs, however, varies with age, sex, altitude, and advance of the season.

But a single litter of young is reared each year. At Mountain Home half-grown young and young recently out of the nest were taken in the latter part of May. From observations of young made near the nest burrows, I judge the average litter numbers four.

Records of occurrence.—Specimens examined, 60, as follows: *Payette County:* 2 mi. S Payette, 31; 3 mi. S Fruitland, 4. *Canyon County:* 2 mi. S Melba, 7. *Ada County:* 14 mi. SE Boise, 2; 7 mi. S Emmett, 2. *Elmore County:* 4-5 mi. S Mountain Home, 14. Additional records (Merriam, 1913:135): *Payette County:* Payette. *Canyon County:* Nampa. *Ada County:* Kuna; Orchard. *Elmore County:* Mountain Home.

Citellus mollis vigilis Merriam
MALHEUR GROUND SQUIRREL

Citellus canus vigilis Merriam, Proc. Biol. Soc. Washington, 26:137. May 21, 1913. Type from Vale, Malheur County, Oregon.

Distribution.—In Idaho, Owyhee County, along the south side of Snake River from Oregon east to Reynolds Creek (see map, fig. 10).

Description.—Adults: General dorsal coloration grayish avellaneous; sides white, faintly tinged with light buff; abdomen pale smoke gray; nose, both surfaces of tail, and outer surfaces of hind feet tinged with cinnamon; terminal hairs of tail with seven alternately light and dark color bands; external ears short. External measurements of three adult males and three adult females from Ontario, Oregon, average respectively 233-57-33 and 225-51-32. Skull: Large (nearly as large as in *idahoensis*). Rostrum relatively short and broad; occipitonasal length averages 39.0 (males) and 37.6 (females); auditory bullae medium, as measured between jugular and postglenoidal foramina, 8.6 (males) and 8.3 (females); dentition medium (alveolar length of maxillary tooth row in both sexes averages 8.0); width of M^2, 2.3; ratio of palatal to postpalatal length in both sexes averages 72.3. Young: Similar to adults, but grayer.

Comparisons.—Compared with *idahoensis* from north and east of the Snake River: Hind foot smaller; tail less bushy; lacks distinct dappling on dorsum; zygomatic arches less bowed anteriorly; dentition weaker (width of M^2, 2.3 as opposed to 2.6; length of tooth row, 8.0, rather than 8.8). Compared with topotypes of *Citellus mollis mollis* with which race *vigilis* intergrades along the south side of the Snake River east of Marsing: General coloration less grayish, that is, more avellaneous; dentition weaker (width of M^2, 2.3 as opposed to 2.5; length of tooth row, 8.0, rather than 8.4); auditory bullae averaging larger.

Remarks.—The major portion of the range of *vigilis* lies in Oregon; it extends a short distance into western Idaho along the south side of the Snake River. This race differs markedly from *C. m. idahoensis* from which it is separated by the Snake River. Near Payette, each race occupies territory along its respective bank of the river, and, so far as I have been able to determine from observation and collecting in that area, neither crosses to the opposite side. Eight specimens (Biol. Surv. coll.), labeled as from Payette and Weiser, that is, from the Idaho side of the river, certainly are referable to *vigilis*. Elsewhere (see under *Remarks* of *Citellus m. idahoensis*) I have commented on them.

Ecology.—Along the west bank of the Snake River near Ontario, Oregon, *vigilis* was found in numbers. Here they were inhabiting waste and pasture lands. These squirrels are highly gregarious and one colony that I observed carefully consisted of several family groups. One large family consisted of the female and eight young, seven of which were taken at different times in one trap set at the main entrance to the home burrow. At the time of my visit, May 25 to 27, 1936, young of the year were about half grown. They were actively engaged in digging separate burrows for themselves. Usually these had a single entrance whereas the home burrows have as many as eight separate openings. Traps placed at the entrances to the small burrows yielded but a single young individual each.

Since a different race of ground squirrel occurs on each side of the river in this area, I was interested in testing the swimming ability of *vigilis*. A young individual, which had been caught in a steel trap by one front leg, was thrown into the river. It fell about one hundred feet from shore, sank out of sight, immediately rose, and swam rapidly *back to the shore from which it was thrown*. When the test was repeated, the animal again swam to the same bank. When the squirrel returned the second time, I captured it and placed it in a cage where it remained overnight. When I opened the cage next morning, the squirrel jumped out, ran to the edge of a ditch four feet wide which was carrying a full head of water, jumped into this, and swam against the current to a small bridge where it escaped. These observations show that *vigilis* can swim well, and, if hard pressed, that it may enter water voluntarily.

That this squirrel returned on two different occasions to its native side of the river may have been accidental, or due to the fact that the home bank was closer. The same result was obtained, however, on three different occasions when individuals of *Citellus armatus* were thrown into the river to test their swimming ability. I infer that these animals have a keen sense of direction which caused them to react as they did. The effects of such instinctive behavior may have important bearing on the distribution of a species, individuals of which have definite places of abode and which normally do not, but can, swim. If by accident one falls into water, one instinctive reaction seems to be to seek safety in the direction whence it came. Perhaps this is one reason why the Snake River along much of its course is such an effective barrier to the movements of ground squirrels.

These squirrels feed largely on native vegetation, especially several species of wild mustard, but they are not averse to cultivated crops. At Ontario, they fed regularly in a field of alfalfa which was but a short distance from their burrows. By standing on the hind legs they reached and pulled down the tender growing tips of the plants, the part most preferred.

All the old individuals taken in the latter part of May were fat and probably nearly ready to hibernate. They were active only in early morning and late afternoon; the young were active nearly throughout the day.

Records of occurrence in Idaho.—Specimens examined, 4, from Owyhee County as follows: Homedale, 3; S. side Snake River, 2 mi. W Reynolds Creek, 1.

Citellus mollis mollis (Kennicott)
PIUTE GROUND SQUIRREL

Spermophilus mollis Kennicott, Proc. Acad. Nat. Sci. Philadelphia, 1863: 157. Type probably from near Camp Floyd [=Fairfield], Wasatch County, Utah.

Synonyms.—*Citellus leurodon* Merriam, 1913:136 (type locality, Murphy, Owyhee County, Idaho) ; *Spermophilus townsendi*, Merriam, 1891:36; *Citellus mollis artemesiae* Merriam, 1913:138, part.

Distribution.—In Idaho, south and east of Snake River from near Murphy east at least to Blackfoot where it intergrades with *Citellus mollis artemesiae* (see map, fig. 10).

Description.—Adults: Two color phases, gray and avellaneous, the former more common. Gray phase: Upper portions grayish, faintly washed with avellaneous, inconspicuously dappled; cheeks and sides of neck near cinnamon buff; sides white, faintly tinged with light buff; abdomen pale smoke gray; nose and outer surfaces of lower hind legs tinged with cinnamon; under surface of tail near cinnamon; terminal hairs of tail with seven indistinct alternate light and dark color bands; ears short. Dark phase: Similar to above but dorsum and top of tail avellaneous, rather than gray. External measurements of three adult males and four adult females from Raft River Valley, Idaho, average respectively 226-48-32 and 223-50.5-32.5. Skull: Medium in size. Rostrum relatively short and broad; occipitonasal length averages 38.3 (males) and 36.9 (females) ; auditory bullae medium, averaging, as measured between jugular and postglenoidal foramina, 8.4 (males) and 8.1 (females) ; dentition heavy, width of M^2 averages 2.6; length of maxillary tooth row averages 8.8 (male topotypes) and 8.4 (females from Raft River) ; ratio of palatal to postpalatal length averages 72.5. Young: Two color phases. Gray phase: Lighter than in adults in same phase, cinnamon buff on cheeks and sides of neck distinct. Avellaneous phase: Much like adults in same phase.

Comparisons.—Compared with *Citellus mollis artemesiae* with which it intergrades in the region north of Blackfoot: General dorsal coloration in adults averages darker, cinnamon buff on cheeks and sides of neck more distinct; tail averages longer; auditory bullae larger, 8.4 as opposed to 7.8 (males) ; dentition heavier, width of M^2, 2.6 as opposed to 2.3 (males) ; maxillary tooth row longer, 8.8 as opposed to 7.8 (males) ; palatal length greater, ratio of palatal to postpalatal length 72.5, rather than 75.5. Compared with *Citellus mollis vigilis* with which it intergrades in northern Owyhee County: See under *Comparisons* of same. Compared with *Citellus mollis idahoensis:* Smaller; less distinctly dappled; bullae smaller; zygomatic arches less bowed anteriorly.

Remarks.—I have been unable to find any characters which distinguish the specimens from near Murphy (type locality of *Citellus leurodon* Merriam) from specimens of *C. m. mollis* taken south of the Snake River farther east. Indeed, all these specimens fall within the range of variation of a series of topotypes of *Citellus mollis mollis* from Utah. Specimens from the Raft River Valley of southern Idaho are nearly typical of *C. m. mollis;* the tail averages longer, however. Specimens from west of Twin Falls apparently are intergrades between *C. m. mollis* and *C. m. vigilis*, but because of heavier dentition they are referred to *mollis*. Specimens from Blackfoot were referred to *C. m. artemesiae* by Merriam (1913:138). All of them are young of the year and, to me, they appear to be intergrades between *mollis* and *artemesiae*. On the basis of longer maxillary tooth row and relatively longer palate (ratio of palatal to postpalatal length 73.0), they here are referred to *mollis*.

Ecology.—These squirrels occupy a variety of habitats in the desert areas of southern Idaho. At Murphy, they were found almost exclusively in areas overgrown with rabbit brush *(Sarcobatus vermiculatus)*, saltbush *(Grayia spinosa* and *Atriplex confertifolia)*, and dwarf sage *(Artemisia spinescens)*. Here they were living in colonies. Each burrow system was marked by a mound of earth; one measured seven feet in diameter and about fourteen inches high. It had 15 openings distributed around the periphery and on top. Burrows connecting with the external openings ramified the mound and formed a complicated network of interconnecting runways before they united with the main deep burrow. Usually the openings near the center of the mound were most used, but one could never anticipate at which opening a squirrel would appear. Such a system of "surface" burrows must be of protective value to the squirrels when they are pursued by weasels, badgers, and coyotes.

These squirrels usually occur in areas where the soil consists of dry, whitish, volcanic ash of flourlike consistency on the surface. Amid such surroundings they are inconspicuous, in fact, so much so that often, when I was searching for them I was unable to detect the presence of individuals which were sitting "picket-pin fashion" on top a mound until they moved. The color of the abdomen and sides is almost identical with that of the soil. Even when one is sitting up with one side toward the observer, bringing the darker colored back into view, the white coloration of the side obliterates the general outline of the animal and causes it to resemble a stump.

In Raft River Valley they preferred deserted dry farms which have been cleared of sagebrush and which now are overgrown with June grass *(Koeleria)*. Here, also, they were colonial, but each burrow system lacked the large surface mound and its accompanying system of interlacing burrows. Hillsides and banks of dry washes were preferred places for the location of burrows.

At Murphy, the squirrels were timid and shy and, when molested, their rate of "recovery" was slow. One adult female, which ran into her burrow when I was fifty yards distant, remained underground forty-five minutes before reappearing at the surface. The rate of recovery in young was more rapid; the average being about ten minutes. These squirrels, if molested, frequently emit faint, high-pitched calls when underground. I have heard several individuals calling which I knew were within a radius of fifty feet, yet none was visible. Often one will sit partly within the burrow with only a portion of its head visible and give warning notes which appear to be heeded by all squirrels within hearing distance.

At Murphy, the squirrels fed extensively on the tender buds and growing tips of *Atriplex, Grayia,* and *Artemisia spinescens*. These animals are adept at climbing and at this locality they did much of their foraging off the ground in the low bushes. Near Malta, they fed occasionally in the tops of tall *Artemisia tridentata*. Probably these places serve also as vantage points from which they have a better view of the surrounding terrain. In Raft River Valley, June grass constituted a large portion of their diet, but near Sublett, on the east side of Raft River Valley, where their burrows were along a fence, they foraged in an adjoining wheat field.

Records of occurrence.—Specimens examined, 71, as follows: *Owyhee County:* Murphy, 6 (Biol. Surv. coll.); 5-9 mi. SE Murphy, 18. *Twin Falls County:* 13 mi. E Twin Falls, 3; Twin Falls, 1 (Los Angeles Mus.); Rogerson, 1 (Biol. Surv. coll.). *Cassia County:* Bridge, 4; 3½ mi. S Declo, 2; 10 mi. E Malta, 1; 14 mi. SE Malta, 2; Raft River Valley, 10 mi. E Declo, 6; Raft River, 2 mi. S Snake River, 2; Oakley, 1 (Biol. Surv. coll.). *Bingham County:* Blackfoot, 7 (Biol. Surv. coll.); 3½ mi. E Wapello, 1. *Power County:* American Falls, 6 (Biol. Surv. coll.). *Bannock County:* Pocatello, 10 (Biol. Surv. coll.). Additional record: Ross Fork Creek, Bannock County ? (Merriam, 1873:664; 1891:37. Whitlow and Hall, 1933:251).

Citellus mollis artemesiae Merriam
SAGEBRUSH GROUND SQUIRREL

Citellus mollis artemesiae Merriam, Proc. Biol. Soc. Washington, 26:137. May 21, 1913. Type from Birch Creek, ten miles south of Nicholia, *in* Clark County, Idaho.

Synonyms.—Spermophilus townsendi, Merriam, 1891:36, part; *Citellus mollis pessimus* Merriam, 1913:138 (type locality, lower part of Big Lost River, Butte County, Idaho).

Distribution.—North and west of Snake River from near Bliss north and east to Birch Creek (see map, fig. 10).

Description.—Adults: General dorsal coloration varying from light gray to avellaneous gray, dappling distinct; sides and abdomen light grayish buff; nose, outer surfaces of hind legs, and undersurface of tail varying from cinnamon to cinnamon buff; terminal hairs of tail with seven indistinct alternate dark and light color bands; external ears short. External measurements of three old adult males and two old adult females from Berenice and Arco average respectively 217-42-33 and 221-45-33. Skull: Smallest of the *mollis* group. Occipito-nasal length averages 37.2 (males) and 36.4 (females); auditory bullae small, averaging, as measured between jugular and postglenoidal foramina, 7.8; dentition relatively weak, width of M^2, 2.3; alveolar length of maxillary tooth row, 7.6; ratio of palatal to postpalatal length averages 75.5. Young: Similar to adults, but averaging darker and more distinctly dappled.

Remarks.—For comparisons, see under *Comparisons* of other races of *mollis* herein discussed. I can find no appreciable differences in the specimens from Birch Creek and ones of comparable age from near Arco. On the basis of the geography of the Lost River country, one would expect the populations at these two localities to be similar because no apparent barrier is present which would affect the distribution of *mollis* ground squirrels. Furthermore, the two localities are less than thirty miles apart, and ground squirrels of this species occur throughout the area. Merriam (1913) based his description of *C. m. artemesiae* on specimens which he took to be adults, but which actually are young of the year. They differ in no respect from young which I collected in the same valley in 1935. Likewise, his description of *C. m. pessimus* is based not upon adults, but subadults which are somewhat older than his specimens from Birch Creek. Even though these squirrels may breed when less than a year old, they are not fully adult until two years of age. This is true of all ground squirrels in Idaho. The differences which Merriam *(ibid.)* found between the specimens from Birch Creek and those from Arco are due to differences in age; this is evidenced by additional material from that general area. Accordingly, the name *Citellus mollis pessimus* is arranged as a synonym of *C. m. artemesiae* which has page priority.

Specimens from Pingree, Taber, and localities farther west average darker than specimens from Arco and Berenice. In the account of *Citellus m. idahoensis,* comment is made on intergradation with that race. Superficially, specimens from Bliss, Gooding, and Twin Lakes, resemble *C. m. mollis,* which is intermediate in size between *idahoensis* and *artemesiae.* They differ, however, from *mollis* and resemble either *idahoensis* or *artemesiae* as follows: Distinctly dappled; undersurface of tail near sayal brown, rather than cinnamon color; tail considerably longer than in typical *mollis;* palate actually shorter, but, relative to occipitonasal length, longer. Of these characters, the color of the undersurface of the tail and length of tail are as in *idahoensis.* The cranial characters are divided: Width of incisors (measured across the tips of the two), length of maxillary tooth row, and size of bullae approach the mean of *idahoensis;* width of M^2, and ratio of palatal to postpalatal length tend toward *artemesiae.* The dappled appearance is common to both races. Dappling is indistinct or lacking in specimens of *mollis* from south of the Snake River east of American Falls, whereas it is distinct in most specimens from north of the Snake River.

An additional reason why I consider the specimens from Bliss, Gooding, and Twin Lakes as intergrades between *idahoensis* and *artemesiae* rather than as *C. m. mollis,* to which race Howell *(in litt.)* refers them, is that the Snake River from Blackfoot westward appears to be an absolute barrier to *all* kinds of ground squirrels. For additional comments on this point, see under *Remarks* in the species accounts of *Citellus mollis vigilis, Citellus mollis idahoensis, Citellus beldingi oregonus,* and *Citellus armatus.*

Ecology.—In the latter part of June, 1935, *mollis* ground squirrels were scarce in Birch Creek Valley, but large colonies were observed, and specimens collected, at Pingree, Taber, Arco, and Berenice. At the last-mentioned place they were extremely abundant. One colony that I observed consisted of both old adults and young of the year. The former were recognized easily by their fat, chunky appearance. These squirrels were living on abandoned farm land and had their burrows in the dikes and along the fences where the land was elevated. To reach green vegetation, other than Russian thistle, they crossed a road and penetrated a woven wire fence which, toward the bottom, was "chicken proof." Usually they climbed the fence until a space of sufficient size to permit easy passage was reached and then jumped to the ground on the other side. The fence was not buried in the ground, but rested on it. I judged, therefore, that the squirrels found it easier to climb over than to dig under. An additional demonstration of climbing ability was given by a subadult individual which was seen sitting four feet from the ground on top of a gnarled, cedar post. When I approached, the squirrel jumped to the ground and disappeared in a patch of weeds. Several knots projected from the post at intervals and these possibly were helpful to the squirrel in reaching the top.

At Pingree, the squirrels occupied a hillock in the middle of a marshy pasture; in the Aberdeen dry-farm area, northwest of American Falls, they occurred commonly along the roads at the edges of wheat fields. Here, entrances to the burrows were located usually near fence posts which the squirrels utilized for concealment and shade. In this respect they reminded me of horned larks which often are observed in similar situations. Near Taber and Arco, squirrels were common along the railroad grade and on the neighboring high ground. At none of these localities did they construct the large mounds and complicated "surface" burrows that squirrels of this species make in northern Owyhee County. Among the squirrels of the species *mollis* these mounds seem to be peculiar to those inhabiting that one area.

Records of occurrence.—Specimens examined, 65, as follows: *Gooding County:* 3 mi. W Bliss, 2; 4 mi. E Gooding, 5. *Minidoka County:* Acequia, 1; 4-5 mi. N Rupert, 2; Twin Lakes, 20 mi. N Minidoka, 1

(Biol. Surv. coll.). *Clark County:* Birch Creek, 6 (Biol. Surv. coll.);
Birch Creek, 2 mi. SE Kaufman, 5; Birch Creek, 8 mi. SE Kaufman, 1.
Butte County: 3 mi. SE Arco, 14; Pioneer, 17 mi. SE Arco, 2; 1 mi.
N Berenice, 10; Big Lost River (near Pioneer), 9 (Biol. Surv. coll.).
Bingham County: 16 mi. NW American Falls, 5; 19 mi. NW American
Falls, 1; 10 mi. WNW American Falls, 1.

Genus **Callospermophilus** Merriam
Mantled Ground Squirrels

Callospermophilus lateralis cinerascens (Merriam)
MONTANA MANTLED GROUND SQUIRREL

Tamias cinerascens Merriam, N. Amer. Fauna, 4:20. October 8,
1890. Type from Helena, 4500 feet, Lewis and Clark County, Montana.
   Synonym.—Spermophilus lateralis, Elliot, 1898:221.
   *Distribution.—*In Idaho, from Canada south through mountainous
portions of state (except in extreme western part) to Snake River
Plains. Probably intergrades with *C. l. lateralis* in southern Wyoming
(see map, fig. 13).
   *Description.—*Adults: Males generally brighter colored than females. General dorsal coloration allevaneous gray; head, ears, and
neck deep rusty chestnut (this portion termed the mantle); three distinct lateral stripes, a whitish one bordered by two black ones, extending from hip to shoulder on each side; sides and abdomen grayish
white, tinged with light buff; outer parts of lower hind legs rusty
brown; undersurface of tail grizzled grayish yellow; lateral hairs of
tail, when viewed from above, with two distinct black bands; upper
surfaces of hind feet grayish white. External measurements of four
adults (one male and three females) from Mill Creek average 290-
101-44-24. Skull: Large (occipitonasal length, 47 mm.) and relatively
slender; posterior extensions of premaxillae broad (each about as
wide as breadth of posterior portions of both nasals); rostrum relatively long and narrow. Young: Similar in external appearance to
adults, but pelage softer and silkier.
   *Comparisons.—*Compared with *C. l. lateralis* with which it probably
intergrades in southern Wyoming: Mantle much deeper chestnut;
inner black stripe much wider and more conspicuous; dorsal coloration grayish, rather than nearly avellaneous; ears considerably larger
(there is considerable variation in this character); tail averages
longer; skull larger; premaxillary tongues much wider; basioccipital
wider. Compared with *C. l. connectens* with which it integrades in
western Idaho: Mantle deeper rusty chestnut; undersurface of tail
grayish yellow, rather than fulvous; skull averages larger; premaxillary tongues average wider. Compared with *C. l. trepidus* from Mt.
Harrison: Mantle much darker; undersurface of tail grayish yellow,
rather than fulvous; ears noticeably larger; white eye ring more
conspicuous; rostrum longer and relatively narrower.

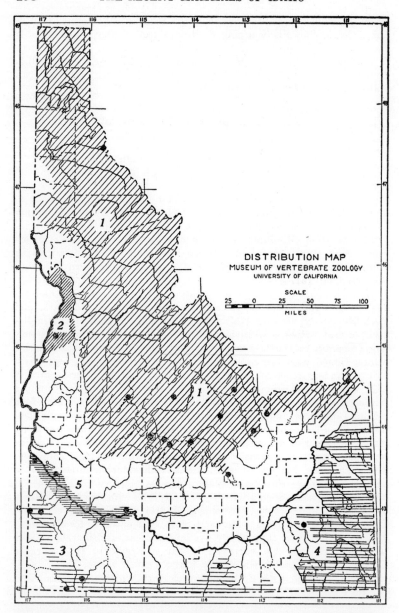

FIG. 13. Map showing the distribution of some ground squirrels in Idaho. Dots indicate localities whence specimens have been examined or recorded. 1. *Callospermophilus lateralis cinerascens*, 2. *Callospermophilus lateralis connectens*, 3. *Callospermophilus lateralis trepidus*, 4. *Callospermophilus lateralis castanurus*, 5. *Ammospermophilus leucurus leucurus*.

Remarks.—Of these four races, *cinerascens* has the largest skull, darkest mantle, and grayest tail; *trepidus* is lightest colored; *lateralis* has the inner black stripe narrowest and often inconspicuous; *connectens* is intermediate between *cinerascens* and *trepidus* as regards most characters.

Merriam (1890) separated the mantled ground squirrels into two groups on the basis of width of inner black stripe and on whether the lateral hairs of the tail have one or two black bands. In one group, characterized by "inner black stripe narrower than outer: lateral hairs of tail with two black bands," he placed *lateralis* (Colorado) and *cinerascens* (Montana). In the other group he placed *chrysodeirus* (California) and *castanurus* (Utah). This combination of characters long has been used to differentiate these two supposed groups but is unsatisfactory as a means of identifying individuals from many parts of Idaho.

In specimens of *cinerascens* from central Idaho the inner black stripe is as wide and as conspicuous as the outer one, and the lateral hairs of the tail have two, in one individual (no. 71984) three, black bands. Here, then, characters of the two groups of Merriam are found combined. All specimens of *chrysodeirus* examined from Oregon, northern California, and Nevada have two black color bands on the lateral hairs of the tail which are obscured in ventral view, but if the tail be viewed from the top, they are conspicuous. It seems that the combinations used by Merriam applied only to the specimens he had available at that time, because additional material demonstrates that a division of the genus based upon these characters no longer is tenable. In fact, I have found no combination of characters which satisfactorily separates the genus into two groups.

Taylor (1910) implied in his description of *C. trepidus* from northern Nevada that this division was unsatisfactory and suggested that *trepidus* was structurally intermediate between the *castanurus (chrysodeirus)* and *lateralis* groups of Merriam. In 75 specimens of *trepidus* from Nevada and southern Idaho, the wide inner black stripe, bright ventral coloration of tail, and relatively short, broad rostrum suggest that *trepidus* actually is intermediate structurally as well as geographically between *chrysodeirus*, to the west, and *castanurus*, to the east. Contrary to Taylor's statement *(ibid.)* that the inner black stripe is narrower than the outer one in *trepidus*, I find that over 75 per cent of the specimens have the inner black stripe as broad as, or broader than, the outer one. Hence, I see no direct relationship between *trepidus* and *lateralis*, as he suggests, but rather an indirect one through *catanurus* and *wortmani*. Allen (1895), in the original description of *wortmani*, pointed out that this race is characterized by almost complete lack of the inner black stripe (a condition occasionally found in *lateralis)* and by fulvous coloration of ventral surface of tail as occurs in *castanurus*. To emphasize resemblances, these races might be arranged as follows: *chrysodeirus—trepidus —castanurus—wortmani—lateralis*.

Even stronger evidence of intergradation is found in specimens from northern California, Oregon, and western Idaho. The recently described *Callospermophilus chrysodeirus connectens* (Howell, 1931) from the Blue Mountains of Oregon and Washington, as Howell *(ibid.)* points out, resembles *C. c. chrysodeirus*. It differs from that race, however, in darker, that is, more rusty reddish, mantle and paler undersurface of tail. These trends are toward *cinerascens*. Four specimens, two adults and two young of the year, collected in late July near Black Lake, Adams County, Idaho, are of particular interest because in dorsal aspect they are but slightly different from specimens of *connectens* from Union County, Oregon. The mantle is a shade darker, and almost exactly intermediate between *connectens* and *cinerascens*. Three of the specimens have the undersurface of the tail fulvous colored as in *connectens;* in the other, an adult male, it is grayish yellow as in *cinerascens* from central Idaho. In many of the specimens of *cinerascens* from central Idaho the undersurface of the tail is considerably more yellowish than in specimens of that race from the Bitterroot Valley, Montana, and in this respect they are intermediate between *cinerascens* (grizzled grayish yellow) and *connectens* (fulvous). In shape of skull, shape of rostrum, and width of premaxillary tongues, the adult specimens from Black Lake are structurally as well as geographically intermediate between *cinerascens* and *connectens* and demonstrate intergradation between the two. Thus, another chain of relationships is suggested: *chrysodeirus—connectens—cinerascens*. Accordingly, the mantled ground squirrels herein discussed are regarded as members of a single geographically variable species, *lateralis*.

Ecology.—In Idaho, *cinerascens* usually is restricted to mountainous areas where it occurs commonly on rocky talus areas in company with pikas *(Ochotona)* and marmots *(Marmota)*. At the head of Big Lost River individuals occupied burrows in open spaces on the hillsides. At Mill Creek they occurred largely on talus areas high above the valley floor. Apparently, as with most ground squirrels, absence of water is not a critical factor in limiting their distribution.

Three of the specimens from Mill Creek, taken July 27-29, are in process of molt.

Records of occurrence.—Specimens examined, 20, as follows: *Bonner County:* 5 mi. W Cocolalla, 1. *Shoshone County:* Glidden Lakes, 2; Lower Glidden Lake, 1. *Valley County:* 5 mi. W Cape Horn, 1. *Custer County:* head Big Lost River, 2; head Pahsimeroi River, 4; Mill Creek, 14 mi. WSW Challis, 5. *Butte County:* Craters of the Moon National Monument, 4. Additional records (Merriam, 1891:43-44, unless otherwise stated): *Lemhi County:* Salmon River. *Blaine County:* head Big Wood River; Summit; Sawtooth Mountains (Elliot, 1898:221). *Clark County:* Birch Creek. *Fremont County:* Henrys Lake (Merriam, 1873:664). *Butte County:* Lost River Mountains.

Callospermophilus lateralis connectens Howell
OREGON MANTLED GROUND SQUIRREL

Callospermophilus chrysodeirus connectens Howell, Jour. Mammalogy, 12:161. May 14, 1931. Type from Homestead, Baker County, Oregon.

Distribution.—In Idaho, known definitely only from Adams County in extreme western part of state (see map, fig. 13).

Description.—Adults: Mantle chestnut; inner black stripe as wide, or nearly as wide, as outer one; general dorsal coloration grayish, tinged with avellaneous; undersurface of tail fulvous. Young similar to adults, but usually lighter colored. External measurements of two adult males from Black Lake average 280-101-43-14.

Comparisons.—See under *Comparisons* in species account of *C. l. cinerascens*.

Remarks.—The Snake River, where it forms the boundary between Idaho and Oregon, transects the range of *connectens* in such a manner that the major portion lies on the Oregon side of the river. Although the mantled ground squirrels from Adams County herein are referred to *connectens*, they differ from specimens taken in Oregon. The general dorsal coloration is less vinaceous, that is, more grayish; mantle deeper chestnut, less vinaceous; undersurface of tail lighter. Their general similarities, however, indicate close relationship, and, to me, suggest that the range of this race in Idaho and Oregon at one time was continuous. The differences noted indicate that the two portions of their present range have been separated for a considerable period of time.

If this interpretation be correct, *connectens* offers additional evidence that the Snake River in this region was blocked at an early time and that, after the course of the river was re-established, it served as an effective barrier to the movements of many kinds of land-dwelling mammals, particularly ground squirrels and pocket gophers.

The specimens from Idaho are intermediate between *C. l. connectens* and *C. l. cinerascens* which hitherto was regarded as races of two full species, *C. chrysodeirus* and *C. lateralis*. This point is discussed more fully under *Remarks* in the account of *C. l. cinerascens*.

The four specimens from Black Lake were the only ones encountered by Borell and Gilmore (MS) in ten weeks of intensive collecting in Adams and Washington counties, Idaho. They were taken at the base of a large rock slide along an old road.

Records of occurrence.—Specimens examined, 4, all from ½ mi. E Black Lake, Adams County (Ralph Ellis coll.).

Callospermophilus lateralis trepidus Taylor
NEVADA MANTLED GROUND SQUIRREL

Callospermophilus trepidus Taylor, Univ. California Publ. Zool., 5:283. February 12, 1910. Type from head of Big Creek, Pine Forest Mountains, 8000 feet altitude, Humboldt County, Nevada.

Distribution.—In Idaho, mountainous areas south of Snake River from Owyhee County east at least to Mt. Harrison, Cassia County (see map, fig. 13).

Description.—Males usually brighter colored than females. General dorsal coloration avellaneous gray; inner black stripe as broad as or broader than outer one; mantle pale fulvous; sides of neck distinctly yellowish; undersurface of tail fulvous; sides and abdomen dark smoke gray, tinged with buff. External measurements of three adult females from Mt. Harrison average 276-94-43-20.

Comparisons.—See under *Comparisons* in species account of *C. l. cinerascens.*

Remarks.—For discussion of relationships and use of the above name for this race, see under *Remarks* in species account of *C. l. cinerascens.*

Ecology.—At Mt. Harrison, mantled ground squirrels were found only in the immediate vicinity of Lake Cleveland and on the summit of the peak. Here they occurred in the vicinity of large boulders and rocky talus areas where they sought refuge when alarmed. At Indian Creek, near Riddle, Owyhee County, I saw a mantled ground squirrel in a rocky canyon, but was unable to collect it. Probably it was of this race.

Records of occurrence.—Specimens examined, 7, as follows: *Owyhee County:* 2½ mi. E Jordan Valley, 2; Silver, 1 (Carnegie Mus.); between Duck Valley Indian Reservation and Juniper Lake Basin, 1. *Cassia County:* Mt. Harrison, 10 mi. S Albion, 3 (1 in Davis coll.).

Callospermophilus lateralis castanurus (Merriam)
WASATCH MANTLED GROUND SQUIRREL

Tamias castanurus Merriam, N. Amer. Fauna, 4:19. October 8, 1890. Type from Park City, Wasatch Mountains, 7000 feet, Summit County, Utah.

Distribution.—In Idaho, restricted to the southeastern portion of the state. Definitely recorded only from the Wasatch Mountains between Preston and Montpelier (see map, fig. 13).

Description.—Males brighter colored than females; similar to *cinerascens*, but mantle paler; undersurface of tail *deep chestnut* (to which character the subspecific name alludes). The ventral coloration of the tail is the best single diagnostic character of this race.

Remarks.—For discussion of relationships see under *Remarks* in the account of *cinerascens*. Whitlow and Hall (1933:251) refer a skull lacking the rostrum from Barrett's

Ranch, Bannock County, to *C. l. lateralis.* Instead, possibly, *C. l. trepidus,* or more probably, *C. l. castanurus* is the race which occurs there.

Ecology.—In the vicinity of Copenhagen Basin, and all along the ridge of that portion of the Wasatch Range we visited in southeastern Idaho, *castanurus* was exceedingly abundant. Like other mantled ground squirrels, they were most common in the rocky areas near the summit of the range. Areas where large boulders bordered alpine meadows were particularly heavily populated, but every rock pile and boulder slope was occupied by one or more individuals. On the west-facing side of the range where boulder-strewn slopes were more common, the mantled ground squirrel was found associating with pikas, marmots, *consobrinus* chipmunks, and bushy-tailed wood rats. In the boulder-rimmed meadows it associated principally with *consobrinus* chipmunks.

At the time of our visit, mid-July, 1937, young of the year were numerous. Family groups of third-grown young were often seen playing about the home burrows, the entrances to which usually were placed at the bases of large boulders. From observation of several such groups I gained the impression that four or five young per litter was the average. One family consisted of six young and the female. The mammae of several adult females that were collected contained milk, indicating that the young probably were still nursing.

Records of occurrence.—Specimens examined, 12, all from near Copenhagen Basin, 20 mi. W Montpelier, in Bear Lake and Franklin counties.

Genus **Ammospermophilus** Merriam
Antelope Ground Squirrels

Ammospermophilus leucurus leucurus (Merriam)
ANTELOPE GROUND SQUIRREL

Tamias leucurus Merriam, N. Amer. Fauna, 2:20. October 30, 1889. Type from San Gorgonio Pass, Riverside County, California.

Distribution.—In Idaho, Snake River Valley from Oregon east at least to Glenns Ferry (see map, fig. 13).

Description.—Adults: General dorsal coloration avellaneous gray; distinct dorsolateral white stripe from hip to shoulder on each side; sides, abdomen, chin, and lower surface of tail pure white; shoulders, outer parts of lower legs, and tops of feet ochraceous tawny; lateral hairs of tail with two distinct black bands; external ears short. External measurements of two adult females from Homedale average 210-56-38-11. Mammae in five pairs. Skull: Relatively narrow and deep, smooth; occipitonasal length averages 38.6; rostrum short and pointed; dentition relatively weak, maxillary tooth row, 6.7; width of Pm^3 less than half the width of Pm^4 (in all other species of ground squirrels examined, width of Pm^3 is more than half as wide as Pm^4). Young: Similar to adult, but lighter colored.

Comparisons.—Readily distinguishable from all others of the squirrel family in Idaho by presence of one dorsolateral white stripe on each side, and white under tail surface.

Remarks.—The shape of skull and ratio of width of Pm^3 to Pm^4 in this squirrel corresponds more closely to conditions in chipmunks *(Eutamias)* than to those in ground squirrels *(Citellus* and *Callospermophilus).* Its systematic position, however, appears to be intermediate between the two.

Antelope Ground Squirrels are uncommon in their restricted range in southwestern Idaho. Here they occur only in the lowlands and appear to have reached this region by way of Oregon and not over the high plateau in southern Owyhee County. As judged from my experiences in the field and from information gathered in conversation with residents of that area, the "white-tailed chipmunks" occur largely south of the Snake River. Two specimens from near Glenns Ferry and a sight record made in 1910 by Stanley Jewett *(in litt.)* of one between Nampa and the Snake River demonstrates that they have reached the north side. One wonders if they crossed the river unaided by man. Two that I saw caged as pets at Mountain Home had been captured south of the river near Bruneau.

Ecology.—Two females were collected May 29 and 30 at the edge of the desert just west of Homedale where the dominant vegetation consisted of *Atriplex* and *Artemisia.* Both had active mammae and recently had been suckling young.

A nest was discovered by accident on May 31 when I set a rat trap baited with rolled oats at the entrance to a burrow in a cut bank at the side of the road. When I returned two hours later, the trap held three third-grown young. I excavated the burrow and found three more. The main burrow was in soft volcanic ash between two layers of "hard pan." It ran about six inches in from, and parallel to, the cut, and about three feet from the top of the bank. It averaged 85 mm. in diameter and had three openings. The nest chamber was merely an enlarged portion of the main burrow and measured, in millimeters, 120 by 115 by 50. It was lined with a compact mass of rabbit fur, shredded bark of *Artemisia,* feathers, grasses, and bits of cotton, and left an inner chamber 75 by 75 by 35 mms. The feathers and cotton probably had been gathered at the near-by city garbage dump.

The specimen from near Bruneau, collected June 3, 1934, is a third-grown young male. This specimen and the young captured at Homedale indicate that the breeding season is later than in typical ground squirrels *(Citellus).*

Records of occurrence.—Specimens examined, 3, all from Owyhee County, as follows: 5 mi. N Bruneau, 1; Homedale, 2. Additional record (A. H. Howell, *in litt.):* *Elmore County:* Glenns Ferry (specimens in Biol. Surv. coll.).

Genus **Eutamias** Trouessart
Chipmunks

Small to medium-sized, diurnal, squirrellike rodents with internal, membranous cheek pouches; dorsum conspicuously marked with longitudinal stripes which pass onto head and cheeks; eyes large; ears prominent, pointed, sparsely haired; forefeet with four functional toes, hind feet with five; claws sharp, those on hind feet longest, modified for climbing; tail bushy, lateral hairs, when viewed from above, with four alternate darker and lighter color bands. Skull smoothly rounded; postorbital processes weak and slender; bullae well inflated, internally divided into three incomplete chambers; stapedial canal large, completely ossified; dental formula $\frac{1\,0\,2\,3}{1\,0\,2\,3}$; cheek teeth rooted, brachydont; Pm^3 rudimentary, less than half the width of Pm^4; molars modified tritubercular, nearly bunolophodont.

Chipmunks are attractive creatures and, because of their diurnal habits, they are familiar to everyone who has spent any time in the open. The group is similar in general habits, yet nearly every species is modified in some way so that it is well adapted to a particular environment. Most of them are associated with forests; here some are largely arboreal, others largely terrestrial or restricted to the underbrush. Some kinds, for example, *E. minimus* and *E. dorsalis,* are adapted to dry, desert conditions; others are restricted to high mountain tops.

These rodents do not hibernate in the true sense of the word. Rather, they are inactive, perhaps torpid, during the most adverse periods of winter, at which time they subsist on food stored in summer and autumn. In known instances (Howell, 1929) the animals do become torpid, but such a condition probably lasts for only a brief period because they have little, or no, reserve of fat stored in the body. Also, it is not uncommon to find chipmunks abroad on warm days in winter.

In northern regions, Idaho included, the breeding season of chipmunks apparently is restricted to a brief period in early spring; a single litter is the rule. In southern climes, southern California for instance, the breeding season may last for six months or more and more than one litter may be reared by a single female.

Nine kinds of chipmunks, of five different species, occur in Idaho.

Key to Adult Chipmunks of Idaho

1 General size small; hind foot 30 mm., or less.

    2 Interlacrimal width near 10.4 mm.; dark dorsal stripes near fuscous black; sides ochraceous or tawny, not buffy.

        3 General dorsal coloration bright; sides bright ochraceous; shoulder patches ochraceous; ratio of tail to head and body near 82%; skull rounded. **E. m. consobrinus,** p. 213

        3' General dorsal coloration duller, more grayish; sides tawny or pale cinnamon; shoulder patches grayish; ratio of tail to head and body near 75%; skull flattened.

                        E. m. scrutator, p. 213

2' Interlacrimal width near 9.7 mm.; dark dorsal stripes near fuscous; sides pale buff; ratio of tail to head and body near 85%; skull rounded.   **E. m. pictus,** p. 208

1' General size medium to large; hind foot more than 31 mm.

    4 Dorsal stripes conspicuous; general coloration ochraceous; hairs on upper side of tail tipped with buff or ochraceous, never with pure white.

        5 Hind foot averaging less than 33 mm.

            6 Ventral coloration buffy; total length averaging near 220 mm.   **E. a. luteiventris,** p. 219

            6' Ventral coloration white or grayish white; total length averaging near 210 mm.

                7 Dorsal coloration buffy.   **E. a. amoenus,** p. 216

                7' Dorsal coloration grayish, with more blackish.
                                E. a. cratericus, p. 222

        5' Hind foot averaging 33 mm., or more.

            8 Tail averaging 112 mm.; sides ochraceous tawny.
                              E. r. simulans, p. 223

            8' Tail averaging 105 mm., or less; sides tawny or sayal brown.

                9 Tail averaging about 105 mm.; rostrum broader, width of the two nasals together near their posterior ends more than 3.0 mm.
                              E. a. canicaudus, p. 221

                9' Tail averaging about 100 mm.; rostrum narrower, width of the two nasals together near their posterior ends 3.0 mm., or less.   **E. umbrinus,** p. 224

    4' Dorsal stripes, especially the lateral ones, obscure; general coloration grayish; hairs on upper side of tail tipped with white.   **E. d. utahensis,** p. 224

Eutamias minimus pictus (Allen)
LEAST CHIPMUNK

Tamias minimus pictus Allen, Bull. Amer. Mus. Nat. Hist., 3:115. June, 1890. Type from Kelton, Box Elder County, Utah.

Synonyms.—*Tamias minimus melanurus* Merriam, 1890:22 (type locality, west side of Snake River near Blackfoot, Bingham County, Idaho); *Eutamias minimus scrutator* Hall and Hatfield, 1934, part.

Distribution.—In Idaho, north of Snake River from Oregon north and east in the sage-covered valleys to Lemhi Valley, thence south along east side of Snake River into Utah (see map, fig. 14). Intergrades with *scrutator* in region south of Snake River between Pocatello and Twin Falls.

Description.—One of the three smallest chipmunks in Idaho. Color (summer) : Top of head varying from smoke gray to buffy gray; dark facial stripes pale fuscous black; postauricular patches conspicuous, grayish; median dark dorsal stripe fuscous black, lateral ones much lighter; rump and thighs smoke gray; sides pale buff; ventral portions grayish white; upper surface of tail grayish black, ventral surface buff, bordered by black band, lateral hairs with four alternate color bands, black, buff, black, buff. External measurements of four males and two females from Shoshone and Minidoka average, respectively, 190-85-27 and 206-88-28; four males and four females from Birch Creek, 190-87-29 and 190-85-28; four males and four females from near Pocatello, 191-87-28 and 194-89-29. Skull smoothly rounded, cranium round-topped; zygoma bowed; interlacrimal breadth averaging less than 10 mm.

Comparisons.—Differs from races of *E. amoenus* in smaller size, shorter hind foot, and paler color. Compared with *consobrinus* with which it intergrades in eastern Idaho: Differs chiefly in grayish, rather than ochraceous dorsal coloration; sides pale buff, rather than ochraceous; skull less arched dorsally; interlacrimal breadth 9.7, as opposed to 10.4. Compared with *scrutator* with which it intergrades south of the Snake River west of Pocatello: Coloration averaging paler; tail, near 85, rather than near 75, per cent of length of head and body; interlacrimal breadth averaging less, rather than more, than 10 mm.; skull rounded dorsally, rather than flattened; zygoma bowed laterally, rather than nearly parallel.

Remarks.—Since Howell's (1929) revision of the American chipmunks, Hall and Hatfield (1934) described a new race, *scrutator,* of the species *minimus,* and assigned to it all the specimens from Idaho which Howell *(ibid.)* referred to *pictus;* simultaneously, they restricted the range of *pictus* to western Utah. It is unfortunate that they had available only 20 specimens of *minimus* from Idaho, all from near Pocatello and Blackfoot, because this circumstance led them to err in assuming that all *minimus* in Idaho, *consobrinus* excepted, are *scrutator.* All specimens (40) examined from north of the Snake River differ from *scrutator,* and agree with *pictus,* in narrow interlacrimal width (less than 10 mm.), ones from Pahsimeroi Valley excepted; rounded skull; relatively long tail (85 per cent, rather than 75 per cent, of length of head and body) ; general lighter dorsal coloration. To be sure, they differ somewhat from topotypes of *pictus,* but the differences are no greater than ones found

within the range of *scrutator* in Nevada and Oregon and
not as great as differences found in *E. amoenus amoenus*.
The main point is that in structural characters they are
closer to *pictus* than to *scrutator*. Because they do not
comment on the 8 specimens they had available from near
Pocatello, I infer that Hall and Hatfield considered them
typical of *scrutator*. Actually, they are intermediates and
perhaps are best treated as intergrades between *pictus* and
scrutator. They possess the relatively long tail and narrow
interlacrimal width of *pictus* and the cranial shape of *scrutator;* color is intermediate.

The disposition of the name *Tamias minimus melanurus*
Merriam requires comment. Merriam (1891:46) and Howell *(ibid.)* placed it as a synonym of *pictus;* later Hall and
Hatfield *(ibid.),* on the assumption that *pictus* is restricted
to western Utah and the fact that specimens formerly referred to *melanurus* differ markedly from *scrutator*, trans-
ferred it to the synonymy of *consobrinus*. Although I have
not examined the specimens on which the name *melanurus*
was based that were available to Hall and Hatfield, I have
examined specimens from Blackfoot and the near vicinity
and also specimens from Big Lost River which Merriam
(1890:22) considered as intermediate between *melanurus*
and *pictus*. These specimens, on the basis of length of tail,
roundness of skull, and laterally bowed zygoma, may be
referred to *consobrinus* or *pictus* with equal propriety because these two races differ chiefly in color. On the basis
of color, and narrow interlacrimal width, however, they
must be referred to *pictus*. Hence, I see no alternative to
returning the name *melanurus* to the synonymy of *pictus*.

The range of *pictus* extends through the lowlands in
southern Idaho from Utah north to the Lemhi and Pahsimeroi valleys and west along the north side of the Snake
River at least to Nampa and perhaps on to the east bank
of the river where it forms the boundary between Idaho
and Oregon. The range of *scrutator* extends into southwestern Idaho, south of the Snake River, and reaches east
about to the vicinity of Twin Falls where intergradation
between *pictus* and *scrutator* is evident. A distribution such
as this gives additional evidence that the Snake River, where

it is of considerable width, is a barrier to the geographic movements of certain kinds of mammals. Although *scrutator* apparently is prevented from extending its range northward by the Snake River, and eastward by the presence of the ecologically similar race *pictus*, *pictus* seems not to have found the river impassable. This circumstance doubtless is due to the fact that the river in the northeastern portion of the range of *pictus* consists of numerous small branches, any one of which chipmunks of this species could cross by way of sand bars, or by swimming a short distance, when the water is low. A similar situation is found in the distribution of *Citellus armatus*, *Citellus mollis*, and *Thomomys talpoides*. Each of these species occupies a range which extends across the headwaters of the Snake River; in western Idaho, the river, there averaging 600 feet in width, prevents them from crossing.

Ecology.—In Idaho, the *minimus* chipmunks, *consobrinus* excepted, are typical of the dry, sage-covered deserts. At Riddle they were abundant in the rocky outcroppings bordering Indian Creek in late May and early June. Here several were caught in snap traps baited with rolled oats. Near Mountain Home they were found in the sage-covered areas, but they were most abundant along weed-choked fences which afforded excellent cover. Here they were occupying underground burrows which apparently they had constructed themselves, whereas at Riddle they resorted for the most part to crevices in rocky outcroppings. For a distance of about 10 miles north of Idavada on Highway 93 they were extremely abundant in September, 1934. Their distribution there seems to be correlated with the presence or absence of basaltic outcroppings, because farther north where the soil was sandy or of claylike consistency they were absent along the highway. They are not averse to sand, however, because one taken north of Rupert was caught on a sage-covered sand hill on which *Dipodomys*, *Citellus mollis*, and *Perognathus parvus* also were taken. Apparently, like that of most desert-dwelling animals, the distribution of *minimus* chipmunks is not correlated with the presence or absence of water. Food and shelter seem to be the chief requisites.

Their food varies considerably. The stomach of one, taken at Deer Flat, September 8, was gorged with large red ants; individuals at Riddle were observed to feed on the flower heads of *Artemisia* and on green vegetation, mostly grasses. North of Idavada, in September, 1934, I watched *minimus* collecting the maturing seeds of the introduced Russian thistle. One that I observed closely for ten minutes climbed into the top of a large thistle, filled its pouches with seeds, and then hurried to a burrow on a hillside about thirty yards distant and disappeared. It was not long before the animal was back and the procedure was repeated. In ten minutes this individual made four round trips, each time carrying a load of seeds. Over a distance of ten miles in this area I collected twelve specimens, mostly young of the year, and saw fully a hundred more. All of them were observed in or near the Russian thistles along the sides of the highway. Although the chipmunks must have stored or consumed thousands of seeds that fall, no effect on the population of thistles was apparent. They appeared to be as abundant in that area the following year as in 1934.

The breeding season of *minimus* chipmunks in Idaho probably is restricted to early spring, April and May. Apparently a single litter of from four to six young is the rule. Females collected June 1 at Riddle, 5300 ft., showed evidence of recently having suckled young; half-grown young were collected near Mountain Home, June 3.

Records of occurrence.—Specimens examined, 56, as follows: *Canyon County* (Biol. Surv. coll.): Deer Flat, 1; Nampa, 3. *Elmore County:* 5 mi. S Mountain Home, 5. *Custer County* (Biol. Surv. coll.): Dickey, 2; Pahsimeroi Valley, 4. *Blaine County:* Craters of the Moon, 1. *Lincoln County:* Shoshone, 4 (Biol. Surv. coll.). *Minidoka County:* Minidoka, 3 (Biol. Surv. coll.); 4 mi. N Rupert, 1. *Twin Falls County:* 1-6 mi. N Idavada, 11 (2 in Davis coll.). *Cassia County:* 1 mi. E Elba, 1. *Clark County:* Birch Creek, 10 (Biol. Surv. coll.). *Butte County:* N. base Sunset Cone, Craters of the Moon National Monument, 1. *Bingham County:* 1 mi. N Fort Hall, 2; 3 mi. S Blackfoot, 1. *Power County:* 4 mi. NE American Falls, 2; 5 mi. NW Michaud, 2; 5½ mi. SW Michaud, 1. *Bannock County:* Fort Hall Indian School, 10 mi. N Pocatello, 1. Additional records (Howell, 1929:40): *Ada County:* Orchard. *Lemhi County:* Junction; Lemhi; Lemhi Valley; Patterson. *Blaine County:* Salmon Valley (near Sawtooth City). *Minidoka County:* Twin Lakes, Snake River Desert. *Cassia County:* Bridge. *Clark*

County: Dubois. *Butte County:* Arco; Little Lost River. *Bonneville County:* Idaho Falls. *Bingham County:* Shelley. *Power County:* American Falls. *Bannock County:* Pocatello. *Oneida County:* Malad City; Juniper.

Eutamias minimus scrutator Hall and Hatfield
GREAT BASIN CHIPMUNK

Eutamias minimus scrutator Hall and Hatfield, Univ. California Publ. Zool., 40:321. February 12, 1934. Type from near Blanco Mountain, 10,500 feet, White Mountains, Mono County, California.

Synonym.—Eutamias minimus pictus, Howell, 1929:40, part.

Distribution.—South of the Snake River from Oregon east to near Twin Falls where it intergrades with *pictus* (see map, fig. 14).

Description.—Size small; tail relatively short, averaging about 75 per cent of length of head and body; general color darker than in *pictus;* sides cinnamon. Skull flattened; zygoma nearly parallel; interlacrimal width averages more than 10 mm. External measurements of two adult males and three adult females from near Riddle average, respectively, 183-82-28 and 188-83-29.

Comparisons.—See under *Comparisons* in account of *pictus.*

Remarks.—Specimens examined from near Riddle are not quite typical of *scrutator;* the tail averages 84 per cent of the length of head and body whereas in typical specimens this percentage is 75. Specimens from near Idavada in south-central Twin Falls County are nearly intermediate between *scrutator,* to the west, and *pictus,* to the east. On the basis of relatively longer tail and an interlacrimal width of 9.7 mm., they are referred to *pictus,* rather than to *scrutator* which they resemble in color. See also under *Remarks* in account of *pictus.*

Records of occurrence.—Specimens examined, 7, from Owyhee County as follows: 2½ mi. E Jordan Valley, 2; 1 mi. S Riddle, 4; Indian Creek, 2 mi. SE Riddle, 1. Additional records (Howell, 1929: 40) : *Owyhee County:* 15 mi. SW Riddle; Silver City.

Eutamias minimus consobrinus (Allen)
WASATCH CHIPMUNK

Tamias minimus consobrinus Allen, Bull. Amer. Mus. Nat. Hist., 3:112. June, 1890. Type from Parleys Canyon, Wasatch Mountains, near present site of Barclay, Salt Lake County, Utah.

Distribution.—Extreme eastern portion of Idaho from Yellowstone National Park south to Bear Lake (see map, fig. 14).

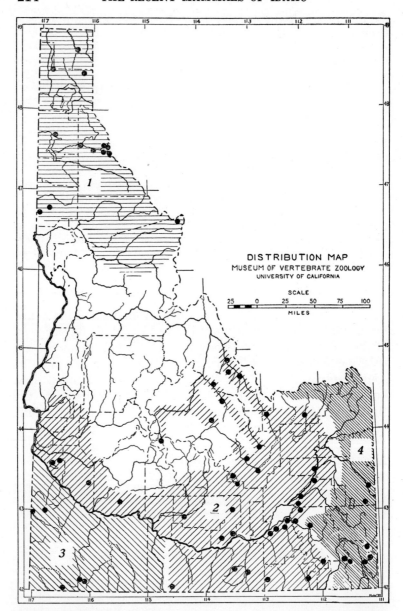

FIG. 14. Map showing the distribution of some chipmunks in Idaho. Dots indicate localities whence specimens have been examined or recorded. 1. *Eutamias ruficaudus simulans*, 2. *Eutamias minimus pictus*, 3. *Eutamias minimus scrutator*, 4. *Eutamias minimus consobrinus*

Description.—Size small. The brightest-colored *minimus* chipmunk in Idaho. Color (summer): Top of head fuscous gray; dark facial and dorsal stripes fuscous black; sides bright ochraceous; rump ochraceous gray; belly white, faintly washed with buff; tail actually and relatively long (ratio of length of tail to length of head and body, 82). Skull smooth, rounded; zygoma bowed laterally; interlacrimal breadth averages 10.4 mm. External measurements of 15 adults from Utah average near 193-87-30 (Howell, 1929:47).

Comparisons.—See under *Comparisons* in account of *pictus.*

Remarks.—The Wasatch Chipmunk is one of the brightest colored of the western races of *minimus*. In Idaho, it is restricted to the mountainous areas in the eastern portion of the state where it associates with the larger *E. a. luteiventris* and *E. umbrinus*. At least *E. umbrinus* and *consobrinus* are separated ecologically, for at Copenhagen Basin, twenty miles west of Montpelier in the Wasatch Mountains, *consobrinus* was abundant in the open boulder-studded alpine meadows and in the talus areas. The larger *umbrinus* occurred commonly in the timbered areas, particularly where slashing and fallen trees were present; seldom was it seen in open meadows and then only near the peripheries where it competed somewhat with *consobrinus* for the flower heads and seeds of small alpine composites. Daily, during our two-weeks' sojourn in this basin, we encountered *consobrinus* in association with mantled ground squirrels, *armatus* ground squirrels, and pikas; *umbrinus* was a part of the community in which the pine squirrel, *Tamiasciurus*, was found. Occasionally *consobrinus* entered the woods, but instances noted were confined to open stands or cut-over areas near talus areas and alpine meadows.

In one meadow occupied largely by *armatus* ground squirrels a dozen or more *consobrinus* chipmunks were engaged in storing seeds in underground burrows in mid-July.

Records of occurrence.—Specimens examined, 10, as follows: *Bannock County:* ¼ mi. W Copenhagen Basin, 1. *Bear Lake County:* crest of Wasatch Mountains, 2½ mi. E Strawberry Creek Ranger Station, 7; W. rim Copenhagen Basin, 2. Additional records (Howell, 1929:48): *Bonneville County:* Grays Lake (10 mi. E of); Irwin (10 mi. SE of). *Bannock County:* Inkom; Swan Lake. *Caribou County:* head Crow Creek. *Bear Lake County:* Montpelier (Howell, 1929, p. 40, recorded as *pictus,* but here tentatively assigned to *consobrinus*); Montpelier Creek.

Eutamias amoenus amoenus (Allen)
KLAMATH CHIPMUNK

Tamias amoenus Allen, Bull. Amer. Mus. Nat. Hist., 3:90. June, 1890. Type from Fort Klamath, 35 miles northwest of Klamath Falls, Klamath County, Oregon.

Synonym.—Tamias quadrivittatus amoenus, Merriam, 1891:44, part.

Distribution.—In Idaho, mountainous areas south of main Salmon River from Oregon east to Lemhi Mountains; also, in mountains south of Snake River desert probably from Oregon east to Swan Lake (see map, fig. 15).

Description.—Medium size. Color (summer): Top of head smoke gray, mixed with cinnamon; dark facial stripes fuscous; median dorsal stripe nearly black, lateral dark stripes fuscous to fuscous black; light dorsal stripes grayish, mixed with cinnamon; postauricular patches white; sides ochraceous tawny; ventral parts whitish; upper surfaces of feet pale cinnamon; rump and thighs smoke gray; tail fuscous black above, cinnamon below, lateral hairs with four alternate color bands, black, cinnamon, black, cinnamon. Average external measurements of 8 adult males and 7 adult females from Mt. Harrison are 210-91-32 and 215-90-32; of 6 adult males and 9 adult females from Washington and Adams counties, 217-94-32 and 223-96-32; of 4 adult males and four adult females from Custer County, 208-84-32 and 208-80-32.5. Skull smoothly rounded.

Comparisons.—Compared with *luteiventris:* Ventral coloration whitish, rather than pinkish cinnamon; skull usually averaging smaller (skulls of *amoenus* from Washington and Adams counties are larger than typical *luteiventris*). Compared with *canicaudus:* Dorsal coloration lighter and brighter, less fuscous cinnamon on shoulders; skull smaller (occipitonasal length 32.8 as opposed to 35.1); total length less (210 as opposed to 235).

Remarks.—Considerable sexual and geographic variation occurs in the populations herein referred to *amoenus.* Females average larger throughout. Individuals from Mt. Harrison are nearly typical of *amoenus* (compared with specimens from Oregon and northern California); those in the mountains north of the Snake River are larger. This is shown in the following tabulation of the "volume" of skulls of adult males (product of occipitonasal length, zygomatic breadth, and depth of skull, in centimeters).

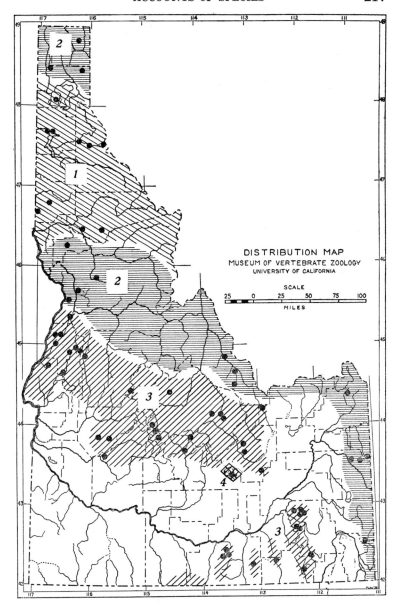

FIG. 15. Map showing the distribution of some chipmunks in Idaho. Dots indicate localities whence specimens have been examined or recorded. 1. *Eutamias amoenus canicaudus*, 2. *Eutamias amoenus luteiventris*, 3. *Eutamias amoenus amoenus*, 4. *Eutamias amoenus cratericus*.

Region	Specimens averaged	"Volume"
Central Oregon	6	7.48 cc.
Mt. Harrison	6	7.72 cc.
Custer County	2	8.35 cc.
Adams and Washington counties	2	8.81 cc.

Specimens of *amoenus* from the Oregon side of the Snake River are smaller than those from the Idaho side. This difference suggests that the Snake River in this region is an effective barrier to geographic movements of chipmunks. If this inference be true, the populations of *amoenus* in central Idaho are isolated from those in Oregon by the Snake River on the south and west and by the presence of another race, *luteiventris,* on the north and east. Were sufficient material available to trace out geographically the variations of *amoenus,* the populations in central Idaho might be found to be subspecifically distinct from *amoenus.* For the present they are best referred to *amoenus.*

Ecology.—These chipmunks are associated with coniferous forests. At Mt. Harrison, they were restricted to the north- and east-facing slopes at elevations ranging from about 6000 to 8000 feet in association with alpine fir, quaking aspen, lodgepole pine, and sagebrush. Here they were trapped in the daytime in sets made near fallen timber and baited with rolled oats. They seemed to be occupying underground burrows, the entrances to which were at the bases of stumps, uprooted trees, and under large rocks. One was caught in a trap set in a deserted badger burrow. In the Sawtooth and Salmon River mountains they were common in all associations except marsh and sagebrush. Here several were seen scampering across talus areas, but they appeared not to be occupying them.

All the specimens collected in June at Mt. Harrison were in winter pelage; some of the males are beginning the summer molt. Specimens collected in July at the head of the Pahsimeroi River, near 9000 feet, have not completed the summer molt; in this process males are more advanced than females. Males from Alturas Lake, late July and early August, are in unworn summer pelage; the females, however, have molted only the fur on the anterior half of the body.

Available data indicate that in Idaho a single litter of from four to six young is born yearly in June or July. A female collected May 10 near Pocatello contained five small embryos; none of the seven females collected in mid-June at Mt. Harrison showed evidence of having suckled young, and only one was pregnant. One female observed June 20 at Lake Cleveland on top of the mountain was transporting dead leaves which probably were being used in constructing a nest. All females collected in middle and late July in the Salmon River Mountains showed evidence of having suckled young recently; third- to half-grown young were observed here.

Records of occurrence.—Specimens examined, 87, as follows: *Idaho County:* Rapid River, near Riggins, 2 (David MacKaye coll.). *Adams County:* 1 mi. N Bear Cr. R. S., 5 (3 in Ralph Ellis coll.); summit Smith Mountain, 4 (Ralph Ellis coll.); 3 mi. W Payette Lake, 2; ½ mi. E Black Lake, 4 (Ralph Ellis coll.). *Valley County:* Sawtooth Range, 5 mi. W Cape Horn, 1. *Washington County:* 1 mi. NE Heath, 15 (12 in Ralph Ellis coll.). *Custer County:* head Pahsimeroi River, 6; Mill Cr., 14 mi. W Challis, 5. *Blaine County:* Alturas Lake, 3; Pettit Lake, 6. *Cassia County:* Howells Canyon, 9 mi. S Albion, 1; Mt. Harrison, 10 mi. S Albion, 20. *Bannock County:* N. Fork Pocatello Creek, 2; W. Fork Rapid Creek, 9½ mi. E Pocatello, 2; Camp Tendoy, 2; Justice Park, 4; Schutt's Mine, 3. Additional records (Howell, 1929:63-64): *Adams County:* Goodrich; New Meadows; Tamarack. *Boise County:* Edna; Idaho City. *Valley County:* Lardo. *Elmore County:* Bald Mountain R. S. *Custer County:* head Big Lost River; Pahsimeroi Mountains; Dickey. *Blaine County:* Ketchum; Sawtooth City; Sawtooth (Alturas) Lake. *Cassia County:* Albion; Bridge. *Clark County:* Birch Creek, 10 mi. S Nicholia; mountains E of Birch Creek. *Butte County:* Arco; Big Butte; Lost River Mountains; Echo Crater (probably referable to *E. a. cratericus*). *Bannock County:* 8 mi. NW Inkom; 14 mi. SE Pocatello; 8 mi. W Swan Lake. *Oneida County:* Blue Spring Hills; Malad.

Eutamias amoenus luteiventris (Allen)
BUFF-BELLIED CHIPMUNK

Tamias quadrivittatus luteiventris Allen, Bull. Amer. Mus. Nat. Hist., 3:101. June, 1890. Type from Chief Mountain (Waterton) Lake, Alberta (3½ mi. N United States-Canada boundary).

Synonym.—*Tamias quadrivittatus amoenus*, Merriam, 1891:44, part.

Distribution.—Most of its range lies in Montana. In Idaho, occurs in extreme northern portion of state; also in central portion mainly north of Salmon River, thence south along the Idaho-Montana and Idaho-Wyoming boundaries to Caribou County (see map, fig. 15).

Description.—Size, medium. Color (summer): Top of head smoke gray, heavily suffused with fuscous; dark facial stripes blackish or blackish fuscous; postauricular patches small, grayish white; dark dorsal stripes blackish or blackish fuscous; rump smoke gray; sides bright ochraceous tawny; upper surfaces of feet cinnamon; upper surface of tail fuscous black, lower surface ochraceous tawny, lateral hairs with four bands, black, ochraceous, black, ochraceous; *abdomen tinged, often heavily washed, with light buff or cinnamon.* Skull smoothly rounded, averaging larger than in *amoenus.* Average external measurements of three adult males and four adult females from Big Hole Mountains are 219-93-31 and 226-99-31.

Comparisons (see also under account of *amoenus*).—*E. a. luteiventris* is by far the brightest-colored race of the *amoenus* group in Idaho. In external measurements and size of skull it is intermediate between *amoenus* and *canicaudus.* This is shown in the following tabulation of measurements of males.

	External measurements	"Volume" of skull
amoenus	210- 91-32	7.72 cc.
luteiventris	219- 93-31	8.48 cc.
canicaudus	235-106-33.5	9.40 cc.

Remarks.—This chipmunk is typically of the central Rocky Mountain area. Its distribution in Idaho is peculiar in that it occurs in two geographically separated regions each of which connects with the main portion of its range in Montana. Its distribution in Idaho seems not to be correlated with geographic or climatic features, but rather with the presence of another race, *canicaudus,* in the region lying between the two arms of its range (see map, fig. 15). It may be that, of these two races, *luteiventris* has a greater range of tolerance to environmental conditions and, thus, is able to succeed in areas to which *canicaudus* is not adapted. This inference is supported by the fact that *luteiventris* occupies a large range which is diversified geographically and climatically, whereas *canicaudus* seems to be limited to a much smaller, more nearly uniform area.

Ecology.—This race usually is associated with coniferous forests although, on occasion, it is found in association with broad-leaved trees and shrubs at lower elevations. Near Swan Valley it was common, along both sides of the South

Fork, in underbrush growing under cottonwood trees. In the Big Hole Mountains it occurred most commonly in small valleys and basins at the edges of the forests. Here, in mid-July, the animals were feeding on ripening berries. Near Victor, they apparently were restricted to coniferous areas for none was observed in the numerous thickets of quaking aspen at the edges of the forest.

A few of the males collected in late July had completed the summer molt, but most of them were still molting; females had just begun to molt—those that showed evidence of having had young lagged behind the apparently sterile ones. The breeding habits of this race probably are similar to those of *amoenus*. None of the females collected in July was pregnant; most of the old females showed evidence of suckling or recently having suckled young. Two-thirds-grown young were observed in mid-July in the Big Hole Mountains.

Records of occurrence.—Specimens examined, 24, as follows: *Boundary County:* 4 mi. W Meadow Creek, 1. *Idaho County:* Castle Creek R. S., 6. *Teton County:* 3 mi. SW Victor, 2. *Bonneville County:* Big Hole Mountains, 8 mi. NE Swan Valley, 7; N. side South Fork, 3 mi. W Swan Valley, 8. Additional records (Howell, 1929:68): *Bonner County:* Cabinet Mountains; Priest Lake. *Lewis County:* Craig Mountains. *Idaho County:* Fiddle Creek; Seven Devils Mountains. *Lemhi County:* Leadore; Lemhi Valley (near Agency); Salmon River Mountains. *Fremont County:* 4 mi. S Trude; Warm River. *Caribou County:* Preuss Mountains (head of Crow Creek).

Eutamias amoenus canicaudus Merriam
LONG-TAILED CHIPMUNK

Eutamias canicaudus Merriam, Proc. Biol. Soc. Washington, 16:77. May 29, 1903. Type from Spokane, Spokane County, Washington.

Distribution.—In Idaho, from near Lake Pend Oreille south to the Clearwater drainage basin (see map, fig. 15).

Description.—Largest of the *amoenus* group in Idaho; tail long (near 100 mm.). Color (summer): Top of head fuscous gray; dark facial stripes fuscous; postauricular patches large, whitish; dark dorsal stripes fuscous black, light ones tending toward gray, rather than white; rump smoke gray; sides grayish cinnamon; ventral portions grayish white; top of tail fuscous black, tawny cinnamon ventrally, lateral hairs with four alternate bands, black, cinnamon, black, buff; tops of feet pale cinnamon. Average external measurements of two adult males and three adult females are 235-106-33.5 and 226-105-33. Skull smooth and rounded; occipitonasal length near 35 mm.

Comparisons.—See under *Comparisons* in accounts of *amoenus* and *luteiventris.*

Remarks.—The long-tailed chipmunk is restricted in range to the north-central portion of Idaho; it occurs also in northeastern Washington. The extremely long tail, large skull, and white ventral coloration distinguish it from all other members of the species in Idaho. In habits, it is similar to *amoenus* and *luteiventris.*

Records of occurrence.—Specimens examined, 23, as follows: *Bonner County:* 5 mi. W Cocolalla, 4. *Shoshone County:* Glidden Lakes, 2; Lower Glidden Lake, 7. *Latah County:* "Latah County," 5 (Chas. R. Conner Mus.). *Clearwater County:* Orofino, 2 (Chas. R. Conner Mus.); 2 mi. NE Weippe, 3. Additional records (Howell, 1929:71): *Kootenai County:* Coeur d'Alene; Fort Sherman; Mission. *Shoshone County:* Osburn. *Latah County:* Moscow.

Eutamias amoenus cratericus Blossom
CRATER CHIPMUNK

Eutamias amoenus cratericus Blossom, Univ. Michigan, Occas. Papers, Mus. Zool., 366:1. December 21, 1937. Type from Grassy Cone, Craters of the Moon National Monument, 6000 feet, Butte County, Idaho.

Distribution.—Lava beds in and near Craters of the Moon National Monument, Idaho.

Description (Blossom, *ibid.*).—"A dull grayish race of the *Eutamias amoenus* group, averaging in body and in skull measurements between *E. a. amoenus* and *E. a. luteiventris* ... top of head Drab, washed with Cinnamon; two upper dark facial stripes Chaetura Drab, lower one Fuscous; three dark median dorsal stripes black, lightly washed with Cinnamon, outer pair Fuscous Black, heavily overlaid with Sayal Brown; median pair of light dorsal stripes Smoke Gray, outer pair Light Smoke Gray ... compared with ... *amoenus* ... duller and darker throughout; underparts less buffy (duller and more grayish) ... skull longer, the zygomatic breadth ... wider, and the nasals are longer."

Remarks.—The specimens collected by me in July, 1937, in comparison with corresponding specimens of other races, bear out the distinctness in color claimed for them by Blossom, but I have had no opportunity to study the skulls.

Records of occurrence.—Specimens examined, 6, as follows: *Butte County:* near Big Cinder Butte, Craters of the Moon, 6. Additional records (Blossom, *op. cit.*, p. 3): *Butte County:* Grassy Cone; Sunset Cone; Broken Top; public camp grounds (Craters of the Moon National Monument); 27 mi. SW Arco. *Blaine County:* 29 mi. SW Arco; 30 mi. SW Arco at S. base White Knob Mountains.

Eutamias ruficaudus simulans Howell
COEUR D'ALENE CHIPMUNK

Eutamias ruficaudus simulans Howell, Jour. Mammal., 3:179. August 4, 1922. Type from Coeur d'Alene, Kootenai County, Idaho.

Distribution.—In Idaho, according to Howell (1929), the extreme northern portion of the state from Canada south to Latah and Idaho counties (see map, fig. 14).

Description (Howell, *ibid.*).—Color (summer): Top of head cinnamon or ochraceous tawny, mixed with fuscous and white; ocular stripe fuscous black; dark dorsal stripes black or fuscous black; rump and thighs mixed clay color and fuscous; tail above fuscous black, ochraceous tawny beneath; underparts grayish white, washed with pale pinkish buff. Skull large (occipitonasal length near 35 mm.); tail long (103-121 mm.). External measurements of ten adults from northern Idaho and northeastern Washington average 238-112-33.5.

Remarks.—According to Howell *(ibid.)*, the species *ruficaudus* differs from all other chipmunks in northern Idaho in whiter belly, longer, more reddish tail, more whitish dorsal stripes, more tawny head, larger skull, and longer rostrum. I have had available too few specimens to permit of my independently making a reliable appraisal of the relationships of this chipmunk. The characters ascribed to it, however, seem to me to be of the nature and degree which ordinarily distinguish subspecies, as Howell, himself (1929, p. 96) has indicated may be the case. The nearest relative of *E. ruficaudus* he regards as *Eutamias umbrinus*.

Records of occurrence.—Specimens examined, 4, as follows: *Kootenai County:* Coeur d'Alene, 1. *Latah County:* Cedar Mountains, 3 (Chas. R. Conner Mus.). Additional records (Howell, *op. cit.*, p. 98): *Boundary County:* Bonners Ferry. *Bonner County:* Cabinet Mountains; Priest Lake. *Kootenai County:* Mission. *Shoshone County:* Kingston; 7 mi. E McKinnis; Mullan; Murray; Osburn; Thompson Pass. *Latah County:* Moscow. *Idaho County:* Packers Meadow.

Eutamias umbrinus (Allen)
UINTA CHIPMUNK

Tamias umbrinus Allen, Bull. Amer. Mus. Nat. Hist., 3:96. June, 1890. Type from Black Fork, Uinta Mountains, Utah.

Distribution.—In Idaho, known from the Big Hole Mountains east of Idaho Falls and the Wasatch, or Bear River, Range in the southeastern part of the state.

Description.—Size medium. Color (summer): Head pale smoke gray; dark facial and dorsal stripes fuscous black; postauricular patches smoke gray, generally indistinct; sides fuscous cinnamon; rump sayal brown shaded with smoke gray; ventral portions white; upper surface of tail fuscous black, ventral surface ochraceous, lateral hairs with four alternate color bands, black, ochraceous, black, buff. Skull large; incisors heavy as in *E. dorsalis*, 1.8 mm. in anteroposterior width.

Remarks.—The heavy incisors, large skull, large size, and distinct dorsal stripes distinguish *umbrinus* from all other kinds of chipmunks in Idaho.

Records of occurrence.—Specimens examined, 17, as follows: *Bannock County:* ¼ mi. W Copenhagen Basin, 1. *Bear Lake County:* N. rim Copenhagen Basin, Wasatch Mountains, 9; W. rim Copenhagen Basin, 7. Additional record (Howell, 1929:95): *Bonneville County:* Big Hole Mountains (near Irwin).

Eutamias dorsalis utahensis Merriam
UTAH CLIFF CHIPMUNK

Eutamias dorsalis utahensis Merriam, Proc. Biol. Soc. Washington, 11:210. July 1, 1897. Type from Ogden, Weber County, Utah.

Distribution.—In Idaho, recorded only from the juniper-covered hills east of Raft River Valley.

Description.—Size medium; general dorsal coloration pale smoke gray; median dorsal stripe fuscous or nearly black, lateral stripes indistinct; dark head stripes fuscous, prominent; ears large, lined with grayish hairs; postauricular patches large, grayish white; sides and upper surfaces of feet cinnamon buff; tail long, between 60 and 75 per cent of length of head and body, bushy, grizzled fuscous blackish above, lateral hairs banded in following sequence; basally blackish, then cinnamon buff, blackish, whitish; mid-ventral hairs of tail cinnamon buff from bases to tips. External measurements of three adult males and of four adult females from near Bridge average, respectively, 215-82-33 and 219-93-33. Skull smoothly rounded; incisors heavy, 1.8 mm. in anteroposterior width; posteroventral margin of maxillary plate of zygoma terminating on a plane between M^1 and Pm^4 (in all other *Eutamias* in Idaho the margin terminates between Pm^3 and Pm^4).

Remarks.—The affinities of the Utah Cliff Chipmunk lie with the *Eutamias townsendii* group which occurs in California, Oregon, and Washington. It is pre-eminently an inhabitant of rocky situations in the semi-arid portions of southwestern North America. In Idaho, where the species reaches its northernmost limit of distribution, it occurs in the juniper-clad mountains to the east of Raft River Valley (Black Pine Mountain).

It usually is a shy creature and lacks much of the curiosity exhibited by the common *amoenus* chipmunk of the mountains. Its general habits have been discussed in part by Cary (1911:81), Davis (1934:20-22), and Merriam (1897:211). Nothing is known concerning its breeding habits in Idaho.

Records of occurrence.—Specimens examined, 6, from near Bridge, Cassia County (Biol. Surv. coll.).

Genus **Tamiasciurus** Trouessart
Red Squirrels or Pine Squirrels

Medium-sized, arboreal squirrels; eyes and ears large; feet large, four functional toes in front, five behind, claws recurved, sharp, modified for climbing; tail semibushy, about 60 per cent of length of head and body; general dorsal coloration reddish or brownish; white ventrally. Skull typically squirrellike; interorbital region nearly as wide as cranium; auditory bullae large, internally subdivided into three incomplete chambers; stapedial artery large, enclosed in complete, osseous tube; cheek teeth brachydont, rooted, roughly quadrangular above and below; Pm^3 reduced to a mere splint. Cowper's glands minute; penile duct and bulbar gland absent; penis long, filiform, os penis lacking (Mossman, *et. al., 1932*).

Red squirrels are typically arboreal in habit, but a considerable portion of their time is spent on the ground. They are strictly diurnal, being most active in early morning and late afternoon. Their distribution in Idaho coincides closely with the distribution of coniferous forests. No squirrels occur, however, in the forested portions in extreme south-central Idaho and in the Great Basin in general. This circumstance perhaps is due to barriers, deserts, which prevent their movement in a westward direction from the Rocky Mountains. It suggests, also, that they migrated from the north into the central Rocky Mountain region *after* the mountains in the Great Basin were isolated by desert conditions.

Red squirrels are active throughout the year. Twining (MS) found them active in January in the Sawtooth Mountains when four feet of snow covered the ground; in winter, trappers in that area frequently catch them in traps set for marten. The breeding season begins in late winter, often before the snow is gone, and by late spring the six or seven young are born. At first they are blind and helpless, but growth is rapid. By July 1 they are nearly half grown and by August they have attained approximately adult size.

Although I have found them to be partial to the seeds of conifers, their diet is highly varied as is shown by the following excerpt from Hatt's (1929:111) monograph which contains a wealth of information concerning the habits and life history of another subspecies in the eastern United States: "In early spring the red squirrel is largely dependent on the buried stores of the previous season and on the winter buds of trees, just as it is in the depth of the winter. Following the thaw, the flowing sap, leaf buds, flower buds and the bark of trees offer variety in its diet. Flowers and leaves follow in their turn; thereupon nesting birds and insect life furnish certain additional items of food to the squirrel. . . . As summer advances nuts, fruits, cones and mushrooms become increasingly important items in its bill of fare. The advent of the fall season is accompanied by increased activity on the part of the squirrels in storing all late ripening nuts, fruits, cones and mushrooms."

The species *T. hudsonicus*, consisting of fourteen geographic races, occurs over most of boreal North America except along the Pacific coast of the United States and in the southern Rocky Mountains where closely related species occur. In Idaho, the red squirrel has differentiated into two geographic races which seem not to intergrade within the bounds of the state. These are distinguished chiefly by the color of the tail; in *richardsoni* it is nearly black, in *ventorum* olivaceous or yellowish.

Tamiasciurus hudsonicus richardsoni (Bachman)
RICHARDSON RED SQUIRREL

Sciurus richardsoni Bachman, Proc. Zool. Soc. London, 1838:100. Type from Wildhorse Creek, head of Big Lost River, Custer County, Idaho.

Distribution.—In Idaho, throughout the timbered areas from the Sawtooth Mountains northward (see map, fig. 16).

Description.—This race is characterized by a tendency toward melanism. Color (summer): Uniform olivaceous above; forefeet, arms, shoulder, and lateral portions of hind limbs ochraceous; lateral line deep black; tail grayish-black below and above except for the deep reddish median area. In winter, darker, with broad dorsal band of rufous; ochraceous areas of summer pelage replaced by sooty gray except on tail; prominent ear tufts black. External measurements of eight specimens from central Idaho average 323-124-51-27.

Records of occurrence.—Specimens examined, 56, as follows: *Bonner County:* 5 mi. W Cocolalla, 1. *Latah County:* Cedar Mountain, 9 (Chas. R. Conner Mus.). *Clearwater County:* Orofino, 1 (Chas. R. Conner Mus.). *Idaho County:* Castle Creek R. S., 1. *Adams County:* 1 mi. N Bear Cr. R. S., 10 (8 in Ralph Ellis coll.); ½ mi. E Black Lake, 2 (Ralph Ellis coll.); 3 mi. E Payette Lake, 3. *Valley County:* 5 mi. E Warm Lake, 1. *Washington County:* 1 mi. NE Heath, 7 (5 in Ralph Ellis coll.). *Custer County:* head Pahsimeroi River, 5; Mill Cr., 14 mi. W Challis, 4; Raney Cr., 4 mi. S Custer, 1; Summit Cr., head Big Lost River, 3. *Blaine County:* Galena Summit, Sawtooth Mountains, 2 (Davis coll.); Baker Cr., 12 mi. N Ketchum, 4; Pettit Lake, 2. Additional records (Allen, 1898:265, unless otherwise stated): *Bonner County:* Soldier Cr., Priest Lake (D. R. Dickey coll.). *Kootenai County:* Coeur d'Alene; Fort Sherman. *Shoshone County:* Mullan. *Benewah County:* Camp Kootenai; St. Mary's (St. Maries?). *Latah County:* Moscow. *Lewis County:* Craig Mountains. *Idaho County:* Fiddle Creek; Seven Devils Mountains. *Lemhi County:* Birch Creek; Lemhi Mountains (Timber Creek and Eight Mile Canyon) (Merriam, 1891:51). *Custer County:* Alturas Lake; head Big Wood River (Merriam, *ibid.*); Sawtooth City (near Alturas Lake). *Butte County:* Lost River Mountains (Merriam, *ibid.*).

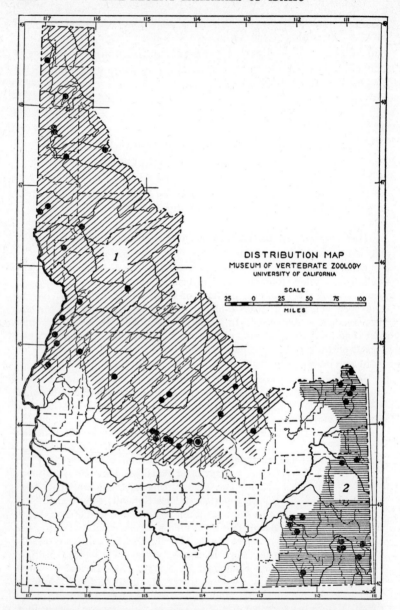

DISTRIBUTION MAP
MUSEUM OF VERTEBRATE ZOOLOGY
UNIVERSITY OF CALIFORNIA

SCALE
25   0   25   50   75   100
MILES

FIG. 16. Map showing the distribution of red squirrels in Idaho. Dots indicate localities whence specimens have been examined or recorded. 1. *Tamiasciurus hudsonicus richardsoni*, 2. *Tamiasciurus hudsonicus ventorum.*

Tamiasciurus hudsonicus ventorum (Allen)
WIND RIVER MOUNTAINS RED SQUIRREL

Sciurus hudsonicus ventorum Allen, Bull. Amer. Mus. Nat. Hist., 10:263. July 22, 1898. Type from South Pass City, Wind River Mountains, Fremont County, Wyoming.

Distribution.—In Idaho, from Montana line near Henrys Lake south through forested areas to Utah; west as far as Pocatello and Malad (see map, fig. 16).

Comparison.—In summer pelage the lighter olivaceous dorsal coloration, usually indistinct lateral line, and lack of predominantly blackish tail coloration readily distinguish this race from *richardsoni*. In winter pelage the contrast is even greater. Then, the general dorsal coloration is distinctly ochraceous reddish; the tail heavily suffused with yellows and reds; pelage shorter. Ten adults from Fremont County, Idaho, average, in external measurements, 336-130-51-26.

Records of occurrence.—Specimens examined, 48, as follows: *Fremont County:* N. Fork Snake River, 10 mi. SW Island Park, 13 (Amer. Mus.); 3-5 mi. S Montana Line at Mount Jefferson, 4 (Amer. Mus.). *Bonneville County:* S. side South Fork, 3 mi. W Swan Valley, 1; Big Hole Mountains, 8 mi. NE Swan Valley, 1. *Bannock County:* Camp Tendoy, 15 mi. SE Pocatello, 5 (2 in Ralph Ellis coll.); Indian Cr., 4 mi. S Pocatello, 3; N. Fork Pocatello Cr., 6½ mi. NE Pocatello, 1; Schutt's Mine, 6. *Oneida County:* Malad City, 1 (Los Angeles Mus.). *Franklin County:* Wasatch Mountains, 2 mi. E Strawberry Cr. R. S., 1. *Bear Lake County:* Montpelier, 1 (Los Angeles Mus.); North Canyon, Wasatch Mountains, 1; Copenhagen Basin, 11. Additional records: *Fremont County:* Henrys Lake (Merriam, 1873:663); Island Park, upper Snake River; Trude (D. R. Dickey coll.). *Bear Lake County:* Crow Creek (head of); Preuss Mountains (Allen, 1898:263).

Genus **Glaucomys** Thomas
Flying Squirrels

Flying squirrels are characterized by long, soft, silky pelage; large eyes and ears; extension of integument laterad between fore and hind legs as a "flying membrane"; tail densely furred and flattened dorsoventrally; soles of hind feet, except for pads, furred; claws sharp, but relatively weak. Brain case rounded, relatively smooth; rostrum short; auditory bullae large, noncancellous, internally subdivided into three incomplete chambers; stapedial artery large, enclosed in complete osseous tube; P³ prominent;

limb segments relatively long; pubic rami directed caudad, as in bats; pubic symphysis short.

Unlike pine squirrels *(Tamiasciurus)*, flying squirrels are strictly nocturnal and spend the day in their nests which usually are placed in hollow stumps or old nest cavities of the larger woodpeckers. Usually male and female occupy separate nests. At Heath, Borell (MS) captured a female and her three helpless young in a hollow, rotten stump which stood on a hillside amidst dead trees, stumps, and down logs. The nest was composed of dry bark and was in a cavity, roughly nine inches in diameter, about five feet from the ground. In addition to nests of this sort, Cowan (1936) found that flying squirrels in southern British Columbia construct globular "outside" nests which probably are occupied only in spring and summer. These usually were placed close to the boles of the trees from five to thirty feet above the ground.

Available data indicate that in Idaho a single litter of young is born yearly, and that in late May or June. Howell (1918:9) states that in the Bitterroot region of Montana large embryos were found in a female collected May 17; a nest located June 11 contained nursing young. The young found by Borell on June 15 were in juvenile pelage and still had their eyes closed; the lateral hairs on the tail are short, and the "flying membranes" are almost naked. The young are hairless at birth; Cowan records the finding of hairless young which he took to be not over three days old.

These creatures eat a variety of foods: lichens, nuts of various conifers, and fruits and leaves of a number of deciduous plants. Sumner (1927) found that flying squirrels in the San Bernardino Mountains, California, were fond of prunes, and he collected a number of specimens in traps baited with this fruit. Cowan, in conversation, stated that he has found dried or smoked fish an excellent bait; William Keubli, Clayton, Idaho, reports *(in litt.)* that he has caught numbers of them each winter in meat-baited marten sets.

Two closely related races of the species *Glaucomys sabrinus* occur within the boundaries of Idaho, where they are more or less restricted to the more heavily forested mountainous areas.

Glaucomys sabrinus bangsi (Rhoads)
BANGS FLYING SQUIRREL

Sciuropterus alpinus bangsi Rhoads, Proc. Acad. Nat. Sci. Philadelphia, 1897:321. June, 1897. Type from Raymond, Idaho County, Idaho.

Synonyms.—Sciuropterus volans sabrinus, Merriam, 1891:51; *Glaucomys bullatus* Howell, 1915:113; *Glaucomys sabrinus bullatus* Howell, 1918:51.

Distribution.—In Idaho, from Idaho County south through the mountainous portions of the state to Utah (see map, fig. 17).

Description.—Dorsal coloration varying from wood brown to ochraceous buff, individual hairs sooty basally; ventral coloration varying from nearly white, through plumbeous white, to ochraceous; cheeks lead gray; eyelids black; upper surfaces of feet dusky, lower surfaces whitish; ears dusky, naked, or nearly so; upper surfaces of "flying membranes" blackish. Color in winter slightly darker. External measurements of five adult females from Adams and Washington counties average 325-148-42-21.

Comparisons.—G. s. bangsi differs from *G. s. latipes* in smaller size and lighter color.

Remarks.—A third race of flying squirrel has been ascribed to Idaho by Howell (1915, 1918) with a range nearly coincident with that of *bangsi.* This race, *G. s. bullatus,* was thought to differ from *bangsi* in larger size, larger skull, more highly inflated auditory bullae, and brighter, more pinkish cinnamon, dorsal coloration. Subsequently, Whitlow and Hall (1933:254) contended this was not a valid race and in support of their contention pointed out the inconstancy of color, among other features, in flying squirrels from near Pocatello. I find also that June-taken specimens from Heath (western Idaho) are pinkish cinnamon dorsally, the color ascribed to *bullatus,* but in size of external parts, skull and auditory bullae fall within the range of variation ascribed to *bangsi.* The same color is found in an individual from Alturas Lake (central Idaho), the type locality of *bullatus,* and also in a June-taken specimen from near Pocatello (southern Idaho). In each of these the bullae and external proportions are as in *bangsi.* Specimens from Smith Mountain (about twenty-five miles northeast of Heath), collected in June and July, are wood brown dorsally, as are October-taken specimens from near Pocatello. The ventral coloration likewise varies irrespec-

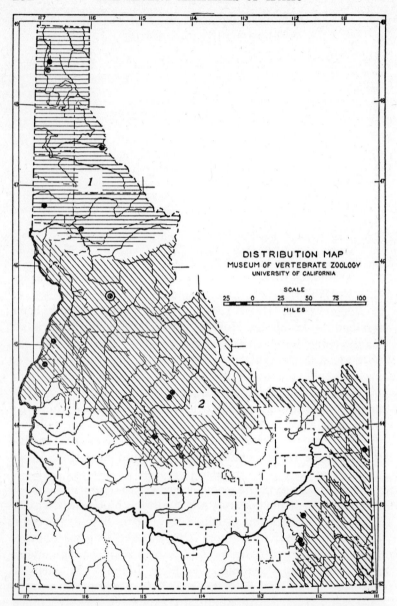

FIG. 17. Map showing the distribution of flying squirrels in Idaho. Dots indicate localities whence specimens have been examined or recorded. 1. *Glaucomys sabrinus latipes*, 2. *Glaucomys sabrinus bangsi*.

tive of age, sex, season, and geographic position, ranging from cinnamon-washed to nearly white. If one were to segregate these specimens on color alone, the series from Heath would stand with the single specimen from Alturas Lake; those from Smith Mountain and Camp Tendoy (near Pocatello) would make up the second group.

As regards the diagnostic value of size of auditory bullae in this species, Whitlow and Hall *(ibid.)* observed that in flying squirrels from Camp Tendoy these structures were large in some individuals, small in others. Size of bullae is not correlated with age, sex, color, or geographic position. Large bullae are present in both sexes, young and old, but the important point is that they are not found in all, or nearly all, individuals from a given locality. For example, of nine specimens from two localities near Stanley (central Idaho), a male from one locality and a female from the other place have large bullae. At Camp Tendoy, one individual of four, a young female, has large bullae; at Smith Mountain the ratio is approximately the same. This state of affairs occurs also in specimens from the Bitterroot Valley, Montana. These ratios suggest that we here are dealing with a single Mendelian character involving one dominant gene and its recessive allelomorph.

External measurements and size of skull are not correlated with color or geographic position. An old female (no. 8720, Ellis coll.) from Smith Mountain has large bullae, a hind foot 46 mm. in length, and a skull 44.5 mm. in occipito-nasal length. These measurements are above the extremes given by Howell *(op. cit.,* p. 52) for *bullatus,* but the color is wood brown, not the pinkish cinnamon ascribed to *bullatus.* An old male (no. 2430, Davis coll.) from Cabin Creek, near Stanley, has large bullae and a skull 43 mm. in length; the hind foot is only 40 mm. in length and the color is wood brown. Each of the characters ascribed to *bullatus* appears independently of the others. It is generally known that rarely if ever do two subspecies of a single mammalian species have coincident ranges unless ecologic differentiation has taken place. No evidence is available which indicates that the large flying squirrels with large bullae are ecologically different from their smaller relatives with normal bullae. Because both kinds occur in the same area and can be taken in the same line of traps, the evidence is rather to the contrary. Therefore, and in view of the facts presented above, *G. a. bullatus* is here treated as a synonym of *G. s. bangsi* which has priority.

Records of occurrence.—Specimens examined, 27, as follows: *Adams County:* 1 mi. N Bear Cr. R. S., 3 (Ralph Ellis coll.). *Washington County:* 1 mi. NE Heath, 5 (Ralph Ellis coll.). *Custer County:* Cabin Creek, 21 mi. NE Stanley, 4; Five-mile Cr., 25 mi. NE Stanley, 5 (1 in Alex Walker coll.). *Blaine County:* Alturas Lake, 1; Baker Cr., 12 mi. N Ketchum, 2 (1 in Davis coll.). *Teton County:* Driggs, 1 (B. Y .U., Zool. Dept. coll.). *Bannock County:* W. slope Scout Mountain, near Camp Tendoy, 4; Schutt's Mine, 1; Justice Park, 1. Additional records (Howell, 1918:39): *Idaho County* (=Raymond, type locality). *Blaine County:* Ketchum.

Glaucomys sabrinus latipes Howell
BROAD-FOOTED FLYING SQUIRREL

Glaucomys sabrinus latipes Howell, Proc. Biol. Soc. Washington, 28:112. May 27, 1915. Type from Glacier, British Columbia, Canada.
Distribution.—In Idaho, north of Idaho County (see map, fig. 17).
Description.—Similar to *G. s. bangsi*, but larger and darker.
Records of occurrence.—Specimens examined, 2, from the Chas. R. Conner Mus., as follows: *Latah County:* Cedar Mountain, 1. *Clearwater County:* Orofino, 1. Additional records (Howell, 1918:49): *Bonner County:* Coolin; Priest Lake. *Shoshone County:* Mullan.

Family GEOMYIDAE
POCKET GOPHERS

Specialized burrowing rodents with large claws on front feet, external fur-lined cheek pouches, short ears, small eyes, short tail, fore and hind legs of about equal length, upper incisors projecting beyond lips. Skull sturdy; cheek teeth rootless, four in number, with transverse enamel plates; auditory bullae usually relatively small, angular; external auditory canal relatively long; stapedial artery small, enclosed in a complete osseous tube.

In North America west of the Rockies all members of this family are assigned to the genus *Thomomys*. They may be segregated into two distinct groups. One group is characterized by the relatively great breadth of the rostrum, presence of large sphenorbital fissure, in having the anterior opening of the infraorbital canal on a plane with, or anterior to, the incisive foramina, and in that the anterior prism of Pm_4 is rounded in outline. To this group belong the members of the "heavy rostrum group" as recognized by Bailey (1915:32-33). It would include all the large-bodied forms of the genus. The second group is characterized by relative narrowness of the rostrum, absence of the sphenorbital fissure, in having the anterior opening of infraorbital canal posterior to the incisive foramina, and in that the anterior prism of Pm_4 is triangular in outline. To this group belong the members of the "slender rostrum group" as Bailey (*ibid.*) designated them.

Pocket gophers, especially the males, tend to increase in size with age. The ultimate size attained appears to be correlated directly with the type of soil inhabited, and indirectly with altitude. At high elevations where the soil usually is shallow and rocky, or at lower elevations where the same general environmental conditions prevail, races and individuals of the genus tend to be small. In places of this kind the skulls of males and females often are indistinguishable; they are smooth and lack ridges. They appear to be juvenile in character, and in many respects they have not developed beyond the subadult stage of forms living under better environmental conditions. If one compares individuals from soils that are poorer for pocket gophers with gophers from progressively better and deeper soils, the size of both sexes is found generally to increase, the male more than the female. Under optimum conditions the actual weight of the skull may average two or even three times that of individuals which live amid adverse conditions. In the lower, deeper soils sexual dimorphism is evident and the skulls of both sexes are angular in outline and have well-developed sagittal, lambdoidal, and temporal ridges.

This general reduction in size at higher altitude is illustrated by specimens from near Pocatello, Idaho. There, the species *Thomomys quadratus* occurs altitudinally from 4400 feet on the floor of Portneuf Valley up to over 7000 feet in the Bannock Mountains. Individuals taken from the valley are considerably larger than those from higher altitudes. The skulls are massive, angular, ridged, have prognathous incisor teeth, and the males are much larger than the females. Individuals taken at progressively higher altitudes are smaller, the skull tends to be less angular and ridged, incisors less prognathous, and the degree of sexual dimorphism is reduced. Taking the product of three dimensions of the skull, basilar length, zygomatic breadth, and palato-frontal depth, in centimeters, as an index of size, the following results were obtained:

	Males	Females	Difference
4500 feet	12.95 cc. (3)*	10.35 cc. (3)	2.60 cc.
5000 feet	13.60 cc. (4)	9.30 cc. (3)	4.30 cc.
5800 feet	10.60 cc. (2)	8.80 cc. (2)	1.80 cc.
6300 feet	9.20 cc. (6)	8.40 cc. (6)	.80 cc.
7000 feet	9.20 cc. (2)	8.50 cc. (1)	.70 cc.

Certain exceptions to the correlations indicated above are to be noted in these figures. Males from 5000 feet are larger than those from 4500 feet; the female from 7000 feet is larger than the average from 6300 feet. These exceptions do not invalidate the general principle because age differences in the males and too few specimens in the females probably account for the deviations from the expected size. A reduction in length of body, length of hind foot, and length of tail accompanies a reduction in "volume" of the skull.

Similar results were obtained in a study of another species, *Thomomys bottae*. In Nevada, this species occurs on the floor of Monitor Valley, 6900 feet, and also on the adjacent Toquima Mountains which rise to over 10,000 feet. Individuals taken at altitudes ranging from 9000 to 10,000 feet on the mountain are considerably smaller than those from the valley; specimens from Meadow Creek Canyon, at 8000 feet on the east side of the mountain, are intermediate in size. Sexual dimorphism is pronounced in specimens from the valley; it is slight in those from above 9000 feet. These facts are evident from the following tabulation.

---

* Indicates the number of specimens averaged.

	Males	Females	Difference
6900 feet	17.75 cc. (6)	12.50 cc. (6)	5.25 cc.
8000 feet	13.20 cc. (2)	10.60 cc. (2)	2.60 cc.
9000 to 10,000 feet..	10.60 cc. (5)	9.20 cc. (2)	1.40 cc.

Aside from consistently smaller size, specimens of both *quadratus* and *bottae* from the higher altitudes are but little different from animals living at low levels. The most significant difference is found in the relatively shorter rostrum in specimens from high altitudes. This I interpret as a neotenous condition, that is to say, one which results from arrested development. Numerous studies have shown that the rostrum in subadults is consistently relatively, as well as actually, shorter than in adults.

A similar transition from large to small size is found in every area studied in the Great Basin where one species occupies both the valley floor and the adjacent mountain. Because of this, it becomes increasingly difficult to reconcile present practices in taxonomy with the actual facts of variation. The tendency of certain students to assign all the populations of pocket gophers occurring on different, isolated mountain tops in southern Idaho to one subspecies and those occurring in the lowlands to another defeats the purpose of systematics. To me, it is illogical to assume that the several alpine populations are closely related *inter se* and genetically different, as a unit, from the populations of the same species occurring in the valleys. Nor does it seem logical to assume that the populations of a species in two valleys separated by a high mountain range on which small individuals occur are genetically related *inter se* and at the same time genetically distinct from the smaller alpine individuals.

Various authors have referred the alpine populations in southern Idaho to *Thomomys uinta* or *Thomomys quadratus uinta* and those in the lowlands to *Thomomys bridgeri* or *Thomomys quadratus bridgeri*. In doing this the topography and geologic history of the area probably was not considered. In this region the mountains certainly are older than the genus *Thomomys* and consequently we cannot assume that populations now restricted to alpine areas once occupied a continuous range which subsequently was disrupted

by geologic changes. Nor can we assume that the population of large pocket gophers moved in and usurped the
lowland portions of a range once occupied by the smaller
animals because such an interpretation must assume a divergence and differentiation of the two at a time earlier
than that which is suggested by cranial characters. Furthermore, it must assume a migration of the large individuals
over high passes in order to explain their present distribution in southeastern Idaho.

In interpreting the past history of *Thomomys quadratus*
in southeastern Idaho I have assumed that during the
Pleistocene most of the mountains were glaciated and the
lower valleys were filled with water so that the intermediate
altitudes alone were available to pocket gophers. It is well
known that the yearly increase of a successful species is
greater than the carrying capacity of the area occupied,
and that as a result of population pressure every available
niche is sought out and occupied. As the glaciers receded
and the lakes decreased in extent, additional territory became available both above and below the former range. This
new territory was occupied by the surplus of the yearly
increase. Those gophers that moved downhill encountered
deeper and richer soils and consequently could grow larger.
Those that moved uphill found conditions progressively
more adverse; the soil was shallower and rockier and plant
food was less abundant, though sufficient to maintain life.
Only individuals with small bodies could survive amid such
conditions. Whether size *per se* be heritable or due to onto-
genetic factors is not of prime importance to the question
at issue because the end result in either instance, small
size, is the limiting factor in shallow soil. Ultimately, from
a population of medium-sized gophers, both the mountains
and the lowlands became populated, the former by small
individuals, the latter by large ones.

Such an interpretation explains many facts of distribution. Each high mountain harbors a population of
dwarfed individuals, in each valley the gophers are large,
and at middle altitudes of intermediate size. The alpine
populations, though on isolated mountain tops, resemble one
another more than they do those in the valleys, yet it is

difficult to conceive of them as being subspecifically related *inter se* and at the same time subspecifically distinct from those at lower elevations. The similar cranial characters of the two extremes, the gradation from large size to small, and the topography and geologic history of the regions they inhabit lend support to this interpretation. For this reason I choose to refer both the alpine and lowland forms in southeastern Idaho to the same subspecies, *bridgeri*, and restrict the name *uinta* to the alpine form occurring in Utah. Whether small individuals would increase in size if transplanted to valley conditions, or whether they would retain their identity is not known. An experiment designed to test this would be well worth while.

Knowledge of the distribution and relationships of the various kinds of pocket gophers in Idaho aids in understanding the relationship and distribution of many of the named kinds of *Thomomys* which occur in the intermountain area outside the political boundaries of that state. In the past, the Snake River has been an important factor in determining the present distribution of the various races. From Blackfoot west to the Oregon boundary the river acts as an impassable barrier to pocket gophers, restricting one species, *Thomomys quadratus*, to the south side of the river and another species, *Thomomys talpoides*, to the north side. At no place have I found evidence that either species has crossed to the opposite side of the river. It is true that *Thomomys fuscus fuscus* (the race herein referred to as *Thomomys talpoides fuscus*) has been recorded (Bailey, 1936) from the Blue Mountains of Oregon, that is, on the southwest side of the river, but this, I think, was an error in identification because all of the specimens that I examined from that region belong to the species *Thomomys quadratus* which elsewhere occurs all along that side of the river in southern Idaho. The fact that in both areas where *Thomomys townsendii* occurs in Idaho, it is found on both sides of the Snake River on first consideration seems to show that the river does not act as a barrier to this animal but in the discussion of it beyond, I shall point out how the river probably affected it as well as the other kinds of pocket gophers.

Along the upper reaches of the Snake River from Idaho Falls northeastward to Yellowstone National Park this clear-cut geographic separation of *quadratus* and *talpoides* does not exist; both species occur on both sides of the river, sometimes together in the same fields. Factors which permit the mingling of the two in this area and not farther to the west are (1) reduction in size of the streams toward the headwaters, thus permitting individuals to cross in times of low water when sand bars are exposed, and (2) a more rigorous climate characterized by a heavy snowfall under cover of which the animals might cross also on the ice.

Pocket gophers are active throughout the year, in winter as well as in summer. From Blackfoot westward the Snake River averages six hundred feet in width and flows through a region which has mild winters and relatively little snow; the river may freeze over for a brief period in winter. North and east of Idaho Falls the river divides into three branches. The South Fork is the largest branch and averages about one hundred feet in width except near the Wyoming boundary where it becomes narrower. Here the deep, lasting snow covering the frozen streams 4 to 6 feet deep affords the necessary means by which pocket gophers can cross from one side to the other.

It is in this area of intermingling that I have found evidence of intergradation between *Thomomys fuscus fuscus* and *Thomomys idahoensis;* also between *Thomomys idahoensis* and *Thomomys pygmaeus*. In its typical form, *T. idahoensis* occurs in the desert areas north and west of Idaho Falls. There it is pale yellowish gray in color, has highly inflated auditory bullae, and six pairs of mammae. At Menan, Jefferson County, on the *east* side of the river, the color tends toward brownish and the auditory bullae are smaller. On the north side of the South Fork, about forty miles southeast of Menan, the coloration is distinctly that of *fuscus,* the mammae are in five pairs *(four in typical fuscus),* and the auditory bullae and length of hind foot are intermediate in size. Specimens from Menan, Shelley, Blackfoot, and Alridge provide a transitional series between *idahoensis* and *pygmaeus*. Specimens from Shelley and Blackfoot have the pale coloration of *idahoensis* and the small skull of *pygmaeus;* the specimens from Menan are intermediate in cranial characters, but tend more toward typical *idahoensis.*

Although Bailey *(ibid.)* treated *idahoensis* and *pygmaeus* as full species, he placed both in the *talpoides* group. These two and *Thomomys talpoides clusius* from Wyoming are closely related as shown by the similar construction of the skulls. I have not seen specimens which demonstrate geographic intergradation between *clusius* and *pygmaeus,* but I judge that specimens from critical localities in west-central Wyoming will show this, and also intergradation between *clusius and ocius.* Because both *idahoensis* and *pygmaeus* are clearly related to *talpoides,* through *clusius,* and since specimens from Idaho demonstrate intergradation between *idahoensis* and *pygmaeus,* they all are here treated as geographic races of the species *talpoides.* Intergradation occurs also between *idahoensis* and *fuscus.* Accordingly *fuscus* is reduced from specific to subspecific rank under the older name *talpoides.*

Near Victor, typical *Thomomys talpoides fuscus* and *Thomomys quadratus bridgeri* occur side by side in the same fields. No specimens taken indicate that intergradation occurs between the two.

In Idaho, *Thomomys townsendii* occurs on both sides of the Snake River in two widely separated localities, one in the vicinity of Pocatello, the other in the Snake River valley from King Hill westward into Oregon. Other species, *quadratus* on the south and *talpoides* on the north, occur along the river between these two areas, and the population of *townsendii* near Pocatello is completely isolated from the remainder of the species.

To judge from the present distribution and the meager fossil record, *Thomomys townsendii* and *Thomomys quadratus* moved into Idaho from the south; the *talpoides* group probably moved in from the north and east.

Pocket gophers are highly specialized for digging and spend most of their time underground. Their burrows vary in detail, but the general plan of structure includes a main burrow from which numerous side branches diverge. Occasionally these reunite with the main burrow but generally end either blindly in the ground or at the surface near mounds of earth. A nest cell usually is present. Unless the occupant of such a system is actually engaged in transporting earth to the surface, each opening is filled with an earth plug. When snow is of sufficient depth it also provides a medium through which the gophers burrow. The characteristic earth cores left by receding snow in spring represent old snow tunnels which were filled with earth brought from underground burrows. This practice of filling unused portions of the burrow system is carried out at other seasons of the year, especially during the dry period. Except in cultivated areas, little harm and much good results from the burrowing activities of pocket gophers. Grinnell (1923) pointed out some of the benefits derived from the activities of burrowing rodents in the way of soil formation and water conservation.

During the breeding season both male and female often occupy the same burrow, and a little later the female and her young, but at other times they appear to be solitary in habit. More than one litter of young is known to be reared by a single female each year and it is not uncommon to find a pregnant female still caring for young of an earlier litter.

Key to Adult Female Pocket Gophers of Idaho*

1 Size large; skull robust, upper incisors prognathous; sphenorbital fissure present; anterior opening of infraorbital canal anterior to, or on a plane with, incisive foramina; anterior prism of Pm_4 rounded in outline.

  2 Hind foot over 35 mm.; nasals over 16 mm.
    T. t. townsendii, p. 244

  2' Hind foot under 34 mm.; length of nasals under 16 mm.

    3 Basilar length averaging 39 mm.; coloration darker; restricted area near Pocatello.   T. t. similis, p. 248

    3' Basilar length averaging 37 mm.; coloration ochraceous buff; restricted to northern Owyhee County.
        T. t. owyhensis, p. 247

---

* Females vary less individually than males and therefore seem more reliable for determining subspecies. Males average consistently larger than females in most races of *Thomomys*.

1' Size small; upper incisors prognathous or opisthognathous; sphenorbital fissure absent; anterior opening of infraorbital foramen posterior to incisive foramina; anterior prism of Pm_4 triangular in outline.

    4 Skull rugged, angular, ridged, upper incisors usually prognathous; plane of lambdoidal crest passing posterior to interparietal, or nearly so.

        5 Color dark, some shade of dark brown.

            6 Posterior margin of nasals distinctly notched; foramen magnum usually wider than high.

                T. q. bridgeri, p. 258

            6' Posterior margin of nasals truncate; foramen magnum usually as high as wide, nearly quadrangular.

                T. q. quadratus, p. 256

        5' Color light, near ochraceous buff.   **T. q. fisheri, p. 258**

    4' Skull smooth, rounded, upper incisors slightly prognathous or opisthognathous; plane of lambdoidal crest passing near middle of interparietal; occipital region rounded, supraoccipital taking part in roof of cranium.

        7 Brain case distinctly sagittate; upper incisors opisthognathous; mammae usually in six pairs; hind foot less than 25 mm.

            8 Total length near 185 mm.; auditory bullae highly inflated; general color light grayish.

                T. t. idahoensis, p. 251

            8' Total length near 170 mm.; auditory bullae normal; general color usually brownish. **T. t. pygmaeus, p. 252**

        7' Brain case narrow, but not sagittate; upper incisors slightly prognathous; mammae usually in four pairs; hind foot more than 25 mm.

            9 Dorsal coloration fuscous; hind foot near 27 mm.

                T. t. fuscus, p. 254

            9' Dorsal coloration deep chestnut; hind foot near 29 mm.

                T. t. saturatus, p. 256

Genus **Thomomys** Wied
Pocket Gophers

Thomomys townsendii townsendii (Bachman)
TOWNSEND POCKET GOPHER

Geomys townsendii Bachman (from Richardson's MS), Jour. Acad. Nat. Sci. Philadelphia, 8:105. 1839. Type from near Nampa, Canyon County, Idaho.

Synonym.—Thomomys nevadensis atrogriseus Bailey, 1914:118 (type locality, Nampa, Idaho).

Distribution.—From near King Hill, Elmore County, Idaho, west along north side of Snake River to Weiser, thence into valleys of Malheur and Owyhee rivers of northeastern Oregon and along south side of Snake River east as far as Homedale, Owyhee County, Idaho (see map, fig. 18).

Description.—The largest pocket gopher in Idaho; males larger than females; typically darker than sepia above, light cinnamon buff below; nose sooty black; postauricular patches black; tail and upper surfaces of feet, chin, and lateral lips white. Skull: Large, angular; zygomatic arch heavy; premaxillae narrow; rostral pits absent; nasals long, extending posteriorly beyond frontal tongues; dentition heavy. External measurements of 4 adult females and 6 adult males from near the type locality average, respectively, 276-90-37 and 294-92-38.

Remarks.—For comparisons, see under accounts of *T. t. similis* and *T. t. owyhensis.* The range of *T. t. townsendii* is transected by the Snake River where it forms the boundary between Idaho and Oregon. Typical individuals of this race occur on the Great Basin side of the river at many localities in Oregon, but at only one (Homedale) in Idaho. From Murphy east along the south side of the river to Indian Cove, another race, *owyhensis,* is found, the range of which is separated from that of *townsendii* on the south side of the river by a northward projection of the plateau between Marsing and Murphy. Since the Snake River, along much of its course, now acts as an impassable barrier to populations of this genus, an explanation of the present occurrence of *T. t. townsendii* on both sides of the river naturally directs one's attention to conditions in the past.

In discussing the geology of this area, Hay (1927) suggests that at the beginning of the Tertiary the Snake River occupied a broad, deep valley and that at some time later,

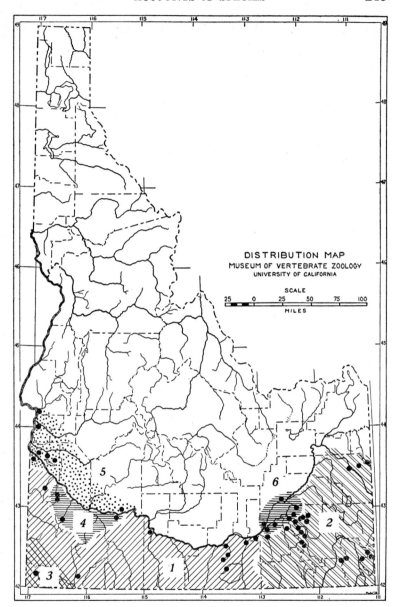

FIG. 18. Map showing the distribution of some pocket gophers in Idaho. Dots indicate localities whence specimens have been examined or recorded. 1. *Thomomys quadratus quadratus*, 2. *Thomomys quadratus bridgeri*, 3. *Thomomys quadratus fisheri*, 4. *Thomomys townsendii owyhensis*, 5. *Thomomys townsendii townsendii*, 6. *Thomomys townsendii similis*.

now supposed to be in the Eocene, the river became obstructed in western Idaho and eastern Oregon by flows of lava or by elevation of the land. One result was the formation of an immense lake which extended in a long curve eastward and northward nearly to the location of the southern boundary of Yellowstone National Park. In time this lake became partially filled by deposits brought down from the surrounding mountains and by volcanic dust. The beds thus laid down constitute what is now known as the Payette Formation. Remains of vertebrate animals have been found at many places in these sedimentary deposits. Cope gave to the more recent of these deposits the name Idaho Formation. Stratigraphically there appears to be no break in the sequence from the Payette Formation to the Idaho. Because of the apparently unquestionable presence, in the Idaho beds, of *Equus, Camelops minidokae,* the genus *Cervus, Bison alleni,* and two species of elephants, *Elephas imperator* and *E. columbi,* Hay refers the formation to Lower Pleistocene.

In late Pliocene and early Pleistocene, this large lake in western Idaho probably extended south into Oregon nearly to the northern limits of Lake Lahonton and existed at about the same times as lakes Lahonton (Nevada) and Bonneville (Utah). If, and when, the Snake River was blocked, the shore line of this lake and its contributary streams might have offered a means by which *T. t. townsendii* could have migrated to the area now occupied by it in western Idaho. Subsequently, hundreds of feet of sediment were deposited in the lake bed, and, after the water rose to a certain level, drainage to the westward along the general course of the present river was re-established. The reformed river may thus have separated the population of this race as we see it today. If this explanation of the separation into two portions of the single subspecies *T. t. townsendii* be accepted, we are led to the conclusion that the effects of isolation have been counteracted either by the homogeneity of the original population or by identical selective factors so that the now separated portions of the population, if they have changed at all, have undergone parallel evolutionary trends. As judged from a comparison of the crania of *T. t. townsendii* with the extinct *Thomomys vetus* from Fossil Lake, Oregon, the latter inference is more likely, because in all Pleistocene *Thomomys* from the Great Basin, the lingual faces of the cheek teeth are more rounded than in their Recent counterparts. This parallel evolution in the *quadratus-, bottae-,* and *townsendii*-groups is interesting, but the point is that change probably has occurred, possibly in the line of *T. t. townsendii* as well as in other stocks.

Specimens from Hammett, Elmore County, are below the mean size of typical *townsendii* and resemble in external appearance specimens of *owyhensis* from Indian Cove south of the Snake River. Differences in cranial characters, however, indicate that no mingling of *owyhensis* and this northern population of *townsendii* has taken place here. The only visible barrier to prevent this is the river which averages about 600 feet in width at this place.

The breeding habits of *townsendii* have been discussed in part by Horn (1923). Of 20 females collected in the vicinity of Vale, Oregon, from March 27 to April 1, 1921, 18 were pregnant and 9 of these showed signs of suckling an earlier litter. He concluded that each female of this race has at least two litters of young in close succession early in the season. None of the 16 females I collected in Idaho from May 28 to August 30 was pregnant, but most of those taken in May and June showed evidence of having had young.

Records of occurrence.—Specimens examined, 23, as follows: *Payette County:* 2 mi. S Payette, 4. *Canyon County:* Nampa, 2 (1 in Los Angeles Mus.); 4 mi. S Wilder, 5. *Owyhee County:* Homedale, 3. *Elmore County:* Hammett, 9. Additional records (Bailey, 1915:43): *Washington County:* Weiser. *Canyon County:* Caldwell.

Thomomys townsendii owyhensis Davis
OWYHEE POCKET GOPHER

Thomomys townsendii owyhensis Davis, Jour. Mammalogy, 18:154. May 14, 1937. Type from Castle Creek, 8 miles south of Oreana, Owyhee County, Idaho.

Distribution.—Owyhee County, Idaho, south of the Snake River, from near Murphy east to Indian Cove (see map, fig. 18).

Description.—Size medium (smaller than *T. t. towsendii*); lighter than sepia above, lighter below; nose sooty black; upper surfaces of feet and tail white. Skull: Small for this species; premaxillae narrow; nasals short, extending to or beyond frontal tongues; maxillary arm of zygomatic arch short. External measurements of 4 adult females and 4 adult males from near the type locality average, respectively, 248-74-33 and 274-88-37.

Comparisons.—Compared with *townsendii:* Nasals actually and relatively shorter (no overlap in length was found); maxillary arm of zygoma shorter, causing a more flattened dorsal outline of skull; squamosal arm of zygomatic arch abruptly curved mediad leaving a wide space between arm and external auditory canal. Hind foot shorter. Compared with *similis:* Smaller; nasals shorter; rostrum actually and relatively narrower.

Remarks.—This race of pocket gopher occurs chiefly in deep, clay-loam soils along watercourses and in irrigated fields at lower elevations in northern Owyhee County. At higher elevations another species, *Thomomys quadratus*, is found. In Reynolds Creek Valley, *owyhensis* does not occur, and here *quadratus* has extended its range north to the Snake River, separating *owyhensis* and *townsendii*. Elsewhere these two are separated by the Snake River. Indian Cove marks the eastern limits of the range of *owyhensis*.

Specimens from the eastern portions of the ranges of *townsendii* (Hammett) and *owyhensis* (Indian Cove) occupy similar types of soil and in external appearance the animals are indistinguishable. In cranial characters, however, they are distinct. Here, only the Snake River separates the two populations, and its effectiveness as a barrier to pocket gophers is indicated by the differences observed in individuals from the two sides of the river.

Records of occurrence.—Specimens examined, 15, all from the south side of the Snake River in Owyhee County, Idaho, as follows: Castle Creek, 8 mi. S Oreana, 6; Indian Cove, 2; 5 mi. SE Murphy, 6; Sinker Creek, 7 mi. SE Murphy, 1.

Thomomys townsendii similis Davis
BANNOCK POCKET GOPHER

Thomomys townsendii similis Davis, Jour. Mammalogy, 18:155. May 14, 1937. Type from Pocatello, Bannock County, Idaho.

Synonym.—*Thomomys townsendii townsendii*, Bailey, 1915:42; Whitlow and Hall, 1933:255.

Distribution.—Occurs on both sides of the Snake River from

American Falls northeast to Pingree, and east along the Portneuf River to Pocatello (see map, fig. 18).

Description.—Size medium *(smaller than T. t. townsendii)*; darker than sepia above, darker than dark mouse gray below; nose and postauricular patches black; tail bicolor, mouse gray above, white below; upper surfaces of feet and throat patch white. Skull: Premaxillae relatively broad; nasals long, extending posteriorly beyond frontal tongues; mastoidal breadth averages 59 per cent of basilar length of Hensel. External measurements of 5 adult females and 5 adult males from near the type locality average, respectively, 241-68-33 and 283-84-38.

Comparisons.—Compared with *townsendii:* Smaller; premaxillae wider; skull smaller, mastoidal breadth actually and relatively less; hind foot in females 33 as opposed to 37. Compared with *owyhensis:* External proportions similar, but skull larger and averaging 30 per cent heavier by weight; incisors wider; zygomatic arch more obtusely angled posteriorly and anteriorly.

Remarks.—This race is restricted to the deep soils in the vicinity of the American Falls reservoir. West of the Snake River it formerly occupied only the river-bottom lands, but due to the construction of the American Falls dam and the subsequent impounding of water in the reservoir, it has migrated to higher lands in the narrow irrigated region from near American Falls north to near Moreland. The presence of the animals on the two sides of the river here in the upper part of its course is more easily understood than in the case of *T. townsendii* farther downstream. Individuals of *T. t. similis* might cross in winter by burrowing through the snow when it covers the frozen river, or in summer when the river is very low. Within historic time the river in the vicinity of Blackfoot has been known to recede to such an extent that in places wagons could be driven across the channel on relatively dry ground. In recent years, however, water-control activities have prevented the river from reaching its previous low levels.

Westward extension of the range of *similis* north of the Snake River is prevented by extensive lava fields and desert land which occur from the river, between Lake Walcott and American Falls, north to the Sawtooth Mountains. North and west of Blackfoot another species of pocket gopher, *Thomomys talpoides idahoensis,* is found. *Thomomys talpoides pygmaeus* and *T. quadratus* occur in the valley of the Portneuf River east of Pocatello, in the surrounding hills, and along the south side of the Snake River from near American Falls west as far as Hagerman, and probably to near Indian Cove, the locality which marks the eastern limits of *T. t. owyhensis*. Thus, *similis* is hemmed in on all sides either by other species of pocket gophers or inhospitable territory, and is distant fully 150 miles from any other known population of the species.

In seeking to account for the geographic position of this population, one would, considering the present distribution of the remainder of the species, infer that at an early time its ancestors moved eastward along the south side of the Snake River and by geographic and biotic changes later were isolated. The finding (Wilson, 1933:122) of fossil remains of pocket gophers closely allied to *T. quadratus* in the Upper Pliocene or Lower Pleistocene beds near Hagerman, on the south side of the river, might argue against this. Migration along the north side of the river is even less likely because of the vast lava fields which have been in existence, and at times active, since the Miocene.

Structurally, individuals of *similis* are most like specimens from near Halleck, Nevada, and accordingly it seems probable that *similis* has been derived from that stock. The headwaters of the Humboldt River are but a few miles west of the westernmost limits of the Pleistocene Lake Bonneville which at one time drained into the Snake River by way of Red Rock Pass and the Portneuf River. Perhaps by keeping to the deeper soils along the northern margin of this lake and its former outlet, migration to the area near Pocatello was accomplished. Since only *Thomomys quadratus* now is known to occur in the country immediately south of Pocatello, and since no specimens of *Thomomys townsendii* have been recorded from Utah, this hypothesis also has serious objections.

Each of two females collected February 23 contained five embryos 10 mm. in crown-rump length. A short, early breeding season is indicated by the fact that none of the thirteen specimens taken in May, June, and July contained embryos. By June 1, young of the year are two-thirds grown.

Records of occurrence.—Specimens examined, 26, as follows: *Bingham County:* 1 mi. E Pingree, 4. *Power County:* 4 mi. NW American Falls, 2; 2½-5½ mi. SW Michaud, 2. *Bannock County:* Fort Hall Indian School, 10 mi. N Pocatello, 2; Pocatello, 15 (1 in Ralph Ellis coll.) ; 4 mi. N Pocatello, 1. Additional record (Bailey, 1915:43) : *Power County:* American Falls.

Thomomys talpoides idahoensis Merriam
IDAHO POCKET GOPHER

Thomomys idahoensis Merriam, Proc. Biol. Soc. Washington, 14: 114. July 19, 1901. Type from Birch Creek, about 6400 feet, ten miles south of Nicholia, Clark County, Idaho.

Synonym.—Thomomys clusius, Merriam, 1891:68.

Distribution.—Occurs in the northwestern part of the Snake River Plains from near Arco and Kaufman east to near Swan Valley and south on the west side of the Snake River to near Blackfoot (see map, fig. 19).

Description.—A small pocket gopher of the species *talpoides;* males and females but little different in size; color typically pale yellowish gray dorsally, lighter below; ears short, but pointed; tail whitish, about 35 per cent of body length. Skull: Small, smooth or with faint, anteriorly converging, temporal ridges; auditory bullae highly inflated with large exposed mastoid bullae; premaxillary tongues extending posteriorly but little, if any, beyond nasals. Average external measurements of twelve adults from Birch Creek and seven miles west of Idaho Falls are 185-48-23.

Remarks.—There is considerable variation in color between different populations. Individuals taken in the light-colored lava-ash soil north and west of Blackfoot are gray with little suffusion of brownish yellow. At Menan the texture of the soil tends toward sandy loam and specimens from that locality are slightly darker than those from Birch Creek; specimens taken on the north side of the South Fork near Swan Valley are still darker, almost fuscous.

Intergradation between *idahoensis* and *fuscus* is indicated by the 14 specimens from Menan and especially so by 4 specimens from three miles west of Swan Valley. In color the animals from near Swan Valley are indistinguishable from typical *fuscus* taken near Victor, Teton County; the general shape of the skull is that of *idahoensis,* and the size of the bullae and length of hind foot are intermediate between *idahoensis* and *fuscus.* Females from Birch Creek have six pairs of mammae, those from near Swan Valley five, and females of *fuscus* from near Victor, four. Specimens from Menan show the same tendencies in cranial characters, but their trend is more toward *pygmaeus*. On the basis of the above findings it seems advisable to consider *idahoensis* and *fuscus* as conspecific. Although Bailey (1915:109) records *idahoensis* from Blackfoot, the specimens available to me from there are referable to *pygmaeus*.

Records of occurrence.—Specimens examined, 30, as follows: *Clark County:* Birch Creek, 2 mi. SE and 2 mi. NW Kaufman, 8. *Madison County:* Menan, 14. *Bonneville County:* 7 mi. W Idaho Falls, 4; N. side South Fork, 3 mi. W Swan Valley, 4. Additional records (Bailey, 1915:109): *Clark County:* Dubois. *Butte County:* Birch Creek Sink; Big Butte; Big Lost River (near sink). *Bonneville County:* Idaho Falls.

Thomomys talpoides pygmaeus Merriam
PYGMY POCKET GOPHER

Thomomys pygmaeus Merriam, Proc. Biol. Soc. Washington, 14: 115. July 19, 1901. Type from Montpelier Creek, about ten miles northeast of Montpelier, Bear Lake County, Idaho.

Distribution.—Occurs on the east side of the Snake River from near Idaho Falls south of Blackfoot, thence east into Wyoming and south from there to the vicinity of Montpelier, Bear Lake County, Idaho (see map, fig. 19).

Description.—Individuals of this race are the smallest members of the genus; sexual dimorphism slight. General coloration varies from pale yellowish gray through light brown to nearly fuscous. Ears small, pointed; postauricular patches sooty black. External measurements of a single topotype are 165-40-20; averages of ten specimens from five miles east of Shelley are 178-52-23. Skull smaller than in *idahoensis*, smooth, and auditory bullae not highly inflated.

Remarks.—Wherever the larger *Thomomys quadratus* occurs within the range of *pygmaeus* the latter apparently is crowded out of the better types of soils and inhabits the claylike, dry areas and barren, rocky, sage-covered hillsides. Intergradation between *pygmaeus* and *idahoensis* is indicated by specimens from Menan, from five miles east of Shelley, from Blackfoot, and from Alridge. There is a gradual transition of color from the pale yellowish gray as observed in specimens from near Shelley, to light brown in

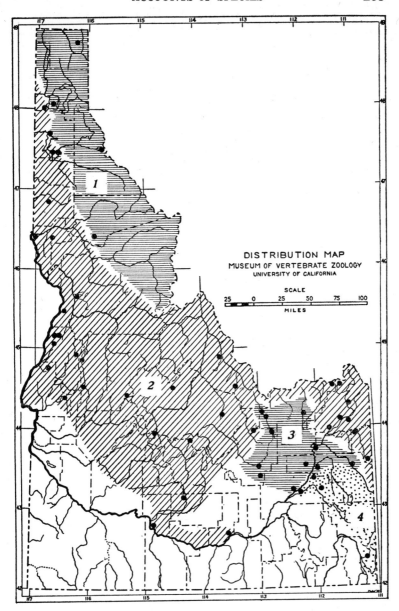

FIG. 19. Map showing the distribution of some pocket gophers in Idaho. Dots indicate localities whence specimens have been examined or recorded. 1. *Thomomys talpoides saturatus*, 2. *Thomomys talpoides fuscus*, 3. *Thomomys talpoides idahoensis*. 4. *Thomomys talpoides pygmaeus*.

specimens from Alridge. Specimens from Menan are nearly typical *idahoensis*, but tend to have smaller skulls and smaller auditory bullae; animals from near Shelley have small skulls and the cranial characters of *pygmaeus*, but they are nearly as large as *idahoensis* and gray in color. Specimens from Alridge, about fifteen miles southeast of Shelley, are typical of *pygmaeus* save for slightly larger average size and paler coloration. Because of this seeming intergradation *idahoensis* and *pygmaeus* are herein arranged as subspecies of a single species.

Records of occurrence.—Specimens examined, 19, as follows: *Bingham County:* Alridge, 2 (Biol. Surv. coll.); Blackfoot, 4; 5 mi. E Shelley, 12. *Bear Lake County:* Montpelier Creek, 10 mi. NE Montpelier, 1 (Biol. Surv. coll.).

Thomomys talpoides fuscus Merriam
BROWN POCKET GOPHER

Thomomys clusius fuscus Merriam, N. Amer. Fauna, 5:69. July 30, 1891. Type from Summit Creek, head of Big Lost River, about 8000 feet elevation, Custer County, Idaho.

Synonym.—*Thomomys fuscus fuscus*, Bailey, 1915:126.

Distribution.—Occurs from the Snake River at Acequia and Hagerman northward to drainage area of Clearwater River. Replaced in nothern portion of state by *saturatus*, with which it intergrades. Save in areas where *Thomomys townsendii* and *T. t. idahoensis* occur on the north side of the Snake River, this stream marks the southern limits of distribution of *fuscus* (see map, fig. 19).

Description.—Size small (external measurements of five adult females from the type locality average 210-67-26); coloration dorsally dark brown or chestnut; mammae in four pairs. Skull relatively slender and readily distinguished from that of other species. Mountain-dwelling individuals lack temporal ridges, but specimens from lower altitudes in deeper soil have these prominently developed. As in *Thomomys t. idahoensis* and *T. t. pygmaeus* the occipital region is swollen, and the supraoccipital bone takes part in forming the roof of the skull. The interparietal is roughly ovoid and projects some distance posterior to the sutures joining the supraoccipital with the two parietals. The rostrum is relatively narrow; nasals truncate or nearly so; premaxillary tongues extend but little, if any, posteriorly beyond nasals; zygomatic arch weak in mountain-dwelling individuals, heavier in those taken at lower altitudes.

Remarks.—The type of soil inhabited by individuals of this race is quite variable. At the head of Big Lost River,

7895 feet, I found them in loose, rocky talus areas, their burrows on the average being less than two inches below the surface. At Mill Creek, 8370 feet, they were common in the moist humus along the stream; sixteen miles north of Shoshone they inhabited the claylike lava ash; and at Acequia the soil was practically all sand.

Specimens from the western part of the state are much darker than those from the type locality and the Snake River Plains. The cranial characters, however, are fairly constant in all but one of the populations I have sampled, and separation of the westernmost populations on the basis of color differences alone, to me, seems unwarranted. A single individual from Lewiston, Idaho, here referred to *fuscus,* differs in so many structural features from typical *fuscus* as to make me wonder if study of additional specimens from that area will warrant their reference to an unnamed race.

Intergradation between *fuscus* and *idahoensis* is indicated by specimens from Victor; 3 mi. W Swan Valley; and Menan. See also under *Thomomys talpoides idahoensis.*

None of the females taken in June, July, and August contained embryos, but many half-grown young were taken in those months.

Records of occurrence.—Specimens examined, 143, as follows: *Latah County:* Cedar Mountain, 1 (Chas. R. Conner Mus.). *Nez Perce County:* Culdesac, 1; Lewiston, 1 (Chas. R. Conner Mus.). *Adams County:* ½ mi. E Black Lake, 9 (7 in Ralph Ellis coll.) ; 5 mi. W Payette Lake, 4; 1 mi. N Bear Cr. R. S., 16 (13 in Ralph Ellis coll.) ; summit Smith Mountain, 16 (13 in Ralph Ellis coll.). *Valley County:* 5 mi. W Cape Horn, 2. *Washington County:* Crane Creek, 15 mi. E Midvale, 8 (Ralph Ellis coll.) ; 1 mi. NE Heath, 19 (15 in Ralph Ellis coll.). *Custer County:* head Big Lost River, 7; head Pahsimeroi River, 2; Mill Cr., 14 mi. W Challis, 7. *Blaine County:* Alturas Lake, 5. *Lincoln County:* 16 mi. N Shoshone, 3. *Gooding County:* 2 mi. S Hagerman, 4. *Minidoka County:* 2 mi. E Acequia, 5. *Clark County:* Taylor Cr., 5 mi. S Montana Line at Sheridan Mt., 1 (Amer. Mus.). *Fremont County:* Black Springs Cr., 4 mi. W Ashton, 5 (Amer. Mus.) ; N. fork Snake River, 10 mi. SW Island Park, 14 (Amer. Mus.) ; 5 mi. W St. Anthony, 1 (Amer. Mus.) ; 3-5 mi. S Montana Line at Mt. Jefferson, 2 (Amer. Mus.). *Teton County:* 3 mi. SW Victor, 10. Additional records (Bailey, 1915:127) : *Bonner County:* Hoodoo Valley. *Kootenai County:* Mission; Blue Lake. *Idaho County:* Freedom; Seven Devils Mountains. *Valley County:* "Lerdo" [Lardo]; Van Wyck.

Lemhi County: Lemhi; Salmon River Mts. *Fremont County:* Ashton. *Butte County:* Lost River Mountains. *Teton County:* Teton Canyon. *Bingham County:* Blackfoot (west of Snake River). *County?:* Mount Carlton; South Fork Ranch.

I have not examined specimens from the above-mentioned localities recorded by Bailey, but from study of the more abundant material collected since his identifications were made, have referred the specimens from Bonner and Kootenai counties to *T. t. saturatus* rather than to *T. t. fuscus*. Also the specimen Bailey records from west of Blackfoot might well be rechecked since specimens I have examined from that vicinity are referable to *T. t. idahoensis*.

Thomomys talpoides saturatus Bailey
COEUR D'ALENE POCKET GOPHER

Thomomys fuscus saturatus Bailey, Proc. Biol. Soc. Washington, 27:117. July 10, 1914. Type from Silver (near Saltese), 4300 feet, in the western corner of Mineral County, Montana.

Distribution.—Occurs in the northeastern part of Idaho from Weippe, Clearwater County, north to Canada and east into northwestern Montana (see map, fig. 19).

Description.—Similar to *fuscus* with which it intergrades, but slightly larger and darker; underparts washed with ochraceous buff.

Remarks.—According to Bailey (1915:128), *saturatus* occurs only on the higher parts of the Coeur d'Alene Mountains in Idaho and Montana. Specimens examined from localities in the central portion of the state listed below are darker than *fuscus* and probably are better referred to *saturatus*.

Records of occurrence.—Specimens examined, 16, as follows: *Boundary County:* 4 mi. W Meadow Creek, 7. *Bonner County:* 5 mi. W Cocolalla, 7. *Kootenai County:* Coeur d'Alene, 1. *Clearwater County:* 2 mi. NE Weippe, 1. Additional record (Bailey, 1915:128): *Shoshone County:* Mullan.

Thomomys quadratus quadratus Merriam
DALLES POCKET GOPHER

Thomomys quadratus Merriam, Proc. Biol. Soc. Washington, 11: 214. July 15, 1897. Type from The Dalles, Wasco County, Oregon.

Synonyms.—*Thomomys uinta*, part, Bailey, 1915:114; *Thomomys quadratus uinta*, Hall, 1931:4.

Distribution.—South of the Snake River from Bonanza Bar (19 mi. SW American Falls) west into Oregon and south into Nevada and Utah (see map, fig. 18).

Description.—Size: Medium; color varying from ochraceous buff to dark brown; tail averaging 43 per cent of body length; mammae in five pairs. External measurements of eight females from Albion and Elba, Cassia County, average 208-61-27. Skull angular in outline; rostrum relatively short and broad; nasals truncate posteriorly, or nearly so; incisors protruding beyond anterior tip of nasals; interparietal wider than long, roughly triangular; occipital region nearly truncate, supraoccipital projecting anteriorly but little onto roof of skull; foramen magnum usually as wide as high; temporal ridges nearly parallel.

Remarks.—The above cranial characters are fairly constant in animals of this race from southern Idaho. Individuals from higher altitudes average smaller, have smooth brain cases, and usually are darker than those from lower elevations. The color is variable and perhaps is correlated with soil conditions. Specimens from Albion and Declo, where the soil is light in color, are ochraceous buff; those from near Riddle, where the soil is largely decomposed basalt, are dark grayish-brown, while specimens taken in sandy soil near Hagerman are pale grayish brown. Three specimens, provisionally referred to *quadratus* from near Riddle are much smaller than any other individuals examined of this species. Their tendency toward dwarfness may be correlated with adverse environmental conditions.

In the arid portions of Idaho, pocket gophers are found in scattered colonies, often in localities isolated by territory inhospitable to them. From observations made near Riddle, it seems likely that these rodents take advantage of deep snow and travel considerable distances through that medium. At the time of my visit there, May, 1934, they were restricted to the vicinity of streams, but evidence of their occurrence the previous winter at localities a mile or more from where they were during the dry season was found in the form of earth cores and old burrow systems.

Intergradation between *quadratus* and *Thomomys quadratus bridgeri* occurs in the region between Declo and American Falls. Hall (1931:4) considers the specimens from Albion as intergrades between *Thomomys uinta* and *Thomomys quadratus fisheri*. Specimens of the species *quadratus* from southern Idaho west of American Falls appear to be referable, on the basis of larger size and heavier skull, to the race *quadratus* rather than to the race *fisheri*. I have examined no specimens from Idaho which I regard as being referable to *uinta* (see under *Thomomys quadratus bridgeri*) though Whitlow and Hall (1933:257) and Bailey (1915: 114) refer specimens from southeastern Idaho to that race.

Records of occurrence.—Specimens examined, 46, as follows: *Owyhee County:* Reynolds Creek, 12 mi. S Snake River, 2; 1 mi. S Riddle, 3. *Twin Falls County:* S. side Snake River, 2 mi. S Hagerman, 10. *Cassia County:* Albion, 10; Declo, 5; Mt. Harrison, 10-12 mi. S Albion, 5; Elba, 8; Raft River, 2 mi. S Snake River, 1. *Power County:* S. side Snake River, 19 mi. SW American Falls, 2.

Thomomys quadratus fisheri Merriam
FISHER POCKET GOPHER

Thomomys fuscus fisheri Merriam, Proc. Biol. Soc. Washington, 14:111. July 19, 1901. Type from Beckwith, Sierra Valley, Plumas County, California.
Distribution.—Definitely known only from the southwestern corner of the state.
Description.—Essentially as in *Thomomys quadratus quadratus* but color much lighter, and at the type locality size smaller.

Remarks.—The animals of this race all were taken in alfalfa fields in the narrow Owyhee River Canyon.

Records of occurrence.—*Owyhee County:* South Fork Owyhee River, 12 mi. N Nevada Line, 8.

Thomomys quadratus bridgeri Merriam
FORT BRIDGER POCKET GOPHER

Thomomys bridgeri Merriam, Proc. Biol. Soc. Washington, 14:113. July 19, 1901. Type from Fort Bridger, Harvey's Ranch on Smiths Fork, six miles southwest of Old Fort Bridger, Uinta County, Wyoming.
Synonyms.—*Thomomys uinta*, part, Bailey, 1915:113; *Thomomys quadratus uinta*, Whitlow and Hall, 1933:257.
Distribution.—South and east of Snake River from near American Falls north to Victor, thence south and east into Utah and Wyoming (see map, fig. 18).
Description.—Size medium to small; average external measurements of five adult females from Montpelier (these are comparable in all respects to topotypes) are 229-70-30.6; of ten adult females from near Pocatello, 215-62-28.5; of two females from near Rapid

Creek, 205-63-28; mammae usually in five pairs, occasionally four. Skull angular and heavily ridged in valley populations, more rounded and less ridged in alpine animals; nasals emarginate posteriorly; rostrum relatively short; interparietal roughly triangular and mainly anterior to lambdoidal crest; supraoccipital truncate in valley gophers, more rounded in alpine specimens, forming little, if any, of roof of skull; foramen magnum usually higher than wide.

Remarks.—In southeastern Idaho individuals of this race vary in size and color. Those from the valley floors are large and generally dull colored; those from higher altitudes average smaller and are brighter colored. Each mountain in this region on which collecting has been done has its population of small pocket gophers. These differ from those occupying the deeper soils in the valleys in having more nearly smooth, more rounded skulls, relatively shorter rostra and nasals, and slenderer zygoma. Whitlow and Hall (1933: 259) make use of the shorter maxillary tooth row in identifying the smaller individuals as *uinta*. The average alveolar length in females from Camp Tendoy and Schutt's Mine, 6300 feet, near Pocatello, is 7.6 mm., while in specimens from Pocatello and Indian Springs, near 4400 feet, it is 8.0 mm. Thus, in specimens from low altitudes the tooth row is on the average only .4 mm., or slightly over 5 per cent, longer than in individuals from alpine areas.

From our knowledge of postuterine development in rodents the differences between the alpine and valley animals are exactly those one would expect to find in stunted or neotenous individuals. In the alpine animals there is little sexual dimorphism, the brain case is relatively smooth, the rostrum is actually and relatively shorter, and the maxillary tooth row is actually shorter, but relatively longer. Because there is gradation from one extreme to the other, and for other reasons stated above (see discussion in introductory paragraphs), I consider all the *quadratus* pocket gophers of southeastern Idaho as constituting a geographically varying race and herein refer them to *T. q. bridgeri.* I should restrict the name *T. uinta* to alpine populations in northeastern Utah.

In this study I have had available for comparison good series of topotypes and near topotypes of both *T. q. bridgeri* and *T. uinta.* If my interpretation of the relationships of the pocket gophers of southeastern Idaho be accepted, *uinta* must stand as a full species until intergradation between it and *bridgeri* can be demonstrated. The animals from Strawberry Creek in Franklin County, and Copenhagen Basin and Geneva in Bear Lake County, though collected to throw more light on the relationship between *uinta* and *bridgeri*, were received too late to permit detailed analysis in this respect.

Although *bridgeri* occurs on common ground with *fuscus* in the vicinity of Victor, Teton County, and in the same general areas with *pygmaeus* and *townsendii*, I have found no evidence that it intergrades with any of them.

Eight females collected between April 1 and May 25 contained an average of six embryos (5-9). At later dates none of the females was pregnant.

Records of occurrence.—Specimens examined, 136, as follows: *Teton County:* 3 mi. SW Victor, 1. *Bonneville County:* Big Hole Mountains, 8 mi. NE Swan Valley, 5; S. side South Fork, 3 mi. W Swan Valley, 7; 10 mi. SE Irwin, 3 (U. S. Nat. Mus.). *Power County:* 9½ mi. SW Pocatello, 6000 ft., 1; Indian Springs, 4 mi. S American Falls, 15. *Bannock County:* 2-3½ mi. SE Pocatello, 6; 5½ mi. SE Pocatello, 1; 11 mi. SE Pocatello, 3; Camp Tendoy, 14 mi. SE Pocatello, 3; Rapid Cr., 4 mi. NE Inkom, 4; 8 mi. S Inkom, 2; 5½ mi. E Pocatello, 6; 12 mi. NE Pocatello, 12; Pocatello, Mink Creek, 8; Pocatello, 1 (U. S. Nat. Mus.); Scout Mountain, 15 mi. SE Pocatello, 2. *Caribou County:* Preuss Mountains, head of Crow Creek, 3 (U. S. Nat. Mus.). *Oneida County:* Malad, 2 (U. S. Nat. Mus.). *Franklin County:* Strawberry Creek [Canyon], 20 mi. NE Preston, 14. *Bear Lake County:* Copenhagen Basin, N. rim 16, W. rim 6; Montpelier, 10 (U. S. Nat. Mus.); Geneva, 5. Additional records (Bailey, 1915:113): *Bear Lake County:* Montpelier Creek. Bailey *(op. cit.*, p. 114) referred specimens, which I have not examined, from Bridge; hills east of Blackfoot; Shelley; and Swan Lake to *T. uinta.* I have examined specimens from Irwin, Malad, and Preuss Mountains which he also referred to *uinta* and these fall within the range of variation of *bridgeri* as outlined above. Consequently, I assume that the other specimens do likewise and herein refer them to *bridgeri*. The specimens from Bridge should be rechecked because specimens from Elba, about fourteen miles to the northwest, are clearly referable to *T. q. quadratus.*

Family HETEROMYIDAE
POCKET MICE and KANGAROO RATS

Geologically speaking, the Heteromyidae is an old family, extending back in time, according to Wood (1935), to the Middle Oligocene where it was represented by the primitive ancestral type *Heliscomys* which has been recorded from Colorado, Montana, Nebraska, and South Dakota. In many respects the genus *Perognathus* is more generalized than *Dipodomys* and it appears to have an older geologic history (Miocene to Recent); *Dipodomys* has been recorded from the Pliocene of Arizona and the Pleistocene of California. At this writing no fossil remains of heteromyids have been reported from Idaho. It is likely, however, that *Perognathus* will be found there; *Dipodomys* seems to have migrated in from the south since the Pleistocene.

In several structural characters, particularly in the structure and number of cheek teeth, the position of the anterior opening of the infraorbital canal far forward on the side of the rostrum, and the presence of external fur-lined cheek pouches, the Heteromyidae is closely related to the Geomyidae. The results of the careful study made by Hill (1937) and published after the present work was in manuscript form led him to include the heteromyids and pocket gophers in the single family, Geomyidae.

Genus **Perognathus** Wied
Pocket Mice

These small rodents are closely related to the kangaroo rats, but differ from them in smaller size, less specialization for saltation, smaller auditory bullae, and rooted rather than rootless cheek teeth. They are nocturnal, about the size of the white-footed mouse, have external fur-lined cheek pouches, and subsist chiefly on seeds. In Idaho they inhabit a variety of habitats, and occur mainly in the arid southern half of the state. At Murphy we found them on volcanic ash amidst *Atriplex, Grayia, Sarcobatus,* and *Artemisia spinescens* and in association with kangaroo rats and white-footed mice; at Salmon Creek they were taken on a boulder talus amongst *Artemisia tridentata*. Here their associates were white-footed and harvest mice. At Crane Creek, Borell and Gilmore (MS) trapped them in tall grass along a stream, in a marsh, and on a sage-covered hillside; and at Fort Hall, Whitlow (MS) took them on fine sand.

These mice are as well adapted to desert conditions as are kangaroo rats. They probably are able to conserve metabolic water to a greater degree than any other mammal known, for Howell (1932:383) kept one on a diet of dry rolled oats, without water, for thirteen months. At the end of this time it was in good condition!

According to Bailey (1936:245) their burrows in mellow soil usually run two or three feet deep and have many branches, winding shafts, storage chambers, and a nest cavity. Although *Perognathus* are not known to hibernate, they probably spend the most adverse parts of the winter underground and subsist then on food which was stored during times of plenty.

Five geographic races of a single species, *Perognathus parvus*, occur in Idaho. Because of insufficient material, I have been unable to work out satisfactorily their relationships and ranges.

Key to Adult Pocket Mice of Idaho

1 Dorsal coloration blackish.

    2   Mastoidal width usually more than 14 mm.; lateral line distinct.
                  P. p. idahoensis, p. 265

    2' Mastoidal width near 13 mm.; lateral line absent, or nearly so.
                  P. p. lordi, p. 266

1' Dorsal coloration grayish or ochraceous buff (may be tinged with blackish).

    3   Hairs on abdomen white to base.

          4   Lateral line distinctly ochraceous; dorsal coloration ochraceous buff.   **P. p. olivaceus**, p. 264

          4' Lateral line indistinct; dorsal coloration grayish or buffy.   **P. p. clarus**, p. 264

    3' Hairs on abdomen plumbeous basally.
                  P. p. parvus, p. 263

Perognathus parvus parvus (Peale)
OREGON POCKET MOUSE

Cricetodipus parvus Peale, U. S. Expl. Exped., 8(Mamm. and Ornith.) :53. 1848. Type probably from The Dalles, Wasco County, Oregon.

Distribution.—Along the Snake River and its tributaries in southwestern Idaho.

Description.—General dorsal coloration grayish buff; lateral line indistinct; hairs of belly usually white or buffy tipped, plumbeous basally. External measurements of a subadult male from Homedale are 165-84-23-8.

Remarks.—For comparisons see under *P. p. olivaceus.* At Homedale, *parvus* was taken on sandy soil where it occurred in association with *Dipodomys ordii;* near Murphy it was taken on lava ash. At Crane Creek, Borell and Gilmore (MS) found it common and collected specimens in tall wet grass along the stream, in a marsh, and on a sage-covered dry hillside.

The specimens from Crane Creek differ constantly from topotypes of *parvus,* and other specimens from western Idaho herein referred to that race, in much darker dorsal coloration and absence of lateral line. In certain respects they resemble *P. p. idahoensis,* but differ from it in lighter color and narrower mastoidal region. They may constitute a new race, but, pending a revision of the genus, I refer them tentatively to *parvus,* the race to which they are nearest in cranial characters and external measurements.

Two females collected at Crane Creek in late May were gravid; one contained five embryos, the other six.

Records of occurrence.—Specimens examined, 26, as follows: *Washington County:* Crane Creek, 15 mi. E Midvale, 14 (Ralph Ellis coll.). *Payette County:* 2 mi. S Payette, between Payette and Snake rivers, 1. *Canyon County:* 4 mi. S Wilder, 1. *Owyhee County:* Homedale, 2 (1 in Davis coll.); 5 mi. SE Murphy, 1; South Fork Owyhee River, 12 mi. N Nevada Line, 4; Little Owyhee River, 4 mi. N Nevada Line, 3. Additional records (specimens in U. S. Nat. Mus., not examined): *Washington County:* Weiser. *Canyon County:* Bowmont; Nampa. *Elmore County:* 8 mi. N Hammett. *Owyhee County:* Murphy.

Perognathus parvus olivaceus Merriam
GREAT BASIN POCKET MOUSE

Perognathus olivaceus Merriam, N. Amer. Fauna, 1:15. October 25, 1889. Type from Kelton, Box Elder County, Utah.

Distribution.—In Idaho, known only from Salmon Creek south of the Snake River.

Description.—General dorsal coloration olive buff with admixture of black-tipped hairs, especially on lower back; cheeks and lateral line distinctly ochraceous buff; hairs on underparts white to base; tail distinctly bicolor, terminating in a short tuft; marginal white spots on ears inconspicuous. External measurements of three adult males and two females from Salmon Creek average 181-95-24-8.

Comparisons.—Compared with *P. p. parvus:* Less grayish, lighter buff; lateral line more pronounced; slightly larger; skull larger. Compared with *P. p. idahoensis:* Less melanistic; mastoidal width less. Compared with *P. p. clarus:* Darker; lateral line more pronounced; tail darker dorsally. Compared with *P. p. lordi:* Buffy, rather than dusky buff; lateral line distinct, rather than wanting; skull slightly larger.

Remarks.—At Salmon Creek *olivaceus* was taken among loose boulders at the base of a basaltic outcropping. In the same area *Peromyscus maniculatus* and *Reithrodontomys megalotis* were taken. One of the two females, collected May 14, contained seven small embryos.

Records of occurrence.—Specimens examined, 5, all from Salmon Cr., 8 mi. W Rogerson, Twin Falls County.

Perognathus parvus clarus Goldman
UINTA POCKET MOUSE

Perognathus parvus clarus Goldman, Proc. Biol. Soc. Washington, 30:147. July 27, 1917. Type from Cumberland, Lincoln County, Wyoming.

Synonyms.—*Perognathus olivaceus* Merriam, 1891:71; *Perognathus parvus olivaceus,* Osgood, 1900:37.

Distribution.—Southeastern Idaho from Wyoming west at least to southern Minidoka County.

Description.—Similar to *P. p. olivaceus* with which it probably intergrades in southern Idaho, but lighter colored; lateral line indistinct. Larger than *P. p. parvus.* External measurements of two adult females from Shelley and Rupert average 166-82-21-8.

Remarks.—A female collected near Shelley on June 29 contained five small embryos. The following day a half-grown young of the year was collected. These meager data suggest that two or more litters are reared yearly.

Specimens from Bear Lake, according to Goldman (1917:148), are intermediate between *clarus* and *P. p. parvus*. Since the range of *P. p. olivaceus* is interposed between the ranges of *clarus* and *parvus* in southern Idaho, it seems better to refer the specimen from Bear Lake to *clarus* which it resembles in color.

Records of occurrence.—Specimens examined, 10, as follows: *Minidoka County:* 4 mi. N Rupert, 1. *Bonneville County:* 5 mi. E Shelley, 2. *Bingham County:* 1 mi. N Fort Hall, 6. *Power County:* 5 mi. NW Michaud, 1. Additional records (Goldman, *loc. cit.*): *Lemhi County:* Lemhi. *Custer County:* Dickey; Pahsimeroi River; Pahsimeroi Valley. *Clark County:* Birch Creek. *Butte County:* Big Butte. *Bingham County:* Blackfoot. *Power County:* American Falls. *Bear Lake County:* Bear Lake (east side) (Osgood, 1900:38).

Perognathus parvus idahoensis Goldman
LAVA-BEDS POCKET MOUSE

Perognathus parvus idahoensis Goldman, Proc. Biol. Soc. Washington, 35:105. October 17, 1922. Type from Echo Crater, Craters of the Moon National Monument, twenty miles southwest of Arco, Butte County.

Distribution.—Apparently restricted to the lava beds north of the Snake River.

Description.—Darkest and largest of the pocket mice occurring in Idaho. Dorsum heavily suffused with black; mastoidal breadth averages 14.5 mm.; lateral line distinct.

Remarks.—The dark color of this mouse probably is correlated with its dark surroundings. It inhabits basaltic outcroppings and old volcanic buttes. A similar correlation between color of background and that of pocket mice is reported by Benson (1933).

Goldman *(loc. cit.)* suggests that *idahoensis* may have an extensive range in the Snake River desert of southern Idaho. None of the specimens I have examined from areas outside the lava beds appear to be of that race, or close to it. A specimen from near Rupert, that is, about forty miles south of Echo Crater, has none of the characters ascribed to *idahoensis*.

A young female collected at the mouth of Little Cottonwood Creek Canyon, about 7 miles northwest of the type
locality, after the above was written, is indistinguishable
in dorsal coloration from specimens of *Perognathus parvus
lordi* from near Vernon, British Columbia, but differs from
them in having the ventral white area more restricted, it
being limited to the throat and a median patch on the chest
in this specimen.

Records of occurrence.—Specimen examined: *Butte County:* mouth
of Little Cottonwood Creek Canyon, Craters of the Moon, 1. Additional records (specimens in U. S. Nat. Mus.) : *Lincoln County:*
Laidlaw Park, 20 mi. N Kimama. *Minidoka County:* Twin Lakes, 20
mi. N Minidoka; Twin Springs, 20 mi. N Minidoka; Sparks Well, 23
mi. N Minidoka. *Butte County:* Echo Crater, 20 mi. S Arco.

Perognathus parvus lordi (Gray)
NORTHWEST POCKET MOUSE

Abromys lordi Gray, Proc. Zool. Soc. London, 1868:202. Type from
southern British Columbia, Canada.
   Distribution.—Plains of the Columbia in northwestern Idaho.
   Description.—Similar to *P. p. parvus*, but much darker dorsally;
abdomen plumbeous white. Differs from *P. p. idahoensis* chiefly in
smaller size and narrower mastoidal region.
   Record of occurrence.—Osgood (1900:40) records a single specimen of *lordi* from Lewiston, Nez Perce County.

Genus **Dipodomys** Gray
Kangaroo Rats

The kangaroo rats of Idaho may be recognized by the
following combination of characters: External fur-lined
cheek pouches; hind legs from two to three times as long as
front legs; plantar surfaces of hind feet well haired; tail
longer than body, terminating in a distinct tuft of hair (the
pencil), and with two black and two lateral white longitudinal stripes; ears short and rounded; eyes relatively large;
general dorsal coloration cinnamon buff; underparts, sides
of nose, postauricular patches, and hip-stripes white. Auditory bullae greatly enlarged; maxillary portion of zygoma
heavy, jugal weak; upper incisors grooved; cheek teeth four
on each side, rootless.

In Idaho these rodents are restricted largely to the Great Basin region where they live in a variety of habitats on both sides of the Snake River. In northern Owyhee County they have been taken on volcanic ash, sandy, and fine gravelly soils amidst *Grayia, Artemisia spinescens, Atriplex,* and *Sarcobatus.* Farther east they occur most commonly on sandy soils amidst *Artemisia tridentata, Atriplex,* and *Sarcobatus.* Although they have been found abundantly in and near irrigated areas, their occurrence there is incidental to the presence of free water which for them is not a necessity.

Kangaroo rats are particularly well adapted to desert conditions. A. B. Howell (1932), who studied the morphology, habits, and adaptations of these animals, points out that their long hind legs and tail are correlated directly with saltatorial habits and permit rapid progress over loose sand; special skin glands secrete an oily exudate that is thought to function in reducing the loss of water through the skin by evaporation, and these creatures are able to dispense with free water for a considerable length of time. Howell and Gersh (1935) report that several species of *Dipodomys* have been kept on a diet of rolled oats, without water, for as long as three months. At the end of this period the animals were in good condition, whereas white rats *(Rattus),* kept on the same diet, were unable to survive longer than one week. These investigators found that *Dipodomys* kept on a dehydrated diet was able to conserve metabolic water chiefly by resorption in the ducts of the renal papillae and in the walls of the urinary bladder. In addition, its habits tend to conserve water. It is strictly nocturnal, hence abroad when the rate of evaporation is at a minimum; during the day it sleeps curled up in an underground chamber which is closed off from the burrow by an earth plug, and moisture which is exhaled then is in part regained at the following inhalation.

The burrow of a *Dipodomys,* in volcanic ash soil near Murphy, averaged 60 mm. in diameter and ran about twelve inches below the surface for a distance of approximately twenty feet. It consisted of a main burrow and several side branches and pockets, one of which contained a nest that was composed chiefly of rabbit fur and seed coats. Numerous flower heads of *Brassica* sp. were strewn along that part of the burrow leading to the nest. Another burrow, in fine sand near Homedale, was approximately eight inches below the surface and consisted of a main burrow five feet long and two shorter ones which diverged from the former at right angles; all terminated in rounded chambers situated about two inches below the surface. Although the burrow was occupied, no nest was found. The small subsurface chambers probably are protective devices for, while I was excavating the burrow system, the occupant broke through the roof of a chamber, in which it probably had been resting, and escaped.

Although Howell *(ibid.)* suggests that kangaroo rats hibernate in the parts of their range where the climate is more rigorous, I know of no instance where this actually has been observed. The fact that these animals store quantities of food indicates that they may be confined to their burrow, but not necessarily hibernating, during severe winter weather. Several specimens of *D. o. columbianus*, now in the Ralph Ellis collection, were collected in December and January near Reno, Nevada. Although no snow was on the ground at that time, the temperature dropped below freezing nightly. I have seen no winter-taken specimens of *Dipodomys* from Idaho, but near Elba on January 1, 1936, I observed their tracks in eight inches of snow. Dr. Richard Bond tells me that he saw their tracks in six inches of snow in December, 1936, in northern California.

Two species, *Dipodomys microps* and *Dipodomys ordii*, occur in Idaho. The two may be distinguished easily by morphological characters, but I have been unable to find significant ecologic differences. Both occur in the same area and may be taken in the same line of traps. Bailey (1936) records, however, that the burrow systems of the two in Oregon differ markedly. According to him, those of *D. microps* are characterized by large surface mounds, from 5 to 12 feet in diameter, with numerous openings.

Key to Adult Kangaroo Rats of Idaho

1 Black stripes on tail wider than white ones; lining of cheek pouches dusky; upper incisors slightly recurved, subequally grooved.

D. m. preblei, p. 271

1' White stripes on tail wider than black ones; lining of cheek pouches white; upper incisors sharply recurved, equally grooved.

D. o. columbianus, p. 269

Dipodomys ordii columbianus (Merriam)
COLUMBIAN KANGAROO RAT

Perodipus ordi columbianus Merriam, Proc. Biol. Soc. Washington, 9:115. June 21, 1894. Type from Umatilla, at mouth of Umatilla River, Plains of Columbia, Umatilla County, Oregon.

Synonym.—Dipodops ordii, Merriam, 1891:71.

Distribution.—The Great Basin region of southern Idaho.

Description.—Medium size with long hind legs and tail. Dorsal coloration cinnamon buff; chin, abdomen, hip stripe, and postauricular patches white; white stripes on tail wider than black stripes; lining of cheek pouches white; length of hind foot usually less than 41 mm.; incisors sharply recurved and equally grooved; maxillary arch usually over 4 mm. in width. External measurements of adults, six males and six females, from Homedale, average, respectively, 251-135-42-14 and 253-159-41-13.5.

Comparisons.—D. o. columbianus differs from *D. microps* as follows: Dark stripes on tail less melanistic, white stripes as broad as, or broader than, black ones; lining of cheek pouches white, rather than dusky; hind foot slender and usually less than 41 mm. in length, rather than broad and usually over 41 mm.; upper incisors sharply recurved, rather than slightly recurved, and equally, rather than subequally, grooved; width of maxillary arch at middle usually more, rather than less, than 4 mm.; auditory bullae smaller.

Remarks.—Specimens of the species *D. ordii* from Idaho differ in several respects, chiefly those associated with larger size, from topotypes of *D. o. columbianus.* Until the relationships of the entire group are better known, however, it seems best to refer the material from Idaho to *columbianus.* In Idaho, I can detect no appreciable differences in the populations on the two sides of the Snake River and infer that the river has little, if any, effect on the distribution of these animals. They are active throughout the year and since they cannot swim, as repeated experiments have demonstrated, it seems likely that they cross the river in winter when it is frozen over and covered with snow. This assumption is supported by the complete lack of *Dipodomys* north of the Columbia and Snake rivers in Washington (Taylor and Shaw, 1929). There the rivers do not freeze over for any appreciable length of time, if at all, and hence a northward extension of range is prevented. The present distribution of the genus, particularly that of *D. o. columbianus* in Oregon and southeastern Washington, indicates that these animals have moved into Idaho and Oregon from the south.

Available data show that the breeding season of *columbianus* extends through several months of the year and suggest that each breeding female bears two or more litters a season. Third-grown young were collected May 30 near American Falls, and gravid females were taken at other localities in southern Idaho in May and June.

The following table shows the number of embryos found in each horn of the uterus in six females of *columbianus*. Differences of a similar nature have been observed in *Thomomys* and other rodents, and these, to me, suggest that some mechanical factor, perhaps the presence of the large stomach on the left side, tends to reduce the number of embryos that develop on that side.

Female	Right	Left
1.	0	2
2.	2	0
3.	1	2
4.	2	1
5.	2	1
6.	3	1

Records of occurrence.—Specimens examined, 75, as follows: *Owyhee County:* Castle Cr., 8 mi. S Oreana, 1; Homedale, 13; Indian Cove, 4; 5 mi. SE Murphy, 7; South Fork Owyhee River, 12 mi. N Nevada Line, 1. *Elmore County:* Hammett, 1. *Minidoka County:* Acequia, 8; 4 mi. N Rupert, 2. *Twin Falls County:* Salmon Cr., 8 mi. W Rogerson, 7. *Bingham County:* Aberdeen, 1; Blackfoot, 5; 3 mi. S Blackfoot, 6; 5 mi. E Shelley, 1. *Power County:* 4 mi. NE American Falls, 4; 6 mi. SW American Falls, 10; 5 mi. NW Michaud, 4. Additional records (Merriam, 1891:71): *Custer County:* Challis. *Clark County:* Birch Creek.

Dipodomys microps preblei (Goldman)
PREBLE KANGAROO RAT

Perodipus microps preblei Goldman, Jour. Mammalogy, 2:233. November 29, 1921. Type from Narrows, Malheur Lake, Harney County, Oregon.

Distribution.—In Idaho, known only from northern Owyhee County.

Description.—Size medium; general dorsal coloration dark cinnamon buff; chin, abdomen, front legs, hip stripe, and postauricular patches white; black stripes on tail wider than lateral white ones; lining of cheek pouches dusky; hind foot broad and usually over 41 mm. in length; incisors slightly recurved and subequally grooved; maxillary arch narrow, usually less than 4 mm. External measurements of an adult male from near Murphy are 261-155-43-13.

Remarks.—For comparison with *D. o. columbianus* see under account of same. The four specimens from Idaho differ from topotypes of *preblei* in larger hind foot, longer skull, wider maxillary arches, longer nasals, longer maxillary tooth row, and greater mastoidal breadth. Until additional material is available, they seem best referred, among named races, to *preblei*.

Records of occurrence.—Specimens examined, 4, all from 5 mi. SE Murphy, Owyhee County.

Family CASTORIDAE
BEAVERS

Large, robust, aquatic rodents; fur soft; eyes small; ears short, valvular, nearly concealed by pelage; tail scaly, paddle-shaped and flattened in horizontal plane; hind feet large, webbed. Skull: rostrum broad and deep; brain case narrow and angular; basioccipital with conspicuous pitlike depression; auditory bullae large, composed of dense, noncancellous bone; auditory tube long; stapedial artery small and apparently (determination from cleaned skulls only) passing to one side of stapes; pterygoid fossae deep; infraorbital canal much smaller than incisive foramen; cheek teeth not ever-growing, but excessively hypsodont and lophodont.

According to Stirton (1935) the oldest beavers found are from Oligocene deposits. They were numerous in the

Middle- and Upper Tertiary and common in the Pleistocene. In Idaho the fossil species *Castor accessor* is known from Upper Pliocene and Lower Pleistocene deposits near Nampa (Hay, 1927) and at Hagerman (Wilson, 1933). Because these essentially aquatic mammals can travel overland from one stream to another, they have occupied most of the watercourses in the state.

In the early part of the nineteenth century, beavers, then abundant in Idaho, attracted many trappers who, in spite of incredible hardships, reaped a "golden harvest." Alexander Ross sums up the activities of his party for one season (1824) in southern Idaho in the following words: "Our returns were the most profitable ever brought from the Snake country in one year; amounting to 5000 beaver, exclusive of other peltries" (Davis, 1935). It was not uncommon for them to capture 100 beavers in a single night; on Big Wood River their average nightly catch in a period of ten days was 55. Although beavers now are greatly reduced in numbers, as compared with 1824, Idaho is fortunate in being well stocked with these valuable rodents. Almost every suitable river and mountain stream has a colony or two. Their value lies not in the pelt alone, but more in the fact that they construct dams which conserve water and tend to equalize the flow of a given stream.

Bailey (1927) reviews briefly the habits and life history of beavers. The animals are colonial; often more than one family group live in the same pond. Their food consists chiefly of the bark and cambium layer of deciduous trees such as willow, cottonwood, and quaking aspen. Females begin breeding when one year old, and the young, three to eight in number, are born in May or June.

A critical examination of ten specimens of beaver from southern Idaho indicates the existence there of an unnamed race which is named and described below.

Genus **Castor** Linnaeus
Beavers

Castor canadensis taylori, new subspecies
SNAKE RIVER BEAVER

Type.—Female, adult, skin and skull; no. 67588, Mus. Vert. Zool.; from Big Wood River, near Bellevue, Blaine County, Idaho; collected April, 1935, by J. M. Wright; original no. 1137, W. B. Davis.

Diagnosis.—A beaver most closely related to *Castor canadensis baileyi* Nelson. Color: Similar to that of *baileyi*, but averaging darker. Skull: Nasals long and narrow (breadth averaging 46 per cent of their length); anterolateral rim of orbit narrow (near 7.0 mm.); occiput nearly vertical.

Range.—The Snake River drainage basin in southern Idaho and northern Nevada.

Comparisons.—Color: Much lighter than *Castor canadensis pacificus* Rhoads, *Castor canadensis leucodonta* Gray, and *Castor canadensis sagitattus* Benson. Similar to *baileyi*, but darker, both dorsally and ventrally. All skins examined of *taylori* are in winter pelage (February and April), while those of *baileyi* are in summer pelage (July and October). Skull: Compared with *leucodonta:* Nasals narrower and more elliptical in dorsal outline (save one specimen, no. 235533, U. S. Nat. Mus., from Boise); bullae smaller; rostral ridges weaker; anterolateral rim of orbit narrower; in adults occiput vertical rather than inclined posteriorly. Compared with *pacificus:* Smaller; nasals shorter and, viewed from above, elliptical in outline (save the one adult from Boise, mentioned above, and in young specimens), rather than parallel anteriorly and constricted posteriorly; no flat triangular area at junction of sagittal and occipital crests; rostral ridges weaker. Compared with *sagittatus:* Rostrum, anterolateral rim of orbit, and nasals narrower, the last less bowed. Compared with *baileyi:* Incisors smaller and less recurved; anterolateral rim of orbit narrower (7.0 mm. as compared with 9.0 mm.); crown length of maxillary teeth greater (28.5 mm. as compared with 26 mm.). Compared with the Pleistocene beaver, *Castor accessor* Hay, described from a right lower fourth premolar recovered from fossil beds near Nampa: The second inner fold in Recent specimens from Idaho is not extended anterolaterally as it is in *accessor*, but is directed laterally and passes posteriorly to the outer enamel fold. To determine possible alteration in position of the last inner fold by wear, I ground a tooth of *C. c. taylori* down nearly to its base and found no appreciable change.

Remarks.—Color of beavers in western North America varies in much the same fashion as that of many other kinds of mammals. It is darkest in the humid, cool northwestern region and palest along the Colorado River in the southwestern desert region. The races in intervening territory offer a transitional series between these two extremes. Races occurring in the Great Valley of California, in the Great Basin proper, and in the southern half of Idaho resemble one another in color.

In the absence of specimens of *pacificus*, I have relied upon the comparative descriptions and figures of Benson (1933), Rhoads (1898), and Taylor (1916).

Although I have not seen the specimens from Teton Canyon listed by Merriam (1873:665), nor the broken skull from the South Fork of the Owyhee River, and although the 4 specimens from Goose Creek are so young that they cannot be identified beyond species, I would tentatively refer all these to *taylori* on the basis of geographic probability.

Specimens examined.—Total number, 15, as follows: IDAHO. *Ada County:* Boise River, 5 mi. W Boise, 4 (U. S. Nat. Mus.) ; South Fork Owyhee River, 12 mi. N Nevada Line, 1. *Lemhi County:* Salmon (City?), 1 (U. S. Nat. Mus.). *Blaine County:* Big Wood River, near Bellevue, 4. *Bannock County:* Portneuf River, 10 mi. NW Pocatello, 1. NEVADA. *Elko County:* Goose Creek, 4.

Castor canadensis sagittatus Benson
BARKERVILLE BEAVER

Castor canadensis sagittatus Benson, Jour. Mammalogy, 14:320. November 13, 1933. Type from Indianpoint Creek, 3200 feet, 16 miles northeast of Barkerville, British Columbia, Canada.

Distribution.—Probably the northern part of the state, south to the Clearwater hydrographic basin.

Remarks.—A single subadult skull is my only record of beaver from northern Idaho. As compared with specimens from southern Idaho, this one is strikingly different, especially in the rostral area. The nasal bones are actually, and relative to their breadth, shorter; they have a "stubby" appearance. Of the named races of beaver occupying the northwestern portion of North America which I have had available for comparison, this specimen resembles *sagittatus* more than any other. I have seen no actual specimens of *C. c. pacificus* or *C. c. missouriensis*, with which the beaver of northern Idaho should be compared before positively identifying it as of the subspecies *sagittatus*.

Record of occurrence.—*Bonner County:* Coolin (Biol. Surv. coll.).

Castor canadensis taylori
Cranial measurements in millimeters

Museum catalogue number	Sex and age		Basilar length of Hensel	Zygomatic breadth	Mastoidal breadth	Cranial breadth	Least interorbital breadth	Length of nasals	Width of nasals	Alveolar length of maxillary tooth row	Vertical diameter of foramen magnum
235532	♂	ad Boise (U. S. Nat. Mus.)	120.5	94.4	64.6	46.5	24.8	51.0	21.6	31.3	14.1
235533	♂	ad Boise (U. S. Nat. Mus.)	116.6	94.0	67.1	43.3	24.8	48.6	24.9	29.8	16.0
235534	♂	sad Boise (U. S. Nat. Mus.)	.....	89.1	62.6	45.5	25.0	46.2	23.2	29.1	.....
67588	♀	ad Bellevue (Mus. Vert. Zool.)	116.1	95.3	67.2	44.0	25.8	50.0	22.6	29.8	16.5
67585	♂	ad Bellevue (Mus. Vert. Zool.)	119.3	.....	70.4	44.9	23.4	51.5	.....	29.8	16.0
67587	♀	sad Bellevue (Mus. Vert. Zool.)	104.2	86.7	63.8	45.0	23.6	45.1	21.0	28.7	15.0
67586	♂	sad Bellevue (Mus. Vert. Zool.)	.....	90.8	64.6	46.0	24.5	47.3	21.5	30.5	.....
243421	♂	sad Salmon (U. S. Nat. Mus.)	107.5	88.1	62.7	45.3	25.1	46.7	21.5	29.8	15.1

Family CRICETIDAE
CRICETID RATS and MICE

This family includes many native New World rats and mice and certain Old World forms (Microtinae). The geologic history of the family is incompletely known back of the Pleistocene. The genus *Peromyscus,* however, has been recorded from Upper Miocene (Mascall) deposits in Oregon (Merriam and Sinclair, 1907). This circumstance suggests that the subfamilies Cricetinae and Microtinae diverged at a relatively early time and, also, that the Cricetinae have been present in North America long enough for the differentiation of the genus *Peromyscus.* At this writing I know of no fossil Cricetinae recorded from Idaho. The Microtinae are known from Pleistocene deposits near Hagerman, Idaho. Remains of *Synaptomys,* now restricted in range to Canada and Alaska, and *Mimomys,* now extinct, occur there.

Subfamily CRICETINAE
WHITE-FOOTED MICE, PACK RATS, and Allies

Genus **Onychomys** Baird
Grasshopper Mice

Small, robust rodents; ears large, projecting well beyond fur; tail about twice the length of hind foot; body and tail bicolor, white below, gray or brownish above; hind foot with four plantar tubercles, proximal half of foot haired; skull smooth, rostrum short, zygomatic arches weak; cheek teeth three on each side, the first one nearly as long as the other two combined; upper incisors ungrooved; lower jaw with long, backward-projecting coronoid process (in *Peromyscus* this process is rudimentary); all three cheek teeth visible when lower jaw is viewed from the side.

Although grasshopper mice are related to, and superficially resemble, white-footed mice, they possess many distinctive characters. The markedly shorter tail, larger front feet, and four plantar tubercles on the soles of the hind feet readily distinguish them from *Peromyscus.*

In Idaho, grasshopper mice appear to be restricted to

the Great Basin part of the state where they occupy a variety of habitats. The specimen from near Michaud was taken on fine clay soil; another from Double Springs was trapped on fine gravelly soil, and a third from near Fort Hall was obtained on fine sand. Their presence in areas where the soil is fine probably is correlated with their requirements for frequent "dust baths" which tend to prevent the accumulation of excessive amounts of natural oil on the fur. Altitudinally, they range from slightly over 2,000 feet, at Weiser, to over 8,000 feet.

The vernacular name "Grasshopper Mouse" was applied by early collectors who found that the stomach of nearly every specimen collected contained grasshoppers. Invertebrates of many kinds, especially insects and arachnids, are readily eaten, but when such food is not available the mice possibly subsist upon small mammals which in captivity they are known to be able to capture and kill. Probably they eat also vegetable matter.

Grasshopper mice are nocturnal and almost exclusively terrestrial in habit. Bailey and Sperry (1929) found that captives rarely attempted to climb even the wire netting of their cages. The disinclination to climb probably is correlated with the short tail, for in *Peromyscus* climbing ability appears to be directly proportional to the relative length of the tail. The large, strong claws on the forefeet are effective in capturing and holding their prey, be it a grasshopper or a mouse. "Most significant, however, is the manner in which a mouse of approximately similar size is grasped with the claws in a death struggle, and while fighting is held and turned until the back of the head is within reach of a daggerlike thrust of the long keen lower incisors, which penetrate the brain and instantly end the struggle." (Bailey and Sperry, *op. cit.*, p. 8.)

No data are available concerning their breeding habits in Idaho. Svihla (1936), working with captive mice of this genus, found that the young are born blind, hairless, and helpless. Their eyes open in about twenty days and at this time they practically were weaned. The gestation period varied from 32 to 47 days, depending on whether the female was lactating or not.

Two races of the species *O. leucogaster* occur in Idaho. These differ only in color, and single specimens are difficult to identify; *fuscogriseus*, especially the young, is darker than *brevicaudus*.

Onychomys leucogaster brevicaudus Merriam
SHORT-TAILED GRASSHOPPER MOUSE

Onychomys leucogaster brevicaudus Merriam, N. Amer. Fauna, 5:52. July 30, 1891. Type from Blackfoot, Bingham County, Idaho.

Distribution.—In Idaho, the semi-arid southern part of the state from Owyhee County east into Wyoming and north to Pahsimeroi Valley (see map, fig. 20).

Description.—Upper parts in adults rich glossy avellaneous; under parts white. Subauricular tufts white at base, buffy distally. Young: above uniform mouse gray; ear tufts inconspicuous. External measurements of an adult female from near Michaud are 128-36-20-18.

Records of occurrence.—Specimens examined, 3, as follows: *Custer County:* Double Springs, 16 mi. NE Dickey, 1 (Davis coll.). *Bingham County:* 1 mi. N Fort Hall, 1. *Power County:* 5½ mi. SW Michaud, 1. Additional records (Hollister, 1914:443): *Owyhee County:* Murphy. *Elmore County:* Glenns Ferry. *Minidoka County:* Minidoka. *Butte County:* Big Lost River. *Bingham County:* Blackfoot. *Bear Lake County:* Montpelier Creek.

Onychomys leucogaster fuscogriseus Anthony
GRAY GRASSHOPPER MOUSE

Onychomys leucogaster fuscogriseus Anthony, Bull. Amer. Mus. Nat. Hist., 32:11. March 7, 1913. Type from Ironside, 4,000 feet, Malheur County, Oregon.

Distribution.—In Idaho, west central part of the state (see map, fig. 20).

Description.—Similar to *brevicaudus*, but darker.

Records of occurrence.—(Hollister, 1914:444): *Washington County:* Weiser. *Canyon County:* Nampa.

Genus **Reithrodontomys** Giglioli
American Harvest Mice

Smallest of the Idaho mice; ears large and conspicuous, inside of pinna covered with short, rusty-colored hairs; body and tail bicolor, white, or grayish white, below, brownish above; tail nearly as long as head and body; brain case smooth and rounded, jugal weak; upper incisors distinctly

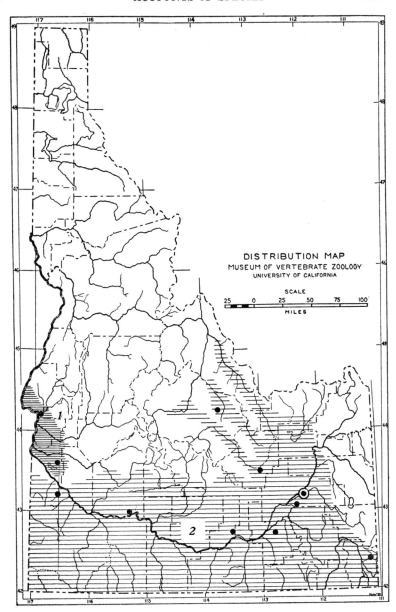

FIG. 20. Map showing the distribution of grasshopper mice in Idaho.
Dots indicate localities whence specimens have been examined or recorded. 1. *Onychomys leucogaster fuscogriseus*, 2. *Onychomys
leucogaster brevicaudus*.

and subequally grooved; cheek teeth three in each jaw, tuberculate, first molar largest, last one smallest; coronoid process of mandible rudimentary.

These small mice often are confused with immature house mice, *Mus musculus*, but may be differentiated by their slightly smaller size, grooved, rather than smooth, upper incisors, and two, rather than three, longitudinal rows of cusps on the upper molars. From *Peromyscus*, harvest mice are distinguished by smaller size, grooved upper incisors, and presence of short rusty-colored hairs in the external ears.

In Idaho, harvest mice have been taken only in the southern half of the state but in a variety of habitats. Usually they frequent meadows in association with meadow mice, *Microtus*, but they occur also in marshes, along weed-covered ditch banks, and occasionally amid nearly typical desert conditions. At Salmon Creek we found them among boulders at the base of a basaltic outcropping in association with pocket mice, *Perognathus*, and white-footed mice, *Peromyscus*. Near Fort Hall, Whitlow (MS) trapped one on fine, sandy soil in association with pocket mice and grasshopper mice.

These creatures are nocturnal and largely terrestrial in habit; however, they can climb. Howell (1914:11) reports them nesting in old woodpecker holes in fence posts and in vines, bushes, and trees some distance above the ground. For the most part they live above ground and construct globular surface nests; frequently they associate with meadow mice and make use of their runways through the grass. Underground burrows, probably vacated by other small rodents, also are used. Their food consists almost entirely of green vegetation and seeds; some animal matter is consumed.

The breeding season in Idaho extends from April to June. Gravid females have been collected May 14 and 31; half-grown young were found in late May at Crane Creek. The length of the breeding season throughout the range of the genus seems to be correlated with geographic position, hence, perhaps with climatic conditions. According to Howell (*ibid.*), in tropical regions the mice breed throughout the year. At Berkeley, California, Smith (1936) found gravid females in each month of the year except January, but the incidence of pregnancy was highest in April, May, and June. None of the females collected in Idaho after May was pregnant.

The center of distribution of the genus is in Mexico; the northern limit of its range in the West runs through southeastern Washington, southern Idaho, and southern Montana. I cannot detect differences in specimens taken on opposite sides of the Snake River. Because of this, I infer that the river has had but little, if any, effect as a barrier. The mice are active throughout the year and could cross easily from one side to the other in winter when the river is frozen over.

Two races of the species *R. megalotis* are ascribed to Idaho. These differ chiefly in color; *nigrescens*, especially in winter, is alleged to be darker than *megalotis*.

Reithrodontomys megalotis megalotis (Baird)
GREAT BASIN HARVEST MOUSE

Reithrodon megalotis Baird, Mamm. N. Amer., 1857:451. Type from between Janos, Chihuahua, and San Luis Springs, New Mexico.

Distribution.—In Idaho, Great Basin region of the state from Oregon east probably into Wyoming; north to Fremont County, and south into Nevada and Utah (see map, fig. 21).

Description.—Dorsal coloration grizzled grayish ochraceous, median dorsal area darker; ventral portions grayish white; decidedly darker in winter. External measurements of seven adults from Salmon Creek average 141-66-16.5-15.

Remarks.—See under *Remarks* in account of *nigrescens*.

Records of occurrence.—Specimens examined, 26, as follows: *Canyon County:* 2 mi. S Melba, 1; Nampa, 1; 4 mi. S Wilder, 2. *Owyhee County:* Castle Creek, 8 mi. S Oreana, 1; 2½ mi. E Jordan Valley, 1; South Fork Owyhee River, 12 mi. N Nevada Line, 3. *Gooding County:* 2 mi. S Hagerman, 4. *Twin Falls County:* Salmon Creek, 8 mi. W Rogerson, 7. *Jefferson County:* Menan, 1. *Bingham County:* 1 mi. N Fort Hall, 1. *Power County:* Bannock Creek, 10 mi. NW Pocatello, 1. *Bannock County:* Pocatello, 3. Additional records (Howell, 1914:29): *Power County:* American Falls. *Bannock County:* Swan Lake.

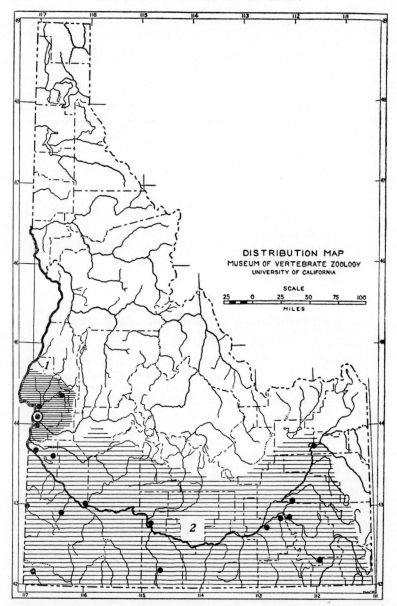

FIG. 21. Map showing the distribution of harvest mice in Idaho. Dots
indicate localities whence specimens have been examined or recorded.
1. *Reithrodontomys megalotis nigrescens*, 2. *Reithrodontomys megalotis
megalotis*.

Reithrodontomys megalotis nigrescens Howell
DUSKY HARVEST MOUSE

Reithrodontomys megalotis nigrescens Howell, N. Amer. Fauna, 36:32. June 5, 1914. Type from Payette, Payette County, Idaho.

Distribution.—In Idaho, extreme west-central part of the state (see map, fig. 21).

Description.—Similar to *megalotis* but darker, especially in winter. External measurements of three adult topotypes average 145-70-17-15.

Remarks.—I have examined thirty-five specimens of *Reithrodontomys* from Idaho, including three topotypes of *nigrescens*. The diagnostic characters mentioned by Howell in the original description of *nigrescens* are: "Similar to *megalotis*, but upper parts more blackish and less buffy," and skull "closely similar to *megalotis*, but with slightly longer nasals." I have compared my topotypes of *nigrescens* and the specimens from Crane Creek (herein referred to *nigrescens*) with other specimens from Idaho; with specimens of *nigrescens* from Prescott, Washington, and Narrows, Oregon; and with specimens of *megalotis* from Nye, Washoe, White Pine, and Lyon counties, Nevada. In respect to the length of nasals, I find that *megalotis* and *nigrescens* are identical. The average of fourteen specimens of *megalotis* from Nevada is 8.0 mm.; that of *nigrescens* is also 8.0 mm. (Howell, *op. cit.*, p. 81).

I have no winter-taken specimens of *nigrescens* from Idaho, at which time the dark color of the dorsum is alleged to be accentuated, but winter-taken specimens from Montague, California (a locality assigned to *nigrescens* by Grinnell, 1933:170), are only slightly darker than winter-taken specimens of *megalotis* from Reno, Nevada, and Pocatello, Idaho. Summer-taken specimens from Payette and Crane Creek (referred to *nigrescens*) average slightly darker dorsally than summer-taken specimens from other localities in Idaho (referred to *megalotis*), and from Nevada; in this respect they are like skins from Prescott, Washington. Since this difference is only slight and because a considerable amount of individual variation in color occurs in specimens from one locality, it seems, to me, that color alone is not a trustworthy subspecific character in these mice. The material seen causes me to doubt the validity of this race.

Records of occurrence.—Specimens examined, 13, as follows: *Washington County:* Crane Creek, 15 mi. E Midvale, 10 (Ralph Ellis coll.). *Payette County:* 2 mi. S Payette, between Payette and Snake rivers, 3. Additional records (Howell, 1914:33): *Washington County:* Weiser. *Payette County:* Payette. Howell also lists five specimens from Nampa, Canyon County, under *nigrescens.* The single specimen I have examined from this locality is very light and certainly is to be referred to *megalotis.*

Genus **Peromyscus** Gloger
White-footed Mice

Mice with large, nearly hairless ears projecting well beyond the fur; tail nearly as long as, or longer than, head and trunk, usually bicolored, white below, dark above; body and head bicolored, white below, dark above; eyes large, black; soles of hind foot with six tubercular pads (five in subgenus *Podomys,* which is not found in Idaho), proximal portion of sole usually hairy; skull smooth, rounded; incisors ungrooved; cheek teeth three in each jaw, the first one largest, in unworn condition with two rows of cusps.

Individuals of this genus are among the commonest mammals found in Idaho. Usually they are terrestrial in habit, but certain races are excellent climbers. Svihla (1933:13) reports that the long-tailed *Peromyscus m. oreas* of western Washington is partly arboreal. Perhaps in these mice the relative length of the tail is a good index to climbing ability, for in such activity a long tail would be useful in maintaining balance. If this be true, the long-tailed mice found in the forested areas in central Idaho may be more arboreal in habit than any of the other races of *Peromyscus* occurring in the state, with the possible exception of the canyon mouse, which is adapted to climbing about in the rocks.

These mice are nocturnal. Trapping records indicate that they leave their daytime abodes early in the evening and remain abroad until shortly after sunup. They live usually in underground burrows or in crevices among rocks; not infrequently individuals are found in or under human habitations in the less densely settled regions. Their food consists of herbage, seeds, roots, bark, and fruits; in fact, nearly anything is eaten which provides nourishment.

White-footed mice do not hibernate. At Elba, early in January, 1936, I studied their activities in winter as recorded by tracks in the snow. A number of individuals had taken up winter quarters in a pile of logs from which they ventured nightly in search of food. The tracks of one animal led from this pile of logs to one sagebrush plant after another in a wandering fashion to the edge of a bare field some 100 yards distant and then back to the starting place. Bits of bark, leaves, and seed coats scattered on the snow beneath many of the bushes indicated that the mouse had climbed into the tops of these in quest of food.

I can detect no differences between specimens from opposite sides of the Snake River. The mice are active throughout the year and could easily cross from side to side in winter when the river is frozen over. In addition, they are excellent swimmers. Orr (1933) records that an individual of *P. m. artemisiae* observed at Cuddy Mountain voluntarily jumped into a fast-flowing stream fully ten feet wide and rapidly swam to the opposite bank.

These rodents are prolific. My data indicate that the breeding season extends from January to August and that several litters of from 3 to 7 young may be reared by each breeding female yearly. Svihla (1932) reports that several females of the subgenus *Peromyscus* kept in the laboratory gave birth to as many as eleven litters in one year. The average gestation period as determined by him is 23 days, and the young are born blind, hairless, and helpless. They grow rapidly and when about four weeks old are weaned.

Two species, each of a different subgenus, occur in Idaho.

Key to White-footed Mice of Idaho

1 Tail considerably longer than head and body, dorsal dark stripe as wide as ventral whitish one; pelage exceedingly long and silky; mammae in two pairs.   **Subgenus HAPLOMYLOMYS**
P. c. crinitus, p. 286

1' Tail shorter than head and body, dorsal dark stripe never as wide as ventral white one; pelage shorter; mammae in three pairs.
Subgenus PEROMYSCUS

   2 Hind foot 22 mm. or less; ears 20 or less; tail usually less than 85; subauricular patches usually inconspicuous.

3 Dorsal coloration dark, seldom ochraceous; occipitonasal
   length averages 26.5.   **P. m. artemisiae, p. 288**

3' Dorsal coloration usually ochraceous buff; occipitonasal
   length usually less than 26.   **P. m. sonoriensis, p. 292**

2' Hind foot over 22; ears more than 20; tail usually more than
   87; subauricular patches usually conspicuous.

                                     P. m. serratus, p. 290

Peromyscus crinitus crinitus (Merriam)
CANYON MOUSE

Hesperomys crinitus Merriam. N. Amer. Fauna, 5:53. July 30,
1891. Type from Shoshone Falls, north side Snake River, Jerome
County, Idaho.

Distribution.—Basaltic outcroppings and canyons in southern
Idaho from near Twin Falls west into Oregon and south into Nevada
(see map, fig. 22).

Description.—Length about 183 mm.; pelage long, soft, and silky;
tail usually longer than head and body, bicolored with brownish dorsal
stripe wider than whitish ventral one, densely covered with short hairs
and with annulations of epidermal scales clearly discernible; color of
upper parts pale ochraceous buff uniformly mixed with dusky; under
parts whitish; two pairs of mammae, inguinal in position; brain case
broad, low, and rounded; rostrum narrow; zygomatic breadth but little
greater than breadth of cranium; palate nearly as long as incisive
foramina; infraorbital canal high and relatively narrow; three cheek
teeth on each side. External measurements of five adult males and
five adult females from Twin Falls County average respectively 183-
94-20-19 and 182-97-20-19. Young are bluish gray in color, but in
proportions of external parts similar to adults.

Comparisons.—Differs from *Peromyscus maniculatus* as follows:
Pelage longer and silkier; tail equal to or longer than head and body,
rather than shorter than head and body; dark dorsal tail stripe wider
than whitish ventral one, rather than the reverse; mammae in two
pairs, rather than in three; brain case more inflated; zygoma less
bowed; rostrum narrower; palatal length about 90 per cent of length
of incisive foramina, as opposed to about 65 per cent of same.

Remarks.—As its name implies, this mouse occurs most
commonly in the numerous rocky canyons and on basaltic
"rimrocks" in southern Idaho. At Salmon Creek it was
caught in numbers at the bottom of a deep gorge in the
lava beds through which the creek flowed. *Peromyscus
maniculatus* appeared to be restricted here to the sage
plains and smaller basaltic outcroppings on each side of

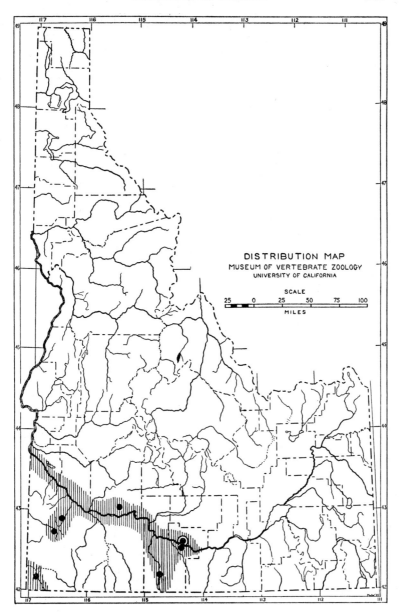

FIG. 22. Map showing the distribution of the canyon mouse, *Pero-myscus crinitus crinitus*, in Idaho. Dots indicate localities whence specimens have been examined or recorded.

the canyon. At Shoshone Falls, both *crinitus* and *maniculatus* occurred in the bottom of the canyon on both sides of the river but *crinitus* was caught only at the bases of rocky ledges and in the numerous "caves" where it associated with the pack rat, *Neotoma cinerea; maniculatus* inhabited areas in which *Artemisia* occurred.

Half-grown young in the bluish gray pelage were taken June 4 on the rimrock near Hammett. A female collected July 11 at Shoshone Falls contained five nearly full term embryos, and on the same day a nearly full grown young was taken which was acquiring its first adult pelage. These data suggest a long breeding season and two or more litters for each breeding female yearly.

Records of occurrence.—Specimens examined, 31, as follows: *Owyhee County:* Castle Cr., 8 mi. S Oreana, 1; South Fork Owyhee River, 12 mi. N Nevada Line, 7. *Elmore County:* Rimrock, 3 mi. NE Hammett, 4 (1 in Davis coll.). *Jerome County:* N. side Snake River, Shoshone Falls, 2. *Twin Falls County:* S. side Snake River, Shoshone Falls, 2; Salmon Cr., 8 mi. W Rogerson, 15. Additional records (Osgood, 1909:231): *Owyhee County?:* Silver Creek.

Peromyscus maniculatus artemisiae (Rhoads)
COLUMBIAN WHITE-FOOTED MOUSE

Sitomys americanus artemisiae Rhoads, Proc. Acad. Nat. Sci. Philadelphia, 1894:260. October 23, 1894. Type from Ashcroft, British Columbia, Canada.

Distribution.—In general, from the Snake River Plains northward, except in the Sawtooth and Salmon River mountains, into Canada (see map, fig. 23).

Description.—Medium-sized mouse; general dorsal color varying from brownish fawn to dusky brown, median dorsal area usually darker; ventral coloration, except for chin and undersurface of tail, white with plumbeous basal color producing a distinctly grayish appearance; subauricular patches never distinctly white. Average external measurements of six topotypes are 167-75-20.5-16.1 (Osgood, 1909:59); of five adults from Cedar Mountain, 175-85-20; of five adults from near Heath, 176-77-21; of seven adults from near Victor, 173-75-22.

Remarks.—For comparisons see under *P. m. serratus.* Typical *artemisiae* occurs in Idaho from Canada south to the Salmon River. Specimens from Washington and Adams

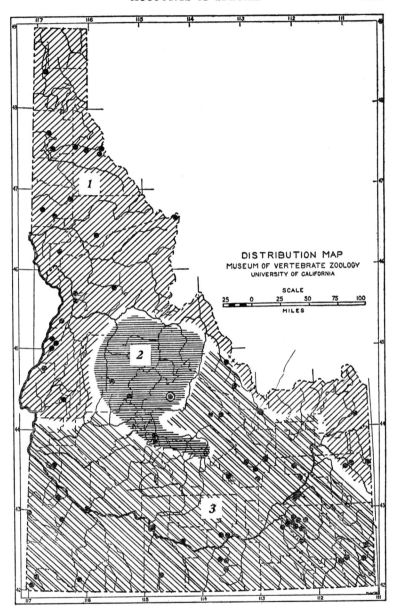

FIG. 23. Map showing the distribution of white-footed mice in Idaho. Dots indicate localities whence specimens have been examined or recorded. 1. *Peromyscus maniculatus artemisiae*, 2. *Peromyscus maniculatus serratus*, 3. *Peromyscus maniculatus sonoriensis*.

counties tend toward *gambelii;* those from near Victor toward *osgoodi;* those from Valley County toward *serratus.* The habitat of *artemisiae* is varied. At Cuddy Mountain, Borell (MS) found it common in wet bogs, along streams, in sagebrush, and from the lowlands to the highest rocky peaks. At Victor, many specimens were taken in the same line of traps in which *Sorex vagrans, Sorex palustris, Microtus mordax, Clethrionomys gapperi,* and *Zapus princeps* were captured. At Glidden Lakes, Orr (MS) took specimens in traps set in grassy, open spaces in the coniferous forest.

Records of occurrence.—Specimens examined, 99, as follows: *Kootenai County:* Coeur d'Alene, 2. *Shoshone County:* Glidden Lakes, 4. *Latah County:* Cedar Mountain, 10 (Chas. R. Conner Mus.); Potlatch River, 5 (Chas. R. Conner Mus.). *Clearwater County:* 2 mi. NE Weippe, 1. *Idaho County:* Castle Creek R. S., 2. *Adams County:* 1 mi. N Bear Cr. R. S., 5 (3 in Ralph Ellis coll.); ½ mi. E Black Lake, 4 (3 in Ralph Ellis coll.); summit Smith Mountain, 2 (Ralph Ellis coll.). *Washington County:* Crane Cr., 15 mi. E Midvale, 15 (Ralph Ellis coll.); 1 mi. N Heath, 18 (12 in Ralph Ellis coll.). *Custer County:* Double Springs, 16 mi. NE Dickey, 4; head Pahsimeroi River, 4. *Fremont County:* Warm River, 1. *Teton County:* 3 mi. SW Victor, 9. *Bonneville County:* N. side Snake River, 3 mi. W Swan Valley, 3; S. side Snake River, 3 mi. W Swan Valley, 10. Additional records (Osgood, 1909:60): *Bonner County:* Priest Lake. *Kootenai County:* Mission. *Shoshone County:* Kingston; Mullan; Osborn. *Latah County:* near Collins. *Clearwater County?:* Bitterroot Mountains. *Lewis County?:* Craig Mountains. *Idaho County:* Fiddle Creek; Freedom; Seven Devils Mountains.

Peromyscus maniculatus serratus, new subspecies
SAWTOOTH WHITE-FOOTED MOUSE

Type.—Female, adult, skin and skull; no. 72330, Mus. Vert. Zool.; Mill Creek, fourteen miles west of Challis, 8370 feet altitude, Custer County, Idaho; collected July 27, 1936, by W. B. Davis; original no. 2290.

Distribution.—Sawtooth and Salmon River mountains in central Idaho; limits of range unknown (see map, fig. 23).

Description.—A member of the *maniculatus* group. Size large (see measurements). Color: Head, shoulders, upper portions of sides, and hips ochraceous buff, broad dorsal stripe darker; ventral parts, cheeks, lower portions of sides, legs, and feet white; tail bicolor, white below with narrow brownish dorsal stripe, terminal hairs white; white subauricular patches conspicuous; distal two thirds of ears black, rimmed with white. Skull: Rostrum long; brain case smooth and large; palate relatively long. Tail averages 92 per cent of length of head and body.

Comparisons.—Compared with *P. m. artemisiae* with which it intergrades toward the west: Distinctly paler, with larger ears and hind feet and longer tail (ratio of tail to head and body, 92, rather than near 80); subauricular patches conspicuous, rather than faint or absent; skull averages larger, cranial portion more inflated; rostrum relatively broader; nasals average longer; auditory bullae larger. Compared with *P. m. sonoriensis* which it resembles most in general coloration: Much larger, with longer tail (ratio of tail to head and body, 92, rather than near 73) and larger ears and hind feet. Skull larger; incisive foramina relatively shorter. Compared with *P. m. osgoodi:* Much larger, with longer tail (ratio of tail to head and body, 92, rather than 68) and larger ears and hind feet.

Measurements.—Average and extreme measurements, in millimeters, of three adults and two subadults from the type locality: Total length, 194 (182-201); length of tail, 93 (89-95); length of hind foot, 24 (24-24); length of ear, from notch, 23 (22-23); occipitonasal length, 27.0 (26.1-27.8); zygomatic breadth, 13.1 (12.4-13.8); length of nasals, 10.7 (10.5-11.3); breadth of cranium, 10.7 (10.5-11.2); length of palate, 4.1 (3.7-4.6); length of incisive foramina, 6.0 (5.8-6.3); postpalatal length, 9.7 (9.2-10.0); length of maxillary tooth row, 3.9 (3.8-4.0). External measurements of an adult male from Alturas Lake are 204-96-24-23.

Remarks.—In size and proportion of external parts this race is nearly as large as *P. m. oreas* of the coastal region of Washington and British Columbia. Although *serratus* occupies territory geographically intermediate between the ranges of *sonoriensis* to the south and *artemisiae* to the west, north, and east, it does not appear to be a race of intergrades or hybrids between the two. For one thing, it is considerably larger than either. Although certain characters of both *sonoriensis* and *artemisiae* are combined in *serratus*, the characters appear to have reached a higher stage of development. For example, *artemisiae* has a longer tail and larger ears and hind feet than *sonoriensis*, but in *serratus* those structures are larger than in *artemisiae*, not intermediate between *artemisiae* and *sonoriensis*. In *sonoriensis* the subauricular patches are white, but not prominent in most instances, while in *artemisiae* they are never white; in *serratus* they are larger and more conspicuous than in *sonoriensis*.

At Mill Creek, *serratus* was caught most frequently in traps set near log piles and brush heaps along the creek. At Alturas Lake specimens were captured in traps set among shrubs in open places in the timber at the north end of the lake; also in traps set near human habitations.

Records of occurrence.—Specimens examined, 25, as follows: *Valley County:* 5 mi. E Warm Lake, 1 (approaching *artemisiae* in size); 5 mi. W Cape Horn, 1. *Custer County:* Mill Creek, 14 mi. W Challis, 13 (1 in Davis coll.). *Blaine County:* Alturas Lake, 10. Four specimens recorded by Osgood (1909:93) from Sawtooth (City?) probably are of this race.

Peromyscus maniculatus sonoriensis (LeConte)
GREAT BASIN WHITE-FOOTED MOUSE

Hesperomys sonoriensis LeConte, Proc. Acad. Nat. Sci. Philadelphia, 6:413. 1853. Type from Santa Cruz, Sonora, Mexico.

Synonyms.—*Hesperomys leucopus*, part, Merriam, 1891:55; *Peromyscus maniculatus osgoodi*, Whitlow and Hall, 1933:262.

Distribution.—Great Basin portion of southern Idaho (see map, fig. 23).

Description.—Size small; dorsal coloration variable, but usually ochraceous buff; ventral portions, including tail, white. Average external measurements of seven adults from Riddle are 168-71-19-17; of six adults from Salmon Creek, 177-75-20-18; of eight adults from Mt. Harrison, 167-70-21-17; of five adults from near Pocatello, 171.5-70-20-17.5. Young are grayish or bluish gray.

Remarks.—For comparisons, see under *P. m. serratus.* Typical *sonoriensis* is found only in the extreme southern portion of the state, where it occurs in a number of habitats. At Riddle, it was taken among bushes of *Artemisia tridentata* and on basaltic outcroppings along Indian Creek. At Mt. Harrison, it was found in numbers at an elevation well over seven thousand feet in *Artemisia tridentata* and in tall herbs among *Populus tremuloides.* At Acequia, it occurred on sandy soil, among *Artemisia tridentata*, in association with *Dipodomys ordii* and *Citellus mollis.*

Specimens from near Pocatello are intergrades between *sonoriensis* and *Peromyscus maniculatus osgoodi* which occurs in typical form in Wyoming and Montana. On the basis of "small size" Whitlow and Hall (1933:262) refer specimens from Pocatello to *osgoodi.* If one averages all specimens "showing wear on the teeth," the results stated by these workers *(ibid.)* are obtained, but if one considers only old adults, the occlusal surfaces of whose molar teeth are much worn, the results are different. Average and extreme external measurements of five such adults are 171.5 (168-177); 70 (66-75); 20 (18-21); 17.5 (17-18). These averages are closer to *sonoriensis* than to *osgoodi* (see Osgood, 1909:90); in fact they are greater, except for length of tail, than the averages of old adults of *sonoriensis* from Riddle. For this reason I herein refer the specimens from Bannock and Power counties to *sonoriensis*, rather than to *osgoodi*.

Records of occurrence.—Specimens examined, 140, as follows: *Canyon County:* 2 mi. S Melba, 8 (approaching *gambelii*); Nampa, 2 (approaching *gambelii*). *Owyhee County:* 2½ mi. E Jordan Valley, 3 (approaching *gambelii*); Castle Cr., 8 mi. S Oreana, 1 (approaching *gambelii*); 5 mi. SE Murphy, 1 (approaching *gambelii*); South Fork Owyhee River, 12 mi. N Nevada Line, 3; Little Owyhee River, 4 mi. N Nevada Line, 1; 1 mi. S Riddle, 8. *Gooding County:* 2 mi. S Hagerman, 3. *Jerome County:* Shoshone Falls, Snake River, 3. *Twin Falls County:* Salmon Cr., 8 mi. W Rogerson, 11. *Minidoka County:* Acequia, 6; 4 mi. N Rupert, 1. *Cassia County:* Elba, 3; Howells Canyon, 8 mi. S Albion, 8; Mt. Harrison, 10 mi. S Albion, 15. *Butte County:* Pioneer, 17 mi. SE Arco, 10 (approaching *artemisiae*). *Bonneville County:* lava beds, 17 mi. W Idaho Falls, 9 (approaching *artemisiae*); Craters of the Moon National Monument, 7. *Bingham County:* lava beds, 7 mi. NW Shelley, 1 (approaching *osgoodi*). *Power County:* Bannock Creek, 1 (approaching *osgoodi*) (Ralph Ellis coll.). *Bannock County* (all approaching *osgoodi*): 3-4 mi. E Pocatello, 16 (3 in Ralph Ellis coll.); 5 mi. W Pocatello, 3; 8 mi. SE Pocatello, 1; Pocatello Creek, 5; Indian Creek, 2; Justice Park, 2; Schutt's Mine, 3; Trail Creek, 1 (Ralph Ellis coll.). *Franklin County:* Strawberry Creek, 20 mi. NE Preston, 1. *Bear Lake County:* W. rim Copenhagen Basin, Wasatch Mountains, 1. Additional records (Osgood, 1909:93): *Lemhi County:* Lemhi. *Butte County:* Arco; Big Butte; Big Lost River. *Clark County:* Birch Creek. *Bingham County:* Blackfoot. *Caribou County:* Crow Creek. *Bear Lake County:* Montpelier Creek. Merriam (1891:56) records 16 specimens from the Salmon River Mountains ["Timber Creek, Lemhi Mountains"] which Osgood *(ibid.)* does not record under any of the races occurring in the state. These probably are to be referred to *sonoriensis*.

Genus **Neotoma** Say and Ord
Wood Rats or Pack Rats

Medium- to large-sized rats; ears large, distal half or two thirds scantily haired, leathery; eyes large, bulging, black; tail more than half the length of head and body, bicolor, white below, dark above; feet white or light colored; brain case narrowing gradually anteriorly; incisive foramina longer than breadth of rostrum; cheek teeth three in each jaw, first one largest, rooted or semirooted, flatcrowned, lophodont; last lower molar with transverse reentrant angles.

Wood rats or "pack rats" may with more appropriateness be called "rock rats" in Idaho, for they occur commonly in rocky situations. Basaltic cliffs, natural caves, and old mine tunnels are favorite haunts. Here their nests, large, bulky structures composed of sticks, grasses, fur, and all sorts of rubbish, are placed in crevices or on protected ledges some distance above the ground. In caves that they have occupied for a long time, masses of hard, flinty, brownish solidified urine are found adhering to the rock walls below the nests. Apparently all the rats in a given colony micturate near one place, for often thick deposits of solidified urine cover several square feet of the rocky walls. These rodents also occupy deserted cabins and other buildings in rural areas.

Wood rats are expert climbers. They experience little difficulty in scaling almost perpendicular rock walls, sides of buildings and trees. In Idaho, this is more true of the bushy-tailed wood rat than of the desert wood rat. For the most part wood rats are nocturnal, but in caves where the light intensity is greatly reduced they often are active in the daytime.

Although largely herbivorous, wood rats eat a variety of foods; seeds, grain, fruit, berries, nuts, and refuse discarded by humans are taken when available. Near Swan Valley one visited our camp during the night and ate nearly a quarter-pound of cheese which had been left on the table. At this same locality a rancher reported that "pack rats" had killed and carried away a number of young chicks.

Whitlow and Hall (1933) record that in stomachs of individuals taken near Pocatello, leaves and bud tips of sagebrush *(Artemisia tridentata)* were found.

In Idaho, the Snake River apparently is not a barrier to the wood rats. They are active throughout the year, and it is possible they cross from side to side in winter when the river is frozen over. This view is supported by the fact that no differences can be detected in specimens from opposite sides of the river.

Two species, of different subgenera, occur in Idaho.

Key to Adult Wood Rats of Idaho

1 Tail bushy; total length over 350 mm.; hind foot 40 or more; occipitonasal length near 50.

    2 Dorsal coloration ochraceous buff, suffused with blackish; auditory bullae large; postpalatine spine absent or greatly reduced; ratio of length of incisive foramina to length of palatal bridge near 124. **N. c. cinerea, p. 297**

    2' Dorsal coloration buff, more heavily suffused with blackish; auditory bullae smaller; postpalatine spine prominent; ratio of incisive foramina to length of palatal bridge near 124.

                  N. c. occidentalis, p. 301

1' Tail terete, never bushy; total length under 300; hind foot under 35; occipitonasal length near 38. **N. l. nevadensis, p. 295**

Neotoma lepida nevadensis Taylor
NEVADA DESERT WOOD RAT

Neotoma nevadensis Taylor, Univ. California Publ. Zool., 5:289. February 12, 1910. Type from Virgin Valley, Humboldt County, Nevada.

Distribution.—In Idaho, southwestern Great Basin portion of the state (see map, fig. 24).

Description.—Adults: General dorsal coloration grayish ochraceous; cheeks, sides, and pectoral areas distinctly buffy; ventral coloration, under side of tail, and feet white; tail terete, bicolor, black or brown above, white below. Young: General coloration bluish slate, dorsal surface of tail nearly black. External measurements of an adult female from near Melba are 285-121-30-30.

Remarks.—Apparently these round-tailed desert wood rats are not common in southern Idaho where they occur in

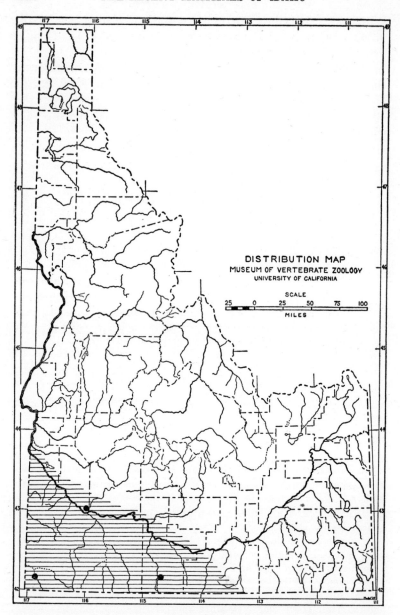

Fig. 24. Map showing the distribution of the Nevada wood rat, *Neo-toma lepida nevadensis*, in Idaho. Dots indicate localities whence specimens have been examined.

isolated colonies in basaltic outcroppings. The two immature specimens from Salmon Creek were collected on a
rocky point about one-half mile east of the dam; those from
near Melba were taken at the foot of rocky cliffs on the
north side of Walters Butte. These localities probably are
near the northern limit of distribution of the species and
they extend its known range considerably to the east and
north.

Four specimens from Canyon and Twin Falls counties
are noticeably different from *Neotoma lepida lepida* as
known to me by specimens from central and southern Nevada. Their closest affinities lie with those desert wood
rats occurring in northern Nevada, southeastern Oregon,
and northeastern California which Taylor described and
named in 1910. All the more important characters which
he ascribes to *nevadensis* are found in the specimens from
Idaho. I have examined Taylor's material, and, in addition,
other specimens from northern Nevada which are referable
to that race. The results of my study accord with Taylor's
views (1911:248) concerning the validity of the name *nevadensis,* and convince me that *nevadensis* is not a synonym
of *lepida.* The six specimens from Owyhee County, received
after the above was written, have not been critically studied.

Records of occurrence.—Specimens examined, 10, as follows: *Canyon County:* 2 mi. S Melba, 2. *Owyhee County:* South Fork Owyhee
River, 12 mi. N Nevada Line, 6. *Twin Falls County:* Salmon Creek,
8 mi. W Rogerson, 2.

Neotoma cinerea cinerea (Ord)
GRAY BUSHY-TAILED WOOD RAT

Mus cinereus Ord, Guthrie's Geog., 2nd Amer. ed., 2:292. 1815.
(Based on ash-colored rat of Rocky Mountains of Lewis and Clark.)
Type locality, Great Falls, Cascade County, Montana.
   Synonyms.—*Neotoma cinerea occidentalis,* part, Goldman, 1919:
102; Whitlow and Hall, 1933:263.
   Distribution.—In Idaho, from Latah County south into Nevada and
Utah, east into Montana and Wyoming (see map, fig. 25).
   Description.—Large, bushy-tailed rat; ears large, prominent, distal
half scantily haired; vibrissae exceedingly long, reaching posteriorly
to, or beyond, shoulders; general dorsal coloration ochraceous buff,
overcast with blackish; ventral portions, under side of tail, and feet

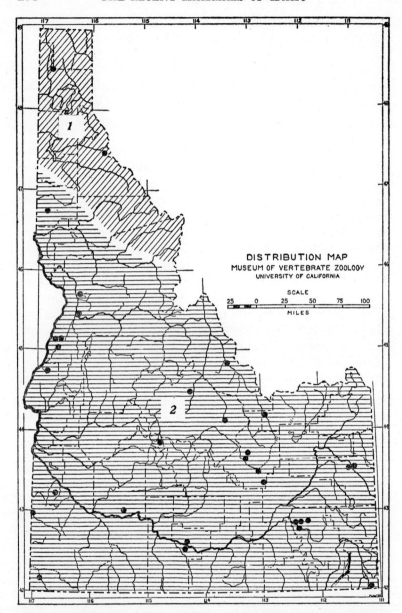

FIG. 25. Map showing the distribution of bushy-tailed wood rats in
Idaho. Dots indicate localities whence specimens have been examined
or recorded. 1. *Neotoma cinerea occidentalis*, 2. *Neotoma cinerea
cinerea.*

white; nasals expanded distally. Young: First pelage black; immature pelage varying from bluish gray to slate gray. External measurements of nine adult females and four adult males from near Pocatello average respectively 370-158-42-33 and 408-168-44-33. An extremely large male from near Heath measures 470-200-49-28.

Remarks.—Apparently placing first reliance upon color in making their decisions, Goldman (1910) and Whitlow and Hall (1933) refer specimens of *Neotoma cinerea* from southern Idaho to *occidentalis*. This race, as illustrated by three specimens, two adults and one immature, from near the type locality, is extremely dark, almost black, dorsally, whereas *cinerea*, the race occurring in Montana and to which specimens from southern Idaho might be referred, is typically ochraceous buff with but slight tendency toward duskiness. Considerable variation in color is present in the large series from near Pocatello. One specimen, in fresh pelage, no. 47058, is bright ochraceous buff, faintly overcast with blackish; the opposite extreme is found in one, no. 46511, in similar pelage which is considerably darker, although not nearly so dark as typical *occidentalis*. All degrees of intermediacy between these extremes are found in the series. Another large series from Adams County exhibits a similar range of color variation, but none of them is as light as the lightest one from near Pocatello. On the average, the specimens examined from Idaho are neither as dark as typical *occidentalis* nor as light as typical *cinerea;* they are intermediate. On the basis of color alone they might, with equal propriety, be referred, among named races, either to *cinerea* or to *occidentalis*.

In searching for morphological characters by which to identify my specimens, I find that the rats from Idaho differ constantly from near topotypes of *occidentalis* in much larger bullae, and absence of distinct postpalatal spine. Because of these osteological differences, I do not feel justified in referring, even as intergrades, any of the specimens from southern Idaho to *occidentalis*. Another argument for excluding *occidentalis* as a possible name for these specimens is that it applies to a *Pacific coastal race occurring west of the Cascades*. None of the other terrestrial rodents occurring in the coastal region of Washington extends in unmodified form to the Columbian Plateau and the Great Basin. The tendency toward darkness in Great Basin specimens I interpret as being due to trends paralleling those of *occidentalis;* one is influenced by dark basaltic surroundings, the other by a humid coastal environment.

With *occidentalis* excluded as a possible name for specimens from southern Idaho, there remain *N. c. orolestes* Merriam, type locality Saguache, Colorado; *N. c. columbiana* Elliot, type locality Ducks, British Columbia; and *N. c. cinerea* (Ord), type locality Great Falls, Montana. Of these, *orolestes* is excluded because the large sphenopalatine vacuities characteristic of that race are absent in specimens from Idaho. Elliot's comments (1899:254) that *columbiana* is lighter colored than *occidentalis* describe the condition of specimens from southern Idaho, but his detailed description *(ibid.,* footnotes on pp. 255-56) of the type, the only specimen he had, does not. Goldman *(op. cit.,* p. 102) examined this type and concluded that the name "*columbianus* was based on a nearly typical specimen of *N. o. occidentalis."* If Goldman implied that this animal closely resembled the coastal animals I have seen, this name, then, cannot be applied to the specimens from Idaho.

As I pointed out earlier, the specimens from Idaho average darker than typical *cinerea;* the ankles are plumbeous, rather than white, and the ochraceous buff of the dorsum is more heavily overcast with blackish. Even with those differences admitted, they are closer in color and cranial characters to *cinerea* than to any other named races. Until additional typical material of *cinerea* is available from Montana for comparison, all the specimens I have examined from Idaho (except from Bonner County) here are referred tentatively to *cinerea.*

The breeding season of *cinerea* in Idaho extends over several months of the year, and probably two or more litters are reared yearly by adult females. Young in the black first pelage were taken from nests near Pocatello, April 3 and May 15. Gravid females were collected May 6 and June 7; half-grown young were collected from the middle of May to the middle of September. The average number of young per litter is 5; one nest found in an old cabin near Murphy on May 23 held 6 young which had their eyes open.

Records of occurrence.—Specimens examined, 54, as follows: *Latah County:* Cedar Mountain, 4 (Chas. R. Conner Mus.). *Idaho County:* Riggins, 2 (David McKaye coll.); 10 mi. S White Bird, 1 (Biol. Surv. coll.). *Adams County:* 1 mi. N Bear Cr. R. S., 4 (Ralph Ellis coll.); ½ mi. E Black Lake, 5 (Ralph Ellis coll.); summit Smith Mountain, 2 (Ralph Ellis coll.). *Washington County:* 1 mi. NE Heath, 2 (Ralph Ellis coll.). *Owyhee County:* 6 mi. W Murphy, 2; 2½ mi. E Jordan Valley, 1; South Fork Owyhee River, 12 mi. N Nevada Line, 2. *Elmore County:* Rimrock, 3 mi. NE Hammett, 1. *Twin Falls County:* Shoshone Falls, 1. *Butte County:* Pioneer, 1. *Bonneville County:* N. side South Fork, 3 mi. W Swan Valley, 1; S. side South Fork, 3 mi. W Swan Valley, 1. *Bannock County:* Pocatello, 4; 4 mi. E Pocatello, 8 (2 in Ralph Ellis coll.); Portneuf, 7 (1 in Ralph Ellis coll.); 1 mi. S Portneuf, 3; Schutt's Mine, 2. Additional records (Goldman, 1910:98 and 102): *Idaho County:* Fiddle Creek. *Lemhi County:* Lemhi. *Custer County:* Challis; Pahsimeroi Mountains. *Blaine County:* Sawtooth (city?). *Jerome County:* Shoshone Falls. *Clark County:* Birch Creek. *Butte County:* Lost River Mountains near Arco; Arco; Big Butte. *Bear Lake County:* N. side Bear Lake.

Neotoma cinerea occidentalis Baird
WESTERN BUSHY-TAILED WOOD RAT

Neotoma occidentalis (Cooper MS) Baird, Proc. Acad. Nat. Sci. Philadelphia, 1855:335. Type from Shoalwater Bay, Pacific County, Washington.

Distribution.—In Idaho, probably restricted to the more humid northern portion of the state (see map, fig. 25).

Description.—Similar in size to *cinerea* but much darker, nearly black, dorsally.

Remarks.—Goldman (1910:102) records specimens of *occidentalis* from the Snake River Plains in Idaho. I have not examined his material, but specimens available from that general region differ importantly in cranial characters as well as in color from near topotypes of *occidentalis* (see remarks under *N. c. cinerea*). For this reason I employ the name *occidentalis* only for specimens from extreme northern Idaho.

Records of occurrence.—Specimens examined, 5, as follows: Priest Lake, 5 (Biol. Surv. coll.). *Shoshone County:* Mullan (Goldman, 1910:102).

Subfamily MICROTINAE
VOLES and LEMMINGS

Genus Phenacomys Merriam
Mountain Voles

Externally, these mice are difficult to distinguish from certain meadow mice *(Microtus)*, particularly those of the short-tailed *montanus* group. The best single diagnostic character of *Phenacomys* is the structure of the molar teeth. No other small microtine in Idaho has the inner re-entrant angles of the lower molars noticeably deeper than the outer ones; all *Microtus* have cement in the re-entrant angles, whereas it is lacking in *Phenacomys*.

In Idaho, *Phenacomys* occur in the mountainous areas where they occupy a range nearly coextensive with that of the coniferous forests. In addition, they often occur above timber line in the numerous alpine heather meadows. Apparently they are absent from the isolated forested mountain masses south of the Snake River.

A study of the present distribution of the *intermedius* group leads me to a conclusion somewhat different from that reached by A. B. Howell (1926) concerning the past history of the terrestrial forms of the genus. Undoubtedly the group is an old one, as evidenced by the rooted molars and the number of recognizably different species, but I hold that it always has occupied a boreal habitat. Had it once been a lowland form that later was forced to a boreal habitat by its inability to compete with more advanced and perhaps better adapted groups *(Microtus* particularly), as Howell *(ibid.)* suggests might have been the case, one would expect it to have retreated altitudinally, as well as latitudinally. In other words, had it been a lowland form during the Pleistocene, its range at that time doubtless would have extended into what is now the Great Basin, and, other things being equal, when the lowland portions of its range were usurped by other better-adapted forms, the impetus to retreat to its present boreal habitat should have been exerted equally in all directions. Hence, we should expect to find relict populations on the isolated mountains in the northern portions of the Great Basin. Not a single specimen is known from any of these mountains in spite of the fact that special efforts have been made to trap them there. Perhaps these mice instead are emigrants from the North which have been unable to extend their range across the lowlands surrounding these mountains. This assumption explains the apparent absence of the genus from all isolated mountains in Idaho, Oregon, Nevada, Utah, Arizona, and California.

At Alturas Lake I caught an adult female in a trap set in a runway in grasses and low shrubs near Alturas Creek; near Payette Lake, Orr (MS) took one in a trap set in a grassy area near a creek, and at Glidden Lakes he captured one in a trap set among sedges. Near the head of the Pahsimeroi River I observed one at an elevation of nearly 9,000 feet on the afternoon of July 23, 1936, at the base of a granite cliff near timber line. It emerged from a thicket of low shrubs about four feet from me, ran unhurriedly across a shelf of rock, and entered a crevice in the rock wall. Although I waited for fully fifteen minutes, it did not reappear. This observation indicates that, like other microtines, *Phenacomys* are not strictly nocturnal.

A female captured at Glidden Lakes, July 23, 1932, contained four embryos which measured 16 mm. in rump-crown length.

Phenacomys intermedius intermedius Merriam
ROCKY MOUNTAIN PHENACOMYS

Phenacomys intermedius Merriam, N. Amer. Fauna, 2:32. October 30, 1889. Type from twenty miles north-northwest of Kamloops, 5500 feet, British Columbia, Canada.

Synonym.—Phenacomys orophilus Merriam, 1891:66 (type locality, Timber Creek, Lemhi Mountains, 10,500 ft., Lemhi County, Idaho).

Distribution.—In Idaho, restricted to the moutainous parts of the state (see map, fig. 26).

Description.—Small, terrestrial rodents; ears of moderate size, rounded, projecting beyond fur, scantily haired; eyes small; tail short, about twice the length of hind foot; color grayish or brownish gray; mammae in four pairs, two inguinal, two pectoral; skull typically microtine in structure; molars rooted in old age, inner re-entrant angles of lower molars much deeper than outer angles, cement lacking in re-entrant angles.

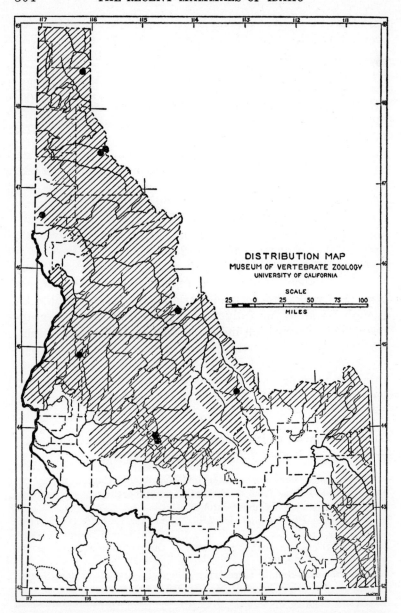

DISTRIBUTION MAP
MUSEUM OF VERTEBRATE ZOOLOGY
UNIVERSITY OF CALIFORNIA

SCALE
25   0   25   50   75   100
MILES

FIG. 26. Map showing the distribution of the mountain vole, *Phena-comys intermedius intermedius*, in Idaho. Dots indicate localities whence specimens have been examined or recorded.

Records of occurrence.—Specimens examined, 7, as follows: *Shoshone County:* Glidden Lakes, 2; Lower Glidden Lake, 1. *Adams County:* 3 mi. W Payette Lake, 1. *Lemhi County:* Horse Creek, 2 (Rocky Mountain Laboratory coll.). *Blaine County:* Alturas Lake, 1 (Davis coll.). Additional records (A. B. Howell, 1926:20): *Bonner County?:* Cabinet Mountains. *Shoshone County:* Mullan. *Latah County:* 8 mi. NE Moscow. *Lemhi County:* Lemhi Mountains (near head of Timber Creek). *Blaine County:* Sawtooth City.

Genus **Clethrionomys** Tsileus
Red-backed Mice

Small, terrestrial rodents; ears large, projecting above fur, scantily haired; eyes small; tail less than three times the length of hind foot, bicolored; dorsal coloration reddish, sides grayish or yellowish; mammae in four pairs, two inguinal, two pectoral. Skull typically microtine in structure; bony palate terminating in a distinct posteriorly projecting bridge (not so in most other microtines); molars rooted, outer and inner re-entrant angles of approximately equal depth; mandible relatively weaker than in *Mictrotus* and *Phenacomys*.

Red-backed mice are boreal creatures and occur throughout the Holartic regions of both the Old World and the New World. Hinton (1926:215-16), in his monograph of the voles and lemmings, separates the American forms of the genus into three groups, each of which, he suggests, has its counterpart in the Old World. According to his view, the American forms would segregate as follows:

GLAREOLUS GROUP: *C. gapperi* and its numerous subspecies; *C. brevicaudus; C. carolinensis;* and *C. idahoensis.*

NAGERI GROUP: *C. phaeus* and *C. wrangeli.*

RUTILUS GROUP: *C. caurinus; C. dawsoni* and its subspecies; *C. orca; C. ungava; C. mazama; C. obscurus; C. occidentalis;* and *C. nivarius.*

He suggests *(loc. cit.)* that *C. californicus, C. mazama,* and *C. proteus* may constitute a fourth group closely related to the Old World *rufocanus* group.

A study of the relationships and distribution of the American forms of the genus leads me to rather different conclusions. This is due, I believe, to the fact that Hinton had available insufficient material, as he points out *(op. cit., p. 3)*, to permit of a detailed study of the American forms. As judged from cranial characters, especially the structure of the palate, and characters of the tail, I should separate the American forms as follows:

RUTILUS GROUP, characterized by incomplete postpalatal bridge until late in life, short, thick tail with closely set bristly hairs, and usually bright colors: *C. rutilus, C. dawsoni dawsoni, C. dawsoni orca, C. dawsoni insularis, C. albiventer.* This group in America is restricted to Alaska and adjacent arctic regions.

GAPPERI GROUP, characterized by complete, posteriorly truncate postpalatal bridge, slender tail set with short hairs except at the tip where they are longer, and usually bright colors: *C. gapperi gapperi, C. gapperi ochraceus, C. gapperi athabascae, C. gapperi rhoadsi, C. gapperi loringi, C. gapperi galei, C. gapperi saturatus, C. gapperi idahoensis, C. brevicaudus, C. carolinensis, C. ungava, C. phaeus, C. caurinus, C. wrangeli, C. limitis, C. proteus.* The range of this group extends from southeastern Alaska and British Columbia southward through the Rocky Mountains and eastward to the Atlantic Ocean.

CALIFORNICUS GROUP, characterized by a complete postpalatal bridge bearing a median, posteriorly directed spine, slender tail covered with short hair, and usually somber colored: *C. californicus californicus, C. californicus mazama, C. californicus obscurus, C. occidentalis,* and *C. nivarius.* This group is restricted to the Cascades and the coastal areas of Washington, Oregon, and northern California.

The *gapperi* and *californicus* groups are not clearly set off from one another; intermediate forms tend to link the two. In color, *C. g. idahoensis* is almost intermediate between *C. c. mazama* and typical *C. gapperi.* In Washington and British Columbia, intermediate stages showing trends from *occidentalis (californicus* group) to *gapperi* are found in *nivarius* from the Olympic Peninsula and *C. caurinus* from the southern coastal area of British Columbia.

I have not had available sufficient material from the

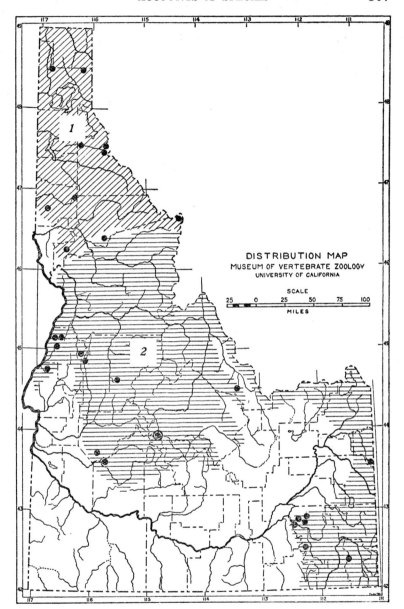

Fig. 27. Map showing the distribution of red-backed mice in Idaho.
Dots indicate localities whence specimens have been examined or
recorded. 1. *Clethrionomys gapperi saturatus,*
2. *Clethrionomys gapperi idahoensis.*

Old World to warrant drawing definite conclusions concerning the relationships of the American forms to those of the Old World. The *gapperi* group may be identical with Hinton's *glareolus* group, but since he reports *(op. cit.,* p. 217) no *glareolus* from east of the Syansk Mountains, 100 miles west of Lake Baikal, in Siberia, it seems probable that the two forms arose from a common stock which diverged early, the two branches undergoing parallel development. The *rutilus* group, on the other hand, occurs at present in Alaska and in Siberia, including the northeastern portion opposite Alaska, and undoubtedly constitutes a natural group which diverged from the *glareolus-gapperi* stem. The *nageri* group at present is confined to Europe and Asia Minor and appears to be a relatively late offshoot from the *glareolus* stem; its affinities are so close to *glareolus* that Miller (1912:641) considered the two as conspecific. None of the American forms I have examined has the simplified M^3 characteristic of the *rufocanus* group which also seems to be an offshoot from the main *glareolus* stem.

In America, the *gapperi* stem appears to have given rise to two groups. One, *gapperi*, followed the general course of the Rocky Mountains southward, thence eastward across boreal Canada to the Atlantic coast; the other, *californicus*, seems to have followed the main axis of the Cascades south through Washington, Oregon, and northern California. This southward extension of range in America probably took place in the Pleistocene, but almost certainly the present southern limits of range of the genus in the West were not reached until late in, or after, that period. The complete lack of *Clethrionomys* in the isolated mountains of southern Idaho, in all of Nevada, and in the Sierra Nevada proper of California supports this view.

The *rutilus* stock seems to have differentiated in Asia and migrated to America in Late Pleistocene after the *gapperi* group had become well established on this continent. Perhaps the Great Ice Sheet played an important role in determining the present distribution of the genus in America. It seems that the *gapperi* group *(gapperi* and *californicus)* moved southward and eastward ahead of the advancing ice; *rutilus* might then have become established on the nonglaciated coastal part of Alaska which at that time probably still was connected by a land bridge with Asia.

In Idaho, red-backed mice occur in scattered colonies throughout most of the mountainous areas. No specimens are available, however, from the isolated mountains south of the Snake River. At Heath, in west central Idaho, Borell (MS) found them occupying a steep wooded hillside; a few were taken along the creek. At Weippe, in the north central part of the state, Orr (MS) took them in traps set in tall grass among lodgepole pines, willows, and smaller shrubs. Near Pocatello, according to Whitlow and Hall (1933:265), they occurred around rotten logs in dry woodland meadows rather than in swampy bogs near the mountain streams. Near Victor, Teton County, I trapped one in tall grass in a grove of quaking aspen *(Populus tremuloides)* along the stream. These data suggest that the *gapperi* group is partial to open, grassy areas in the forests where fallen timber is present; also, that they may occur, on occasion, in typical riparian habitats where they compete more or less directly with meadow mice *(Microtus)*.

These mice do not hibernate. This circumstance permits them to move about freely in winter under the snow. Because of this, the larger rivers in Idaho that freeze over in winter have had but little, if any, effect on their present distribution in that state. Their food consists largely of grasses, but, in season, seeds, bark, and other vegetable materials are eaten. Their nests are constructed in underground burrows, under logs, or under piles of debris. Available data indicate that in Idaho two or more litters, averaging four young each, may be reared yearly. Half-grown young were taken in late June and early July near Heath and Bear Creek; in the same trap lines several gravid females and others showing evidence of having suckling young also were taken.

Two closely related races of the species *C. gapperi* occur in Idaho. These differ mainly in the shape of the cranium and amount of reddish pigmentation on the dorsum; in *idahoensis* the cranium is relatively long and narrow, and the dorsum is dark reddish, in *saturatus* the cranium is more nearly ovoid and the dorsum bright reddish.

Clethrionomys gapperi idahoensis (Merriam)
IDAHO RED-BACKED MOUSE

Evotomys idahoensis Merriam, N. Amer. Fauna, 5:67. July 30, 1891. Type from Sawtooth (Alturas) Lake, 7200 feet, east base of Sawtooth Mountains, Blaine County, Idaho.

Distribution.—In Idaho, from Clearwater County south to the Snake River Plains; from Oregon east to Wyoming, thence south in mountains of southeastern part of state to Utah (see map, fig. 27).

Description.—Dorsal coloration chestnut or hazel, sides grayish, abdomen grayish white, throat patch white; tail distinctly bicolor, whitish below, dark brown above; skull long, slender, and angular (smoothly rounded in young and subadults). External measurements of five adult males and five adult females from Heath and Bear Creek average respectively 152-45-19.4-12 and 156-46-19.6-12.

Comparison.—Compared with *C. g. saturatus:* Cranium narrower; rostrum longer and relatively narrower.

Remarks.—Bailey (1897), in his revision of the American forms of *Clethrionomys,* considered *idahoensis* as differing specifically from all other members of the genus in having clear gray sides, ears not tipped with rufous, and a narrow, smoothly rounded skull. In the account of *C. g. saturatus,* however, he remarks that in external characters *saturatus* resembles *idahoensis* "from which it differs in broad, angular skull, narrower interpterygoid fossa, and in minor details." The cranial characters ascribed to *idahoensis* are evidently those of subadults, for additional material from Idaho reveals that the skulls of adults are not smoothly rounded, but decidedly angular. The only characters that I can find distinguishing *idahoensis* from topotypes of *saturatus* are longer and narrower brain case and slightly more intensely pigmented dorsum. These slight differences suggest no more than subspecific differentiation of the two, and accordingly I follow Whitlow and Hall *(ibid.)* in placing *idahoensis* as a subspecies of *gapperi.*

Specimens from the Blue Mountains of Oregon and from the Idaho side of the Snake River to me are indistinguishable. Also, the Oregon-taken specimens are inseparable from specimens taken in central Idaho. Consequently, I refer the Oregon-taken specimens to *idahoensis* rather than *saturatus,* to which race Bailey (1897 and 1936) refers them. The race *C. g. saturatus* appears to be restricted to northern Idaho and southeastern British Columbia.

Eight specimens, only two of which are adult, from Bannock County, Idaho, approach *C. gapperi galei* of Colorado, and differ from specimens of *idahoensis* from north of the Snake River Plains in having short tails and small auditory bullae. The dark dorsal coloration and narrow cranium, however, are suggestive of *idahoensis*, to which race they tentatively are assigned. The four specimens from Bear Lake County were received too late for critical study and may be the means of giving us a better knowledge of the relationships of *idahoensis* and *galei* if compared with specimens from Utah.

Records of occurrence.—Specimens examined, 85, as follows: *Clearwater County:* 2 mi. NE Weippe, 1. *Adams County:* 1 mi. N Bear Cr. R. S., 17 (16 in Ralph Ellis coll.) ; ½ mi. E Black Lake, 14 (11 in Ralph Ellis coll.) ; 3 mi. W Payette Lake, 6; summit Smith Mountain, 7 (Ralph Ellis coll.). *Valley County:* 5 mi. E Warm Lake, 1. *Washington County:* 1 mi. NE Heath, 26 (20 in Ralph Ellis coll.). *Teton County:* 3 mi. S Victor, 1 (Davis coll.). *Bannock County:* Camp Tendoy, 2; Barrett's Ranch, 2; Indian Creek, 2; N. Fork Pocatello Creek, 1; Schutt's Mine, 1. *Bear Lake County:* N. rim Copenhagen Basin, 4. Additional records (Bailey, 1897:132) : *Lemhi County:* Salmon River Mountains [Timber Creek, Lemhi Mountains]. *Blaine County:* Alturas Lake. Whitlow and Hall (1933:265) record specimens from: *Boise County:* Edna. *Blaine County:* Sawtooth City.

Clethrionomys gapperi saturatus (Rhoads)
KOOTENAI RED-BACKED MOUSE

Evotomys gapperi saturatus Rhoads, Proc. Acad. Nat. Sci. Philadelphia, 1894:284. October 23, 1894. Type from Nelson, on the Kootenai River, 30 miles north of the Washington Line, British Columbia, Canada.

Distribution.—In Idaho, from Canada south to Lewis County (see map, fig. 27).

Description.—Similar to *idahoensis* but with wide, rather than narrow brain case. External measurements of two adults from Cedar Mountain average 140-45-17. These measurements suggest that *saturatus* is slightly smaller than *idahoensis*.

Remarks.—Although intergradation between *saturatus* and *idahoensis* is not evident in the material at hand, I think that specimens from Clearwater County will demonstrate it.

Records of occurrence.—Specimens examined, 13, 12 from Cedar Mountain, Latah County (Chas. R. Conner Mus.), and one from Lower Glidden Lake, Shoshone County. Additional records (Bailey, 1897:129): *Kootenai County:* Mission. *Shoshone County:* Kingston; Mullan. *Lewis County?:* Craig Mountain.

Genus **Microtus** Schrank
Meadow Mice

Members of this genus in Idaho are medium- to large-sized mice with long, loose pelage and comparatively short tails. Ears short, rounded, well furred and nearly concealed by pelage; legs relatively short; thumb vestigal; hip glands usually present in males; molars folded into series of triangles and loops, M_3 with 3 or 4 loops (3 in Idaho); upper incisors ungrooved; general dorsal coloration grayish brown, gradually changing ventrally to grayish.

Typically inhabitants of meadows and streamsides where vegetation is present in quantities sufficient to afford protective cover, these mice construct numerous runways in the course of their foraging activities. Small piles of cut grass and fresh, elongate fecal pellets in the runs, or in small side "rooms," give additional evidence of the presence of meadow mice. The surface runways usually can be followed to openings of underground burrow systems in which nests are located. Since the advent of irrigation these mice have extended their range and are found in hayfields, pastures, weed patches, along irrigation ditches—in fact, in nearly every place where suitable cover and food are available.

In winter, as determined in Nevada by Borell and Ellis (1934:33), they are active and travel considerable distances through or under the snow over areas too dry and open to be occupied in summer. In late summer and autumn the population pressure and the resulting increased competition for the necessities of life must be great and perhaps give impetus to the mice to spread out in winter under the protection of snow. Under favorable circumstances this would lead to wider dispersal of the species. During a period of years when the snowfall is heavy, the maximum essentials for life may be present in areas which, in another part of the climatic cycle, lack even minimum essentials, but which in times of plenty may act as "stepping stones" from one permanently habitable area to another some distance removed. Probably many of the now isolated colonies of these rodents in the Great Basin became established in the manner just indicated.

In summer, their food consists largely of green vegetation and ripening seeds. In winter, they resort to shoots and bark of perennial plants when green plant food is not available. In regions of heavy snowfall, however, this period is relatively short because plants start growing under the snow. Meat-baited traps frequently take *Microtus*, although in nature flesh is thought to be an unimportant part of their diet.

Meadow mice breed throughout the greater part of the year. Hatfield (1935:263) found that in the California meadow mouse *(Microtus californicus)* some females breed at the age of only three weeks, males at twice that age. He found also that the period of gestation is approximately twenty-one days and the number of young in a litter varies directly with the age of the female.

In Idaho there are four species of meadow mice (genus *Microtus*), one of which has two geographic races within the state.

Key to Adult Meadow Mice of Idaho

1 Tail less than 50 mm., less than 40 per cent of length of head and body; hind foot 21 mm. or less.
  2 M^2 with 4 closed angular sections and a rounded, internal, posterior loop; general dorsal coloration blackish brown.
    3 Hind foot near 18 mm.   M. p. drummondii, p. 316
    3 ' Hind foot 20 mm. or more.   M. p. modestus, p. 315
  2 ' M^2 with 4 closed angular sections and no posterior loop; general dorsal coloration grayish, or grayish brown.
                              M. m. nanus, p. 316
1 ' Tail more than 60 mm., more than 40 per cent of length of head and body; hind foot 21 mm. or more.
  4 Medium size, hind foot near 22 mm.
                          M. m. mordax, p. 319
    4 ' Large size, hind foot near 25 mm.
                          M. r. macropus, p. 322

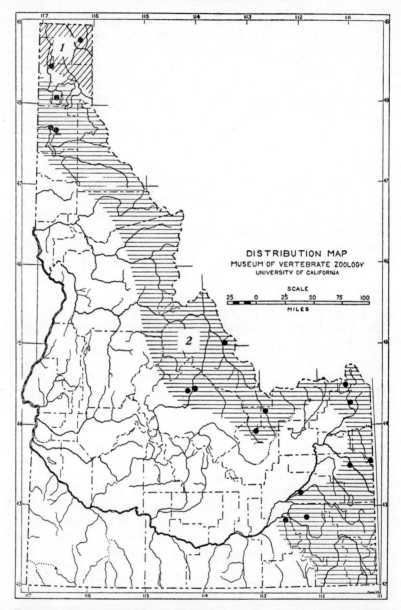

FIG. 28. Map showing the distribution of *pennsylvanicus* meadow mice in Idaho. Dots indicate localities whence specimens have been examined or recorded. 1. *Microtus pennsylvanicus drummondii*, 2. *Microtus pennsylvanicus modestus*.

Microtus pennsylvanicus modestus (Baird)
SAWATCH MEADOW MOUSE

Arvicola modesta Baird, Mamm. N. Amer., 1857:535. Type from Cochetopa (Sawatch) Pass, Saguache County, Colorado.

Synonym.—Arvicola riparius, Merriam, 1891:58.

Distribution.—In Idaho, reaches its western limit of distribution along the western flank of Rocky Mountains from Coeur d'Alene, Kootenai County, southeastward to near Pocatello, Bannock County (see map, fig. 28).

Description.—General dorsal coloration blackish brown; hind foot small (20 to 21 mm. in length); tail less than 40 per cent of length of head and body; second upper molar with four closed triangles and a rounded posterior loop. Differs from *drummondii* in larger size and longer and broader skull. Average external measurements of eight adult specimens from Fremont County, Idaho, are 178-47-21.

Remarks.—In Idaho this race occurs most commonly in the vicinity of water at middle elevations; where cool streams descend from the mountains, its range may extend into the lower valleys. The colonies found at Pocatello and Blackfoot are examples. Like other meadow mice, this one inhabits grassy or marshy areas where cover is available. At Victor it was found in association with jumping mice *(Zapus princeps),* another meadow mouse *(Microtus mordax),* red-backed mice *(Clethrionomys gapperi),* and shrews *(Sorex vagrans);* near Swan Valley it occurred with *Microtus montanus nanus.*

Adults from near Pocatello differ from topotypes of *modestus;* they are larger, heavier, and darker colored. Also, the nasals are relatively shorter, the palate longer, and the postpalatal pits deeper. Specimens from Fremont County near the headwaters of the Snake River, to me, are indistinguishable from topotypes of *modestus.*

Four females collected June 11, 1932, near Pocatello, and two collected August 1, 1935, in Fremont County contained embryos, the average number being 5.4 with extremes of 4 and 6.

Records of occurrence.—Specimens examined, 27, as follows: *Fremont County:* N. fork Snake River, 10 mi. SW Island Park, 3 (Amer. Mus.); 5 mi. S Montana Line at Mt. Jefferson, 7 (Amer. Mus.). *Teton County:* 3 mi. SW Victor, 4 (1 in Davis coll.). *Bonneville County:* S. side South Fork, 3 mi. W Swan Valley, 3. *Bingham County:*

Blackfoot, 1. *Power County:* Bannock Creek, 4 mi. S Portneuf River, 1. *Bannock County:* Rapid Creek, 9½ mi. E Pocatello, 8. Additional records (Bailey, 1900:21): *Kootenai County:* Coeur d'Alene; Fort Sherman. *Lemhi County:* Lemhi Indian Agency. *Custer County:* Challis; Salmon River (near Challis). *Clark County:* Birch Creek.

Microtus pennsylvanicus drummondii (Audubon and Bachman)
DRUMMOND MEADOW MOUSE

Arvicola drummondii Audubon and Bachman, Quadr. N. Amer., 3:166. 1854. Type from "Valleys of the Rocky Mountains," probably in the vicinity of Jasper House, Alberta, Canada.

This meadow mouse is essentially like *modestus*, differing from it in smaller size, narrower skull, smaller hind foot (near 18 mm.), and shorter tail. In Idaho it occurs in the extreme northern portion of the state south to Cocolalla, Bonner County. Most of its range lies north of the United States.

Records of occurrence.—Specimens examined, 6, as follows: *Boundary County:* 4 mi. W Meadow Creek, 2. *Bonner County:* 5 mi. W Cocolalla, 4. Additional records (Bailey, 1900:24): *Bonner County:* Priest Lake.

Microtus montanus nanus (Merriam)
DWARF MEADOW MOUSE

Arvicola (Mynomes) nanus Merriam, N. Amer. Fauna, 5:63. July 30, 1891. Type from Pahsimeroi Mountains, head of Pahsimeroi River, 9350 feet altitude, Custer County, Idaho.

Synonyms.—*Microtus nanus*, Bailey, 1900:30; *Microtus nanus nanus*, Whitlow and Hall, 1933:266.

Distribution.—In Idaho, in general throughout lower valleys from Clearwater drainage basin southwestward into northeastern Oregon; east into portions of Montana and Wyoming; south to Nevada (see map, fig. 29).

Description.—Tail short (averaging about 30 per cent of body length); and hind foot small (usually under 20 mm. in length). Average specimens weigh 35 grams and measure 143-33-18.

Remarks.—In color *nanus* resembles *Microtus mordax,* a long-tailed species, and differs from *Microtus pennsylvanicus,* which has a short tail, in being grayish brown instead of brownish black. This species is the commonest meadow mouse on the Snake River Plains and in the numerous semi-

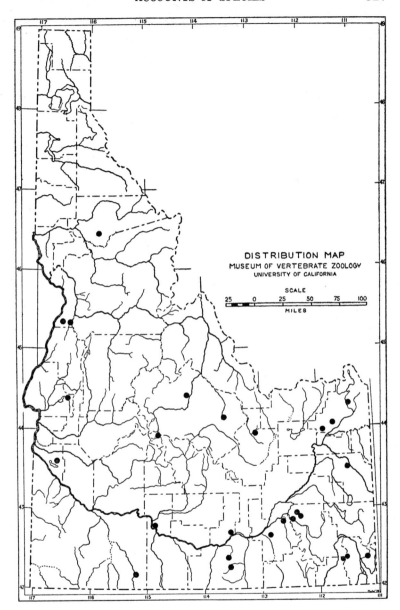

Fig. 29. Map showing the distribution of the dwarf meadow mouse, *Microtus montanus nanus*, in Idaho. Dots indicate localities whence specimens have been examined or recorded.

arid valleys of the Lost River region. Often it is associated with *pennsylvanicus*, but occurs usually in greater numbers at lower elevations than do either *Microtus mordax* or *Microtus richardsoni*. Along the Snake River, *nanus* inhabits sloughs and marshes overgrown with cattails, rushes, and sedges, and, where irrigation is practiced, it lives in hayfields, ditch banks, and pasture lands. In Idaho it apparently has a wider range of tolerance than other meadow mice, for it has been taken at elevations ranging from 2000 feet to over 9000 feet. At higher elevations, however, it is relatively uncommon. There it may be crowded out by the larger *mordax* which is seemingly better adapted to higher altitudes. In the valley at Elba, Cassia County (elevation near 4500 feet), only *nanus* was found, while five miles away on Mt. Harrison, at an elevation of approximately 7000 feet, 500 trap nights yielded only one *nanus* and about thirty *mordax*. When Merriam and his associates visited the head of the Pahsimeroi River in 1890, and took specimens of *nanus*, *mordax* apparently was greatly reduced in numbers, for none was taken. In the summer of 1936 conditions were reversed; two hundred trap nights yielded many *mordax* and only one *nanus*.

Three specimens from Montpelier Creek are too young to identify with certainty. In external appearance they are indistinguishable from young of other races of *montanus* occurring in that general region. *Microtus montanus caryi* has been recorded (Bailey, 1917:30) from Border, Wyoming, only fifteen miles southeast of Montpelier Creek. Possibly adults from southeastern Idaho would be referable to *caryi*. Similarly, the specimens from Three Creek also are young individuals and therefore not certainly identifiable as to subspecies. *Microtus montanus micropus*, described from northern Nevada, may occur in Idaho.

Records indicate that breeding is likely to occur throughout the year, although confined mainly to the warmer seasons. Pregnant females or juveniles have been taken from March 13 to November 4. Embryo counts average 6 with extremes of 4 and 8.

Records of occurrence.—Specimens examined, 78, as follows: *Clearwater County:* 2 mi. NE Weippe, 1. *Idaho County:* Rapid River,

near Riggins, 1 (David MacKaye coll.). *Washington County:* Crane
Cr., 15 mi. E Midvale, 13 (Ralph Ellis coll.). *Canyon County:* Nampa,
1. *Owyhee County:* Three Creek, 3 (Biol. Surv. coll.). *Custer County:*
Pahsimeroi Mountains, head Pahsimeroi River, 1. *Blaine County:*
Alturas Lake, 1. *Twin Falls County:* 2 mi. S Hagerman, 2. *Minidoka
County:* 2 mi. E Acequia, 2. *Cassia County:* Elba, 5; Mt. Harrison,
10 mi. S Albion, 1. *Fremont County:* 4 mi. W Ashton, 1 (Amer.
Mus.); 5 mi. W St. Anthony, 1 (Amer. Mus.); N. fork Snake River,
10 mi. SW Island Park, 2 (Amer. Mus.). *Bonneville County:* S. side
South Fork, 3 mi. E Swan Valley, 3. *Power County:* Bannock Cr., 10
mi. NW Pocatello, 8 (5 in Ralph Ellis coll.); Indian Springs, 4 mi. S
American Falls, 3. *Bannock County:* Pocatello, 17 (1 in Ralph Ellis
coll.); E. fork Pocatello Creek, 1; Pocatello Cr., 6 mi. from Pocatello,
2. *Franklin County:* Strawberry Creek, 20 mi. NE Preston, 5. *Bear
Lake County:* N. rim Copenhagen Basin, Wasatch Mountains, 1;
Montpelier Creek, 3 (Biol. Surv. coll.). Additional records (Bailey,
1900:31): *Idaho County:* Seven Devils Mountains. *Custer County:*
Challis. *Butte County:* Lost River Mountains.

Microtus mordax mordax (Merriam)
LONG-TAILED MEADOW MOUSE

Arvicola (Mynomes) mordax Merriam, N. Amer. Fauna, 5:61.
July 30, 1891. Type from Alturas Lake, east foot of Sawtooth Mountains, 7000 feet, Blaine County, Idaho.

Synonym.—Microtus mordax, Bailey, 1900:48.

Distribution.—In Idaho, throughout the mountainous areas from
the Canadian border south to Nevada and Utah. It has not been
found on the Snake River Plains (see map, fig. 30).

Description.—Size medium; tail long (averaging 54 per cent of
body length, general coloration grayish with admixture of dull reddish along dorsum, hind foot near 21 mm. Average measurements of
seven adults from the type locality are 193-66-21. Large individuals
may attain a total length of 212 mm., and in this respect equal average
individuals of the Big-footed Meadow Mouse, but the weight of these
large *mordax* is only about half that of the latter. The average
weight of *mordax* is about 45 grams.

Remarks.—Although it is essentially a boreal species
and seldom is found below the lower limit of coniferous
forests, *mordax* occurs in a variety of habitats. At an elevation of approximately 7000 feet on Mt. Harrison it was
common in the sagebrush areas during the middle of June.
A few were taken along the stream and in a *Pentstemon*-
covered clearing in a grove of quaking aspen. At Alturas
Lake it was found near water in thickets of soft chaparral

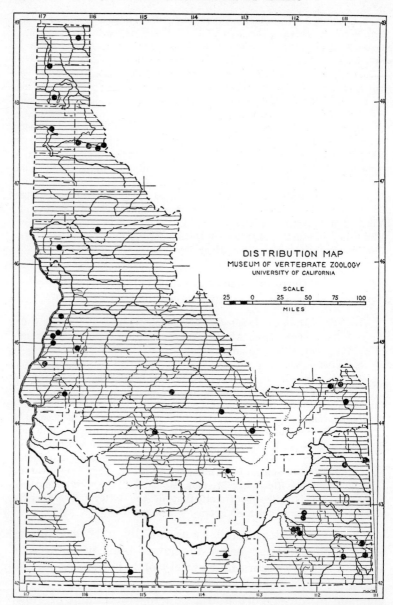

FIG. 30. Map showing the distribution of the meadow mouse, *Microtus mordax mordax*, in Idaho. Dots indicate localities whence specimens have been examined or recorded.

among lodgepole pines, and at the head of the Pahsimeroi
River it inhabited boggy areas along the stream. Raymond
Gilmore captured an adult female September 3 in a rock
slide at an elevation of 8,500 feet on Mount Sheridan. Here
it was fully a mile from the nearest water and in association with pikas. At the head of the Pahsimeroi River several were caught in traps placed at the bases of willow
clumps where I could perceive no evidence of runways in
the short herbage. Others were taken at the edge of the
stream in traps intended for water shrews.

In summer these mice frequently are found in association with other species of meadow mice and also with
jumping mice *(Zapus princeps)*, red-backed mice *(Clethrionomys gapperi)*, shrews *(Sorex vagrans* and *Sorex palustris)*, and white-footed mice *(Peromyscus maniculatus)*.

Females captured in each month from May 10 to September 21 contained on the average 5 (3 to 7) embryos.
Half-grown young were common at Mt. Harrison in June,
and near the head of the Pahsimeroi River half-grown
young and smaller individuals hardly three weeks old were
taken in late July. In August several young were captured
at Alturas Lake. These records indicate an extensive breeding season and that several litters may be reared each year.

Records of occurrence.—Specimens examined, 133, as follows:
Boundary County: 4 mi. W Meadow Creek, 4. *Bonner County:* 5 mi.
W Cocolalla, 7. *Shoshone County:* Glidden Lakes, 1. *Clearwater
County:* 2 mi. NE Weippe, 3. *Adams County:* 1 mi. N Bear Cr. R. S.,
4 (2 in Ralph Ellis coll.) ; 3 mi. W Payette Lake, 6; ½ mi. E Black
Lake, 3 (Ralph Ellis coll.) ; summit Smith Mountain, 2 (Ralph Ellis
coll.). *Washington County:* 1 mi. NE Heath, 27 (25 in Ralph Ellis
coll.) ; Crane Creek, 15 mi. E Midvale, 1 (Ralph Ellis coll.). *Custer
County:* Mill Cr., 14 mi. W Challis, 7; head Pahsimeroi River, 8.
Blaine County: Alturas Lake (type locality), 13. *Cassia County:*
Mt. Harrison, 10 mi. S Albion, 12. *Clark County:* Taylor Cr., 5 mi. S
Montana Line at Sheridan Mountain, 3 (Amer. Mus.). *Fremont
County:* 5 mi. S Montana Line at Mt. Jefferson, 2 (Amer. Mus.) ; N.
fork Snake River, 10 mi. SW Island Park, 2 (Amer. Mus.). *Butte
County:* N. base Sunset Cone, Craters of the Moon National Monu-
ment, 1; Grassy Cone, Craters of the Moon National Monument, 1.
Teton County: 3 mi. SW Victor, 4. *Bonneville County:* S. side South
Fork, 3 mi. W Swan Valley, 7. *Bannock County:* Camp Tendoy, 1;
Indian Creek (near head of), 1; Justice Park, 5; Barrett's Ranch, 1;

Schutt's Mine, 5. *Bear Lake County:* N. rim Copenhagen Basin, Wa-
satch Mountains, 2. Additional records (Bailey, 1900:49): *Bonner
County:* Priest Lake. *Kootenai County:* Coeur d'Alene. *Shoshone
County:* Kingston; Osborn; Mullan. *Lewis County:* Craig Mountains.
Idaho County: Seven Devils Mountains. *Owyhee County:* Three Creek.
Lemhi County: Lemhi Indian Agency; Salmon River Mountains. *Butte
County:* Lost River Mountains. *Caribou County:* Preuss Mountains.
Bear Lake County: Montpelier Creek.

Microtus richardsoni macropus (Merriam)
BIG-FOOTED MEADOW MOUSE

Arvicola (Mynomes) macropus Merriam, N. Amer. Fauna, 5:60.
July 30, 1891. Type from Pahsimeroi Mountains, head of Pahsimeroi
River, 9350 feet altitude, Custer County, Idaho.

Distribution.—In Idaho, occurs in the mountainous portions from
Canada south to Utah (see map, fig. 31). Its range extends also into
the Blue Mountains of Washington and Oregon, and along the Rocky
Mountains from Montana to Colorado.

Description.—Largest species of the genus; hind foot is much
larger than in any other meadow mouse (near 25 mm.). Average
external measurements of five adults from central Idaho are 215-67-
27. Extremely large individuals may measure 220-70-29 and weigh
as much as 100 grams.

Remarks.—This species is semiaquatic in habit and
strictly boreal in occurrence. Apparently it is more closely
restricted to the vicinity of water during the summer than
are other meadow mice. Near Victor several were caught
in traps placed in midstream on mats of water cress *(Radicula nasturtium-aquaticum);* others were trapped in runways under overhanging banks which paralleled the edge
of the stream. Many of their runs traversed the cress-
choked springs, the vegetation serving to support the weight
of the animal in transit.

At Black Lake, Borell (MS) found them under heavy
brush, alders, and grass at the very edge of the stream.
Here they had burrows entering the banks just at or under
the level of the water. Some of their forage runways extended for many feet out among the herbs and grasses
along the stream, and often their trails came out of the
water, crossed a small neck of land, and re-entered the
water. Some of the runs were so situated that the mice

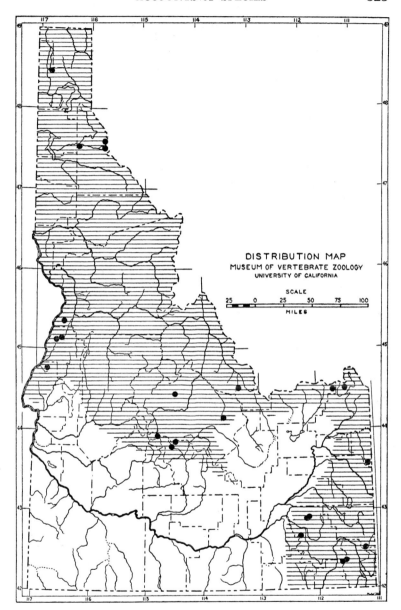

Fig. 31. Map showing the distribution of the big-footed meadow mouse,
Microtus richardsoni macropus, in Idaho. Dots indicate localities
whence specimens have been examined or recorded.

would have to go entirely under water in using them. As indicated by trapping records, runways which paralleled the stream, and ran through the water much of the way, were used more than were forage runways on dry land.

At Smith Mountain, Adams County, Borell (MS) dislodged an adult from the tall grass in a small boggy meadow. It ran along a runway to the creek, entered the water, and without splashing swam freely with most of the body above the surface. It crossed the creek and entered a burrow, the entrance to which was under water. Upon excavation the burrow was found to have four entrances, each of which led to a cavity under a wet, rotten stump. At Alturas Lake a nest was located in a wet, rotten log which was partly buried in the mud at the edge of a bog. Entrance to the nest cavity was gained by means of a single opening. Another nest was found underground among the roots of an old stump. This, too, had but a single entrance.

My records of pregnant females are for July only. Half-grown young taken July 19 and September 28 indicate the possibility of at least two litters a season. The average number of young in a litter is 5, with extremes of 4 and 6.

Records of occurrence.—Specimens examined, 38, as follows: *Shoshone County:* Glidden Lakes, 2. *Adams County:* ½ mi. E Black Lake, 10 (Ralph Ellis coll.) ; summit Smith Mountain, 6 (Ralph Ellis coll.). *Washington County:* SW slope Cuddy Mountain, 1. *Custer County:* Mill Creek, 14 mi. W Challis, 1. *Blaine County:* Alturas Lake, 2. *Clark County:* Taylor Creek, 5 mi. S Montana Line at Mt. Sheridan, 4 (Amer. Mus.). *Fremont County:* Mt. Jefferson, 3 mi. S Montana Line, 5 (Amer. Mus.). *Teton County:* 3 mi. SW Victor, 2 (1 in Davis coll.). *Bannock County:* Camp Tendoy, 1; W. fork Rapid Creek, 9½ mi. E Pocatello, 1; Schutt's Mine, 1. *Franklin County:* Strawberry Creek, 20 mi. NE Preston, 1. *Bear Lake County:* N. rim Copenhagen Basin, Wasatch Mountains, 1. Additional records (Bailey, 1900:61, unless otherwise stated): *Bonner County:* Priest Lake. *Shoshone County:* Thompson Pass; 7 mi. E McKinnis (D. R. Dickey coll.). *Idaho County:* Seven Devils Mountains. *Lemhi County:* Salmon River Mountains. *Custer County:* Pahsimeroi Mountains. *Blaine County:* Big Wood River (head of) ; Summit. *Caribou County:* Crow Creek (head of).

Genus **Lemmiscus** Thomas
Short-tailed Voles

Small, mouselike; pelage long and soft, light gray in color dorsally, whitish ventrally; ears medium, partly concealed by pelage, antitragus present; eyes small; tail short, less than twice the length of hind foot, bicolored; feet moderately large with five plantar tubercles, claws of hind foot larger than those of front foot; tarsal and metatarsal portions of hind foot densely haired. Skull typically microtine in structure, but decidedly flattened and angular, often saddle shaped in dorsal outline; zygoma heavy, wide spreading; auditory bullae large, projecting posteriorly beyond plane of occiput, consisting of foamlike bone with tympanic annulus embedded deep below the surface; molars anteroposteriorly compressed, rootless, re-entrant angles filled with cement; M_3 with four prisms consisting of two transverse loops and two median triangles; incisors simple, ungrooved.

About seventy years ago Cope (1868, p. 2) described the first known American species of this genus and named it *Arvicola curtata*. Later, Miller, in his revision of the genera and subgenera of voles and lemmings (1896), placed *Arvicola curtata* Cope, *Arvicola pauperrimus* Cooper, and *Arvicola (Chilotus) pallidus* Merriam, along with certain Old World species, in the subgenus *Lagurus* under the genus *Microtus*. In doing this, Miller apparently accepted the opinion expressed by Merriam (1895a:759) that the species showed no characters which would separate it generically from *Microtus arvalis*. Thomas (1912:401) raised *Lagurus* to generic rank. He says *(ibid.)*, "It appears to me that the *Lagurus* group is amply worthy of separate generic rank, its general characters, lemming-like appearance, and especially its peculiar M_3 making it readily distinguishable from all other voles." Simultaneously he set off the American forms as a subgenus of *Lagurus* with the following comment: "And, further, I would separate as a special subgenus the American members of the group from the Old World ones, on the ground of their rather less lemming-like form, longer tails, and the possession of only four prisms in

M_3. This subgenus might be called *Lemmiscus* with *Lagurus (Lemmiscus) curtatus,* Cope, as its type. . . . " My own study leads to the view that the American forms of *Lagurus* are worthy of separate generic rank. The following comparisons indicate certain of the differential features of *Lemmiscus.*

Lagurus	*Lemmiscus*	*Microtus*
Skull flattened	Skull flattened	Skull usually not flattened
Stapedial canal complete	Stapedial canal complete	Stapedial canal incomplete*
Bullae foamlike in structure	Bullae foamlike in structure	Bullae with hard outer shell and inner cancellous portion with trabeculae
Mastoidal portion of bulla projects posteriorly beyond plane of occiput	Mastoidal portion of bulla projects posteriorly beyond plane of occiput	Mastoidal portion of bulla terminates on a plane with, or anterior to, occiput
External auditory canal long	External auditory canal medium	External auditory canal short
M_3 with five prisms	M_3 with four prisms	M_3 with three transverse loops
Cement lacking in re-entrant angles of molars	Cement present in re-entrant angles of molars	Cement present in re-entrant angles of molars
Antitragus absent	Antitragus present	Antitragus present
Ears one-third length of hind foot	Ears over one-half length of hind foot.	Ears over one-half length of hind foot
Narrow dorsal stripe present	No conspicuous dorsal stripe	No conspicuous dorsal stripe

One species of *Lemmiscus* occurs in Idaho. It seems to be closely related, perhaps conspecifically, to *curtatus* of Nevada, but as yet no specimens are available which demonstrate intergradation between these two kinds of voles.

---

* Hinton's (1926:66) statement that in *Microtus* the stapedial artery is enclosed in a bony tube is subject to qualification to the extent that in all species I have examined *(M. abbreviatus, M. miurus,* and *M. (Pedomys) minor* excepted) the stapedial canal is incomplete in the region where it passes over the cochlea and in the region of the stapes. Perhaps it is complete in certain of the Old World species, but the canal is not complete in *M. arvalis* and *M. gregalis.*

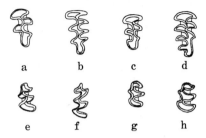

a   b   c   d

e   f   g   h

FIG. 32. Outline drawings, reduced to same scale, of occlusal surface of third upper molar (top) and third lower molar (bottom) of four microtines. *Lemmiscus* (no. 38477, M.V.Z.), a, e; *Lagurus* from Siberia (no. 41290, M.V.Z.), b, f; subgenus *Pedomys* (no. 5443, M.V.Z.), c, g; *Microtus* (no. 47036, M.V.Z.), d, h. Note the lack of cement in the re-entrant angles in *Lagurus;* its presence in *Lemmiscus, Pedomys,* and *Microtus.*

Lemmiscus pauperrimus (Cooper)
SAGEBRUSH VOLE

Arvicola pauperrima Cooper, Amer. Nat., 2:535. December, 1868. Type from plains of the Columbia, near the Snake River, southwestern Washington.

Synonyms.—*Arvicola pauperrimus*, Merriam, 1891:64; *Microtus pauperrimus*, Bailey, 1900:69; *Lagurus pauperrimus*, Whitlow and Hall, 1933:267.

Description.—Smallest microtine in Idaho; dorsal coloration light gray, overcast with fulvous, ventral coloration whitish; ears medium in size, nearly hidden in the fur; tail but slightly longer than hind foot, bicolor, whitish below, fulvous gray above; pelage long and soft; skull typically microtine in structure, but decidedly flattened; auditory bullae swollen and projecting posteriorly beyond plane of occiput; molars rootless, with cement in re-entrant angles; M³ with one transverse loop, two median triangles, and a posterior loop; M_3 with two transverse loops and two median triangles.

Remarks.—These small mice are readily distinguished from all other microtines by their light gray color, short tail, hairy sole of hind foot, flattened skull, large bullae, and structure of the last lower molar.

A summary of the known facts concerning the life history of *Lemmiscus* is given by Hall (1928). The species *pauperrimus* appears to be partial to dry grassy areas and barren hills. In Idaho it ranges altitudinally from the Snake River Plains, where one was captured by Whitlow on fine,

wind-blown sand, up to at least 9000 feet in the Lemhi
Mountains. It is not common in collections, a circumstance
which perhaps is due to insufficient knowledge of its habits.

Records of occurrence.—Specimen examined, 1, from 1 mi. N Fort
Hall, Bingham County. Additional record (Bailey, 1900:70) : Salmon
River Mountains.

Genus **Ondatra** Link
Muskrats

Large aquatic microtines; hind feet much larger than
front ones, partly webbed, with fringe of stiff hairs on free
margins, including web, toes, and metatarsus; tail nearly
as long as body, laterally compressed with distinct dorsal
and ventral keels, scantily haired, scaly; ears small, concealed by dense pelage; eyes relatively small; dorsal coloration variable, but always with browns predominating. Skull
typically microtine in structure, robust, angular, ridged;
auditory bullae small, lacking internal cancellous material;
stapedial artery enclosed within an osseous tube as far as
the stapes; pterygoids platelike, lacking distinct hamuli;
posterior border of palate terminating in spinous process;
cheek teeth three in each jaw, rooted in old age, lacking
cement in re-entrant angles; mandible normal, M_3 slightly
displaced lingually by incisor; root of incisor in condylar
process above mandibular foramen.

In certain respects, especially character of palate and
structure of cheek teeth and auditory bullae, *Ondatra* is
primitive and probably derived from *Phenacomys*-like ancestors. In character of pelage and structure of the tail and
hind feet, however, it is highly specialized for aquatic life.
The fur is "water proof," made up of dense, soft, underfur
in which myriads of minute air bubbles that prevent water
from reaching the skin are entangled, and numerous, long,
stiff guard hairs; the tail, laterally compressed, is used as a
rudder in swimming; the asymmetrically constructed hind
foot has the fourth digit longest, as in most aquatic mammals. The osseous stapedial canal, although not modified
for an aquatic life, shows that *Ondatra* is some distance re-

moved from true *Phenacomys,* in which the stapedial artery is naked.

Muskrats are native only to North America where they occur from the Arctic, southward to near the southern boundary of the United States. They are closely associated with fresh water. Nearly every hydrographic basin harbors its population of muskrats, and where such basins are isolated, the Great Basin for instance, morphological differentiation has resulted. In his revision of the genus (1911), Hollister recognized twelve kinds, belonging to three species. One race of the species *Ondatra zibethica* occurs in Idaho. Two extinct species have been described (Wilson, 1933) from Pleistocene deposits at Hagerman and Grand View.

Ondatra zibethica osoyoosensis (Lord)
ROCKY MOUNTAIN MUSKRAT

Fiber osoyoosensis Lord, Proc. Zool. Soc. London, 1863:97. Type from Lake Osoyoos, British Columbia.

Synonym.—Fiber zibethicus, Merriam, 1891:68.

Distribution.—Occurs throughout the state from Canada south into the Snake River drainage basin.

Description.—Aside from generic characters mentioned above, *osoyoosensis* is characterized by dark dorsal coloration, large size (external measurements of 10 near topotypes average 589-271-83, Hollister, *op. cit.,* p. 25), heavy, relatively narrow skull, and long rostrum. Specimens from the Snake River Valley average smaller and are lighter colored.

Remarks.—Specimens from the Snake River Valley are intergrades between *osoyoosensis,* the race occurring typically in the northern portion of the state, and *mergens,* a race occupying the Great Basin. Whitlow and Hall (1933: 268) mention the intermediacy in color of some specimens from near Pocatello. Other specimens which I have examined from southern Idaho are light in color like *mergens.*

My findings fail to confirm the conclusion reached by Whitlow and Hall *(ibid.),* that the skulls of specimens from near Pocatello are most like those of *osoyoosensis.* It is true that these specimens, as well as others from farther west in the Snake River Valley, are intermediate between *osoyoosensis* and *mergens* in cranial characters, and as regards width of nasals, width of jugal, and alveolar length of the upper molar series, are like *osoyoosensis*, but in length of nasals, basilar length of Hensel, and palatal length they are like *mergens*. In addition, external measurements of five adult males from the Snake River Valley average 575-249-80; of three adult females, 548-248-80. These averages are closer to *mergens*. Thus, the Snake River drainage area must be considered as a zone of intergradation between these two geographic races. The subspecific name *osoyoosensis*, rather than *mergens*, is here applied arbitrarily to the specimens from the Snake River area; merely for the sake of convenience.

Muskrats, because of the large numbers trapped yearly, constitute an important source of revenue. Nearly every youth in the rural areas of Idaho contributes a few pelts yearly to the fur trade. During the winter of 1935-1936, David Krause, near Heyburn in the Snake River Valley, trapped well over three hundred muskrats, the pelts of which grossed on the average ninety cents each. In this area the "rats" occupy the drain ditches which ramify the irrigated areas and hence are close at hand and relatively easily trapped.

None of the females collected in late fall and winter was pregnant. The only young individual available was trapped June 2, 1935, near Payette; it is about the size of a rat and nearly black in color.

Records of occurrence.—Specimens examined, 35, as follows: *Payette County:* 2 mi. S Payette, 2. *Owyhee County:* Castle Creek, 8 mi. S Oreana, 1; South Fork Owyhee River, 12 mi. N Nevada Line, 3. *Elmore County:* Hammett, 1. *Custer County:* head Pahsimeroi River, 1. *Blaine County:* Wood River, 2 mi. N Ketchum, 1; Wood River, 8 mi. N Ketchum, 1. *Lincoln County:* Shoshone, 5. *Minidoka County:* 2 mi. E Heyburn, 13. *Cassia County:* Cassia Creek, Elba, 1. *Power County:* S. side Snake River, 19 mi. SW American Falls, 1; Bannock Creek, 4 mi. S Portneuf River, 2. *Bannock County:* Portneuf River, 1 mi. N Pocatello, 2; Arimo, 6 mi. S McCammon, 1. Additional records (Hollister, 1911:26): *Kootenai County:* Fort Sherman. *Idaho County:* Packer Meadow. *Lemhi County:* Lemhi. *Blaine County:* Sawtooth (Alturas) Lake.

Family MURIDAE
OLD WORLD HOUSE MICE, NORWAY RATS,
and Allied Forms

Skull essentially as in Cricetidae; cheek teeth three in each jaw, the upper teeth with three functional longitudinal rows of tubercles. No fossil record for North America.

Genus **Rattus** G. Fischer
Old World House Rats

Rattus norvegicus norvegicus (Erxleben)
NORWAY RAT

[*Mus*] *norvegicus* Erxleben, Syst. Regni Anim., 1:381. 1777. Type from Norway.

Distribution.—Probably occurs in those parts of Idaho permanently occupied by man.

Description.—Size large; tail usually as long as, or longer than, head and body, thinly haired with conspicuous annulations; ears moderately large, leathery, pubescent; pelage harsh, a feature produced by numerous coarse guard hairs interspersed with the soft fur; thumb reduced, clawed; skull with prominent temporal beading, no sagittal crest; palate extending noticeably behind M^3; mandible robust, coronoid process rising above level of condyle; incisors simple, robust; cheek teeth brachydont, rooted.

Remarks.—No specimens of *Rattus* are available from Idaho, but warehousemen at Pocatello and other cities report rats which probably are of this species. The Norway Rat is an introduced rodent which first gained a foothold in America in seacoast cities. Of late it has spread, following generally the railroads, over much of the United States. In Idaho, it probably is confined largely to the metropolitan and suburban areas.

Genus **Mus** Linnaeus
Old World House Mice and Allied Forms

Mus musculus Linnaeus, subsp.?
HOUSE MOUSE

[*Mus*] *musculus* Linnaeus, Syst. Nat., ed. 10, 1:62. 1758. Type from Upsala, Sweden.

Distribution.—Probably widely distributed throughout those parts of the state permanently occupied by man.

Description.—Mouse size, tail about as long as head and body, thinly haired, annulations conspicuous; ears moderately large, leathery, pubescent; pelage soft, often shorter than in Cricetidae; general color dull, light wood-brown, irregularly darkened with slaty and blackish along dorsum; ventral coloration grayish or brownish, never pure white; feet drab or dusky, never pure white. Skull small, smooth, brain case rounded; incisive foramina very long; palate extending from one to two millimeters behind last upper molar; pterygoid fossae wider than interpterygoidal space; incisors ungrooved, but with conspicuous subapical notch behind enamel plate; molars brachydont, rooted, the crown of first upper molar decidedly longer than that of second and third together, its area nearly one and one-half times greater; upper molars with three longitudinal rows of tubercles, lower molars with two rows; mandible short and deep, coronoid process small.

Remarks.—The house mouse was introduced into America by man's own activities. Its spread in this country has been rapid; it is equaled only by the spread of the English sparrow. It is of interest to note that Merriam (1873 and 1891) does not record this species in Idaho. Whether it had reached there by 1890 is problematical, but at present it is widely distributed in areas occupied by man.

In rural areas it may take to fields, weedy ditch banks, and fence rows where it constructs runways through the vegetation. It is typically a house mouse, however, and, especially in winter, prefers the protection offered by human habitations and other man-made structures. In metropolitan areas it frequents garbage dumps, warehouses, and nearly all buildings to which it can gain entrance. I have no record of its occurrence at any locality far removed from human activities.

House mice do not hibernate. They are prolific breeders and where they have access to dry, warm winter quarters, as many as twelve or thirteen litters, averaging four or five young each, may be reared yearly.

Records of occurrence.—Specimens examined, 14, as follows: *Washington County:* Crane Cr., 15 mi. E Midvale, 4 (Ralph Ellis coll.). *Canyon County:* 4 mi. S Wilder, 1. *Owyhee County:* 5 mi. SE Murphy, 1; Homedale, 1. *Blaine County:* Bellevue, 1. *Gooding County:* 2 mi. S Hagerman, 1. *Twin Falls County:* S. side Snake River, 2 mi. S Hagerman, 1. *Bannock County:* Pocatello, 3; 5 mi. N Pocatello, 1.

Family ZAPODIDAE
JUMPING MICE and Allies

Mouselike, tail longer than head and body, scaly; hind legs elongated for saltation, front legs short; ears medium-sized, hairy, projecting above fur; skull small, with large infraorbital foramina; upper incisors grooved; upper cheek teeth three or four; Pm⁴, when present, a mere peg.

This family's present differentiation and distribution, particularly its occurrence in isolated mountains in southern Idaho and in the Great Basin in general, suggest that it has occupied much of the region now inhabited for a considerable time. In fact, the genus *Zapus* must have been present in the Great Basin during the Pleistocene because no other plausible explanation is at hand for its distribution in the Great Basin today. These mice are unable to live amid true desert conditions, and so they could not migrate today from one mountain range to another wherever the intervening lowlands are desert.

The jumping mice so far found in Idaho are all of the species *Zapus princeps*. In addition to possessing the general family characters stated above, they are characterized as follows: Upper parts with distinct, broad, dark, dorsal stripe; sides ochraceous or grayish; belly usually pure white; tail distinctly bicolored, white below, brownish above. The only small, long-tailed mammals with which jumping mice might be confused are kangaroo rats and pocket mice, both of which have external cheek pouches; these are lacking in *Zapus*.

Ecology.—In Idaho, jumping mice are found most commonly in the vicinity of water. At Mt. Harrison, Cassia County, we found them at the head of Howells Canyon (near 8000 ft.) on an east-facing slope in association with quaking aspen, sagebrush, and numerous herbs, among which a species of *Pentstemon* was most common. In the same trap line white-footed mice *(Peromyscus maniculatus)*, meadow mice *(Microtus mordax)* and shrews *(Sorex vagrans)* were taken. Near Victor, Teton County, they were found in heavy herbage along a small stream bordered by quaking aspen. Here they were in association with meadow mice *(Microtus mordax, Microtus pennsylvanicus,* and *Microtus richardsoni),* red-backed mice *(Clethriononys gapperi),* and shrews *(Sorex vagrans* and *Sorex palustris).* At Alturas Lake, Mill Creek, and the head of the Pahsimeroi River they were found, in association with the mammals just listed, along streams bordered by willow, rose, alder, huckleberry, sedges, and herbs of various kinds. At Cuddy Mountain, Washington County, Borell and Gilmore (MS) found them in flat, boggy places along the creek under yellow pines, Douglas fir, serviceberries, willows, alders, dogwood, and currant.

Jumping mice not only prefer moist places, but as I learned at Mill Creek enter the water at times, and there two were taken in traps set on artificial islands of stones in the middle of the creek where the water was about six inches deep. Apparently the only way the mice could have reached the traps was by swimming. At Pahsimeroi River I took several, mostly young of the year, in swampy areas.

In rapid progression jumping mice move by series of zigzag hops. One young of the year found in tall grass near Victor made horizontal leaps of approximately three feet. The zigzag course was difficult for me to follow, and I was led to wonder if this mode of locomotion were not advantageous to the mice in eluding animals that would do them harm.

In making such leaps the long tail aids in maintaining balance. Svihla and Svihla (1933:133), in observing the actions of a jumping mouse released from a rat trap in which its tail had been lost, noted that at the end of its leaps the mouse could not land on its feet properly, but instead turned somersaults and landed on its back every time. With the loss of its tail there was no compensation made for the vigorous push of the long hind legs. When not in a hurry, they progress on all four feet.

Although jumping mice have runways, they are not so distinct as are those of meadow mice. At Mt. Harrison their runways were more like broad trails among the herbage. Occasionally they make use of *Microtus* runways as is evidenced by the fact that I have taken both animals on successive nights in the runway of *Microtus.*

For the most part jumping mice are nocturnal, but occasionally they are seen in tall grass during the day. At Black Lake, Adams County, Borell (MS) observed "many" of them during the day when he walked through the low grass and herbs. Usually they were "jumped" from their globular surface nests composed of dry grasses. Apparently they emerge from their resting places later in the evening than do white-footed mice *(Peromyscus maniculatus)* and meadow mice *(Microtus mordax)*. At any rate, a line of thirty-five traps, left in the same place for a week at Mt. Harrison, took, on the first night, only *Peromyscus* and *Microtus*. On succeeding nights *Zapus* were taken to the number of 1-1-2-2-4-5. The number of other mice taken nightly during this period gradually decreased from 12 to 4. In all, 15 *Zapus* were taken on 175 trap nights, most of them after the other species had been reduced in numbers.

Jumping mice themselves are often difficult to detect, but long sections of cut grass piled in runways is good evidence of their presence. *Microtus* also pile grass in this manner, but the pieces are seldom over an inch and a half long whereas those cut by *Zapus* may be as long as four inches. In addition to green herbage, jumping mice are fond of seeds. On July 29, at Black Lake, Borell (MS) noted a disturbance among a dense stand of a composite *(Senecio)* which stood two or three feet tall and records: "The composite was in full bloom and I soon learned that a *Zapus* was busily engaged in obtaining these flower heads. It would climb up the stalk rapidly (almost on the run) until its weight caused the flower stalk to bend over to the ground and then with a bite or two it would cut off the flower heads. It pulled down seven or eight heads during the fifteen minutes I watched it." Moore (1928:155) examined the stomachs of seven specimens taken during September in central Utah and found that six of them contained only a white, starchy, glutinous paste, while the seventh showed traces of a brown seed coat. The main seed eaten appeared to be that of an introduced bromegrass which was common in the area. Also, they are fond of meat, a trait common to many rodents, as evidenced by their capture in meat-baited traps. Svihla and Svihla *(op. cit.*, p. 132) have used fish as bait in trapping *Zapus.*

In July, August, and September, *Zapus* becomes excessively fat in preparation for the long winter hibernation. For the intermountain region, I know of no records of capture later than September and infer that hibernation begins in that month or the next. The time of emergence probably varies, according to the season, from March to May. Edson (1932:55) found a hibernating jumping mouse on April 20 at Bellingham, Washington, in its nest among the roots of a decayed tree stump. The position it assumed during hibernation was much like that of the ground squirrel. The animal rested on its hind legs with its head curled far under the body, and its nose between its heels.

The breeding season in Idaho probably is May and June, and indications are that only a single litter a season is reared. Two of three females collected June 19 and 20 at Mt. Harrison contained five and six 2 mm. embryos; the third contained six 12 mm. embryos. Two others taken on June 8 near Pocatello contained four and five embryos. In two of the three females collected at Mt. Harrison the right horn of the uterus contained more embryos than did the left (3R - 2L; 4R - 2L). The third female carried three on each side. I have noted this disproportion in other rodents and have wondered if the presence of the large stomach on the left side may not in some way hinder the development of embryos in the uterine horn of that side.

According to Svihla and Svihla *(ibid.)*, newly born young of this genus are even smaller than those of the harvest mouse *(Reithrodontomys megalotis)*, adults of which are only about half as large as adults of *Zapus.* The young at birth are pink in color, hairless, and the eyes and ears are closed. Postuterine development is rapid, and by mid-July young of the year are about half grown.

From a study of the present distribution of this genus in Idaho, Oregon, and Nevada, it seems to me that jumping mice migrated into these regions from the north. By such a route they were able to become established, perhaps before or during the Pleistocene, in areas which now are isolated by surrounding deserts.

Genus **Zapus** Coues
Jumping Mice

Key to Adult Jumping Mice of Idaho

1 Lateral line distinctly ochraceous; dorsal area heavily suffused with black; width of incisive foramina more than half their length; distribution west-central Idaho. **Z. p. oregonus**, p. 341

1' Lateral line indistinct or lacking; dorsal area less heavily suffused with black; width of incisive foramina less than half their length.

    2 Dorsal coloration ochraceous, suffused with black; auditory bullae large; distribution central Idaho. **Z. p. idahoensis**, p. 339

    2' Dorsal coloration grayish, suffused with black; auditory bullae small.

        3 Skull narrower; incisive foramina relatively narrower; distribution northern Idaho. **Z. p. kootenayensis**, p. 337

        3' Skull broader; incisive foramina relatively wider; distribution southern Idaho. **Z. p. cinereus**, p. 342

Zapus princeps kootenayensis Anderson
Kootenai Jumping Mouse

Zapus princeps kootenayensis Anderson, Ann. Report Nat. Mus. Canada for 1931:108. November 24, 1932. Type from near summit of Green Mountain, head of Murphy Creek, about 10 miles north of Rossland, British Columbia.

Distribution.—In Idaho, from Canada south as far as the Clearwater drainage basin where it intergrades with *idahoensis* (see map, fig. 33).

Description.—Grayish-colored jumping mouse; skull relatively narrow; incisive foramina narrowest of races occurring in Idaho. External measurements of four adults from Glidden Lakes average 236-142-30-16.

Remarks.—The major portion of the range of this race lies in southern British Columbia where, according to Anderson (1932), it occurs in the more humid parts of the Transition and Canadian life zones from the eastern summit of the Cascades east to the Selkirk Range.

The Kootenai Jumping Mouse differs from *idahoensis*, the race with which it intergrades in central Idaho, in the following respects: Coloration averaging grayer, that is, less ochraceous yellow; skull smaller and relatively nar-

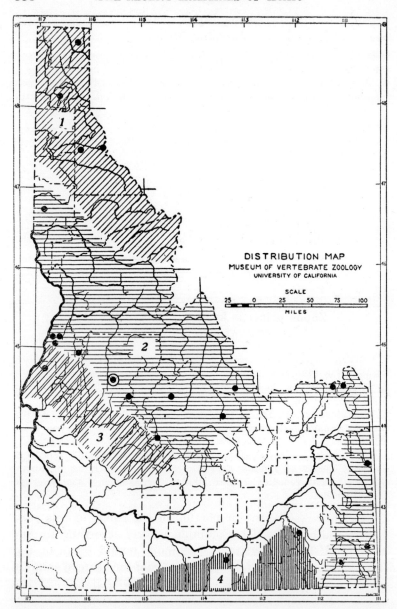

Fig. 33. Map showing the distribution of jumping mice in Idaho. Dots indicate localities whence specimens have been examined or recorded. 1. *Zapus princeps kootenayensis*, 2. *Zapus princeps idahoensis*, 3. *Zapus princeps oregonus*, 4. *Zapus princeps cinereus*.

rower; auditory bullae less inflated; incisive foramina narrower. It may be distinguished from *oregonus* by grayish rather than blackish dorsal coloration; smaller and relatively narrower skull and much narrower incisive foramina. Specimens from Weippe are thought to be intergrades, but are referred to *idahoensis*.

Records of occurrence.—Specimens examined, 8, as follows: *Boundary County:* 4 mi. W Meadow Creek, 2. *Bonner County:* 5 mi. W Cocolalla, 2. *Shoshone County:* Glidden Lakes, 4. Additional records (specimens not examined): *Shoshone County:* 7 mi. E McKinnis (D. R. Dickey coll.).

Zapus princeps idahoensis Davis
CENTRAL IDAHO JUMPING MOUSE

Zapus princeps idahoensis Davis, Jour. Mammalogy, 15:221. August 10, 1934. Type from 5 miles east of Warm Lake, 7000 feet, Valley County, Idaho.

Synonyms.—*Zapus hudsonius*, Merriam (1891:72-73); *Zapus princeps princeps*, Preble (1899:23).

Distribution.—In Idaho, from the Sawtooth Mountains north to Cedar Mountain, Latah County, and from the Seven Devils Mountains east to, and perhaps into, Montana and Wyoming; south to the Preuss Mountains, Caribou County, where it intergrades with *utahensis* (see map, fig. 33).

Description.—Similar to *kootenayensis* but dorsal coloration more ochraceous; auditory bullae much larger; incisive foramina relatively wider; average external measurements of six adults from the type locality are 240-144-31; of four adults from Fremont County, 238-140-32.

Remarks.—Geographically, *idahoensis* is intermediate between *oregonus* and *utahensis*. From the former it is distinguished by lighter coloration, smaller hind foot, more highly inflated tympanic bullae, narrower incisive foramina, the width of which amounts to less than half their length. From *utahensis* it differs as follows: In general, smaller; foramen magnum smaller; brain case narrower; upper tooth rows nearly parallel rather than divergent anteriorly; tail shorter; coloration lighter, that is, more yellowish.

In an earlier paper (1934:226) I referred three subadult specimens from Weippe, Clearwater County, and a single specimen in the Chas. R. Conner Museum from

Cedar Mountain, Latah County, to *kootenayensis*. Since then I have examined the specimen (skin only) from Cedar Mountain which had been identified by Dr. R. M. Anderson as *Z. p. oregonus*. I have compared it with typical *oregonus* and find the dorsal coloration much lighter. It compares favorably with certain specimens of *idahoensis* and should, perhaps, be considered as a nontypical specimen of that race or as an intergrade between *oregonus* and *idahoensis*. Also, the three nontypical specimens from Weippe, upon re-examination, seem better referred to *idahoensis* with the understanding that they are intergrades between that race and *kootenayensis*.

Additional specimens from Alturas Lake make it necessary to reconsider the systematic status of jumping mice in that area. In 1934 *(op. cit.*, p. 225), I referred two specimens from there to *oregonus* and pointed out that they were not typical because the tympanic bullae were considerably larger and more highly inflated, the incisors longer, and the color of the sides much grayer than in typical specimens. Five additional specimens from Alturas Lake appear, on the basis of cranial characters, to be referable to *idahoensis*. This area appears to be one where intergradation occurs between *oregonus* and *idahoensis* with most of the intergrades showing greater similarity to *idahoensis*.

Likewise, specimens from Smith Mountain and Black Lake are not typical of *idahoensis*. In color they approach *oregonus*, but in cranial characters, and length of hind foot are most like *idahoensis* and herein are referred to it.

Additional material from Clark, Fremont, and Teton counties in the upper Snake River area appear to be good *idahoensis*. Five specimens from the head of Crow Creek, Preuss Mountains, in southeastern Idaho indicate intergradation between *idahoensis* and *Z. p. utahensis* Hall which occurs typically in the Uinta Mountains of northeastern Utah. In color they resemble *utahensis*, but in cranial characters they are most like *idahoensis*. The ratio of anterior width of palate to posterior width of palate averages 80, with extremes of 74 and 83.5, and the average ratio of zygomatic breadth to occipitonasal length is 50, with extremes of 47.5 and 51.5. According to Hall (1934), in *utahensis* these respective ratios average 74 and 52.4. In *idahoensis* they average 78.5 and 50.6 in specimens from Warm Lake; 82 and 52.3 in specimens from Mt. Jefferson.

Records of occurrence.—Specimens examined, 87, as follows: *Latah County:* Cedar Mountain, 1 (nontypical) (Chas. R. Conner Mus.). *Clearwater County:* 2 mi. NE Weippe, 3 (nontypical). *Valley County:* 5 mi. W Cape Horn, 1; 5 mi. E Warm Lake, 6 (type locality). *Adams County:* 3 mi. W Payette Lake, 4; 1 mi. N Bear Cr. R. S., 13 (11 in Ralph Ellis coll.) (nontypical); summit Smith Mountain, 10 (7 in Ralph Ellis coll.) (nontypical); ½ mi. E Black Lake, 8 (Ralph Ellis coll.) (nontypical). *Lemhi County:* Salmon River Mountains, 5 (Biol. Surv. coll.). *Custer County:* head Pahsimeroi River, 2; Mill Cr., 14 mi. W Challis, 1. *Blaine County:* Alturas Lake, 7. *Clark County:* Taylor Cr., 5 mi. S Montana Line at Sheridan Mountain, 3 (Amer. Mus.). *Fremont County:* 3-5 mi. S Montana Line at Mount Jefferson, 11 (Amer. Mus.). *Teton County:* 3 mi. SW Victor, 5. *Caribou County:* Crow Creek, Preuss Mountains, 5 (Biol. Surv. coll.). *Franklin County:* Strawberry Creek, 20 mi. NE Preston, 2.

Zapus princeps oregonus Preble
OREGON JUMPING MOUSE

Zapus princeps oregonus Preble, N. Amer. Fauna, 15:24. August 8, 1899. Type from Elgin, Blue Mountains, Union County, Oregon.

Distribution.—In Idaho, restricted to the Weiser River drainage basin (see map, fig. 33).

Description.—Largest and darkest race of the species; nearly black, dorsal coloration with sharply contrasting yellowish brown sides; hind foot large (33 mm.); width of incisive foramina more than half their length; auditory bullae relatively small. External measurements of ten adults from Washington County are 244-144-33.

Remarks.—As compared with *idahoensis*, the race with which it intergrades in central Idaho, *oregonus* differs as follows: Hind foot larger; incisive foramina wider; auditory bullae smaller; dorsal coloration darker. As judged by Bailey's (1936:234) measurements of 232-138-33, for an average typical adult from Oregon, it seems that in Idaho the animals may differ in larger size. Otherwise the jumping mice inhabiting the Weiser drainage basin in Idaho are typical *oregonus* while those found in the vicinity of Smith Mountain in northern Adams County, on the peripheries of the ranges of *oregonus* and *idahoensis*, exhibit characters which indicate intergradation between these two races. The

Smith Mountain specimens resemble *oregonus* in coloration, but in cranial features, to which I assign greater weight, they are like *idahoensis,* the race to which they here are referred. Intergradation between these two races occurs also in the vicinity of Alturas Lake. From a geographical point of view, it seems probable that jumping mice inhabiting the drainage basins of rivers to the south and west of the Sawtooth Mountains will be found to be referable to *oregonus.*

The major portion of the range of *oregonus* lies in Oregon where, according to Bailey *(loc. cit.),* it covers practically all of the Transition and Canadian Zone areas east of the Cascades, including such scattered desert ranges as Yamsay, Hart, Steens, and Mahogany mountains, and the high country at the headwaters of the Owyhee River. If my interpretation of his statement be correct, Bailey would include southwestern Idaho within its range. At present I know of no specimens from that area. Its range extends also into southeastern Washington south of the Snake River (Taylor and Shaw, 1929:27).

Records of occurrence.—Specimens examined, 20, as follows: *Washington County:* 1 mi. NE Heath, 20 (15 in Ralph Ellis coll.).

Zapus princeps cinereus Hall
GRAY JUMPING MOUSE

Zapus princeps cinereus Hall, Univ. California Publ. Zool., 37:7. April 10, 1931. Type from Pine Canyon, 6600 ft., Raft River Mountains, 17 miles northwest of Kelton, Box Elder County, Utah.

Distribution.—In Idaho, restricted to boreal areas south of the Snake River (see map, fig. 33).

Description.—General coloration of sides grayish; auditory bullae small; skull relatively broad and short. External measurements of nine adults from near Albion average 243-142-32.3.

Remarks.—The Gray Jumping Mouse geographically is intermediate between *Z. p. nevadensis* Preble and *Z. p. utahensis* Hall. By means of external features alone, these three races are difficult to distinguish, but by means of cranial characters this may be accomplished with relative ease. From *nevadensis, cinereus* differs as follows: Auditory bullae much smaller; postpalatal length relatively less; skull relatively shorter and broader. According to Hall (1934:4), *cinereus* may be distinguished from *utahensis* as follows: Zygomatic breadth relatively less; skull shorter, but upper tooth rows longer; upper tooth rows parallel, rather than divergent anteriorly. From *Z. p. idahoensis, cinereus* differs as follows: Auditory bullae smaller; zygoma weaker; skull relatively narrower.

Since *cinereus* was described from nine specimens, only two of which are near adult, one cannot place much value on the coloration ascribed to it by Hall (1931:7). The type specimen is much lighter and grayer dorsally than is the near adult paratype which was collected the same day. As judged from cranial characters, eighteen specimens from near Albion, Idaho (about 50 mi. N of the Raft River Mountains, Utah), are clearly *cinereus,* but only one is gray like the type specimen. Most of the specimens from Albion are as dark, or darker than, the paratype; this condition indicates that grayish tendencies prevail in only a small proportion of the population and are not typical of the race. Likewise, the external measurements given by Hall *(op. cit.,* p. 11) appear to be below average. This is indicated by the following average external measurements of nine adults from near Albion: 243-142-32.3.

If my identification of the Albion specimens be correct, it appears that *cinereus* is not a race of small, grayish, short-tailed individuals, but one much like *nevadensis* in size and external proportions, but differing from it in paler, less pinkish, lateral coloration, and in certain cranial characters mentioned above.

This race occupies semiboreal areas in the isolated mountains in northwestern Utah and southern Idaho. A discontinuous distribution such as this leads one to consider the now isolated populations as relicts. Probably during the Pleistocene before the present desert conditions came into being, the species *princeps* occupied a nearly continuous range.

Records of occurrence.—Specimens examined, 20, as follows: *Cassia County:* Mt. Harrison, 10 mi. S Albion, 18 (2 in Davis coll.). *Bannock County:* Camp Tendoy, 2.

Family ERETHIZONTIDAE
AMERICAN PORCUPINES
Genus Erethizon F. Cuvier
North American Porcupines
Erethizon epixanthum epixanthum Brandt
YELLOW-HAIRED PORCUPINE

Erethizon epixanthus Brandt, Mem. Acad. Imp. Sci., St. Pétersbourg, ser. 6, 3 (Sci. Nat., 1) :390. 1835. Type from California. (See Hollister, Canadian Alpine Journal, special no., p. 27. February 17, 1913.)

Synonym.—Erethizon epixanthus, Merriam, 1891:72.

Distribution.—In Idaho, from Canada south into the mountains south of the Snake River.

Description.—Large, robust rodent with hairs of back and tail modified as barbed quills; tail short, broad, strong; eyes small; ears relatively short; feet large, with strong sharp claws; skull heavy, angular; infraorbital canal larger than foramen magnum; alisphenoidal canal and formen lacerum medius about half the size of foramen magnum; auditory bullae large, with dense, noncancellous bone; stapedial artery naked in its course through middle ear; dentition heavy, $\frac{1\ 0\ 1\ 3}{1\ 0\ 1\ 3}$, brachydont, rooted; premolars largest, with four lateral salient loops; angle of mandible curved medially; posterior termination of lower incisor in front of mandibular foramen. External measurements of three adult males from Bannock and Cassia counties average 735-200-97-28; a single female from near Pocatello measures 620-160-85-30.

Remarks.—Gazin (1935) records fossil porcupines from the Pleistocene deposits near American Falls. Taylor (1935) gives an excellent account of the habits and life history of the porcupine and its relation to forests; he discusses, also, methods of control. Suffice it to say here that the porcupine is widespread in North America; its range coincides closely with the distribution of coniferous forests. Although it is arboreal in habit, it is at home on the ground and often is found at some distance from trees. It frequents rocky ledges and boulder slopes where it establishes its den and rears its single young; it is active the year round.

Records of occurrence.—Specimens examined, 11, as follows: *Adams County:* summit Smith Mountain, 2; 1 mi. N Bear Cr. R. S., 2 (all in Ralph Ellis coll.). *Washington County:* 1 mi. NE Heath, 3 (Ralph Ellis coll.). *Cassia County:* 6 mi. SE Albion, 1. *Bannock*

County: Schutt's Mine, 3. Additional records: *Washington County:* tracks noted at Crane Creek (Borell, MS). *Owyhee County:* tracks noted in Bruneau Mountains (Merriam, 1891:72). *Jerome County:* tracks noted near Shoshone Falls (Merriam, 1891:72). *Cassia County:* sight records at Howells Canyon and Mt. Independence (Davis, MS). *Clark County:* one found dead near Birch Creek (Merriam, *ibid.*). *Fremont County:* Henrys Lake (Merriam, 1873:666). *Butte County:* Big Lost River; Lost River Mountains (Merriam, *ibid.*). *Bannock County:* sight record 1 mi. E Portneuf (Whitlow and Hall, 1933:269).

Order LAGOMORPHA
Rabbits, Hares, and Pikas

Family OCHOTONIDAE
Genus **Ochotona** Link
Pikas

Small, rabbitlike; ears short, rounded, scantily haired; fore and hind legs of nearly equal length; digits 5 in front, 4 behind; soles of feet haired, digital pads naked; tail rudimentary, often invisible externally; pelage long and soft. Skull moderately arched; postorbital processes lacking; palate but little longer than width of maxillary tooth row; infraorbital canal small; jugal extended far posteriorly as a spinous process; auditory bullae highly inflated, of alveolar structure; teeth rootless, dental formula $\frac{2\ 0\ 3\ 2}{1\ 0\ 2\ 3}$; I^2 a mere peg placed directly behind the large, grooved I^1; clavicle complete.

Although this family is related to the hares and rabbits, its present distribution, distinctive and amazingly constant morphological features, and the paleontological record (see Romer, 1933) suggest a divergence from the primitive lagomorph stem at a period not later than Eocene. The short, rounded, ratlike ears, nearly equal length of fore and hind legs, absence of fenestrations in the skull, and lack of supraorbital processes suggest retention of primitive lagomorph characters.

Today the family is holarctic in distribution. There is but a single genus. The present distribution in western North America, particularly in the Great Basin region, suggests its presence on this continent at least as early as the Pliocene. In the southern portion of its range it is restricted usually to high altitudes, often on isolated mountains, where it occurs in rocky outcroppings and boulder slopes. In Idaho, it occurs commonly in the mountains north and east of the Snake River Plains; as yet it has not been recorded from south of the river west of the Wasatch, or Bear River, Range.

Pikas are diurnal and active the year round. They spend much time in summer and autumn storing food for winter use. In mid-July individuals of a colony in a boulder slope near the head of the Pahsimeroi River were so spaced that each appeared to have a definite home territory in which it lived and stored its "hay." The forage grounds, however, were community property. They were most active, foraging, running hurriedly from rock to rock, and making hay, in early morning and late afternoon. At midday they usually rested in the shade of boulders or retreated to recesses among the rocks.

Their food consists mainly of grasses and herbs. These are collected and stored in piles in recesses under overhanging rocks. One haystack that I examined near Mill Creek consisted of about one half a bushel of cured grasses, several different kinds of herbs, chiefly composites, and a few pine needles and pine cones.

The breeding season probably is restricted to late spring. None of the females collected in July and August contained embryos or had active mammae. In these months, however, a number of half-grown young were seen. Howell (1924) records that the young are brought forth "from late in May or early in June to early in September."

The pikas of Idaho previously have been referred (Howell, *ibid.*) to two species, *O. princeps* and *O. schisticeps.* Borell (1931), however, has demonstrated that all the recognized races in Idaho should properly be referred to *O. princeps,* which name has priority.

The presence of seven races of pikas in Idaho illustrates the effects of isolation and diverse environmental conditions upon a plastic species of mammal. In general, pikas are limited in Idaho to rocky slopes at elevations above 4000 feet, and, thus, colonies on isolated mountains at the periphery of the main mountain mass in central Idaho are hemmed in by valleys which appear to act as impassable barriers. Once such a colony is effectively isolated, genetic variations which are not detrimental or are of an adaptive nature may persist and escape the swamping effect that occurs where a species occupies a continuous range.

The pikas in the Craters of the Moon National Monument are of particular interest. Here, a melanistic race has evolved on the dark, basaltic cinder cones. The controlling influences in the evolution of this race appear to be those of isolation and a dark-colored environment. Climatic conditions seem to have had little effect because the humidity and temperature in this area are nearly identical with those in the southern portion of the Lemhi Mountains where the lighter-colored race *O. p. lemhi* occurs. Benson (1933 b) has discussed this phenomenon at considerable length in connection with his report on a study of mammals in a limited area in New Mexico.

Ochotona princeps princeps (Richardson)
ROCKY MOUNTAIN PIKA

Lepus (Lagomys) princeps Richardson, Zool. Journal, 3:520. 1828. Type from headwaters of Athabaska River, near Athabaska Pass, Alberta, Canada.

Distribution.—Bitterroot Mountains in the northern half of the state.

Description.—Size medium; skull relatively narrow with rather long nasals, narrow interpterygoid fossa, and moderately wide palatal bridge; winter pelage uniform buffy drab or mouse-gray; summer pelage clay color or pinkish cinnamon, heavily shaded with blackish (Howell, 1924:12). External measurements of 5 males and 5 females from Glidden Lakes average, respectively, 203-15.5-33-22.5 and 202-16-32.5-22.

Records of occurrence.—Specimens examined, 30, as follows: *Shoshone County:* Glidden Lakes, 8; Glidden Creek Canyon, 2 mi. E Burke, 17; Lower Glidden Lake, 5. Additional records (Howell, 1924: 14): *Shoshone County:* Mullan; Thompson Pass. *Idaho County:* Bitterroot Mountains (west of Hamilton, Montana).

Ochotona princeps cuppes Bangs
BANGS PIKA

Ochotona cuppes Bangs, Proc. New England Zool. Club, 1:40. June 5, 1899. Type from Monashee Divide, Gold Range, 4000 feet altitude, British Columbia, Canada.

Distribution.—In Idaho, restricted to the extreme northern part of the state.

Description.—Similar to *princeps* but coloration darker, the upper parts and sides (in summer pelage) suffused with ochraceous-tawny instead of cinnamon-buff, the underparts pinkish cinnamon instead of pinkish buff (Howell, 1924:27). A male from near the type locality measures 203-15-32-19.

Record of occurrence (Howell, *ibid.*).—*Boundary County?*: Cabinet Mountains.

Ochotona princeps lemhi Howell
LEMHI PIKA

Ochotona uinta lemhi Howell, Proc. Biol. Soc. Washington, 32:106. May 20, 1919. Type from Timber Creek, Lemhi Mountains, 10 miles south of Junction, Lemhi County, Idaho.

Synonym.—*Lagomys princeps*, part, Merriam, 1891:73.

Distribution.—The mountainous central part of the state.

Description.—Size small; colors very pale; similar in winter pelage to *princeps*, but upperparts paler and underparts more whitish; in summer decidedly paler (less blackish) above and less buffy below; skull small and relatively narrow, with narrow nasals (Howell, 1924: 17). External measurements of 3 males and 5 females from the head of the Pahsimeroi River average, respectively, 180-22-32-24 and 185-23-30-24; of 4 males and 3 females from Mill Creek, 180-15-30-23 and 181-17-30-25; of 3 males and 3 females from Pettit Lake, 188-16-30-24 and 195-16-31-24.

Remarks.—Specimens from Pettit Lake are larger than typical *lemhi,* and in this respect tend toward *howelli;* their color, however, is typical of *lemhi.*

Records of occurrence.—Specimens examined, 51, as follows: *Valley County:* 5 mi. W Cape Horn, 12. *Custer County:* head Pahsimeroi River, 9; Mill Creek, 14 mi. W Challis, 7. *Blaine County:* Alturas Lake, 2; Pettit Lake, 6; Sawtooth Mountains, 5 mi. NW Galena, 1. Additional records (Howell, 1924:18): *Valley County:* Elk Summit. *Lemhi County:* Leadore (mountains east of); Timber Creek, Lemhi Mountains. *Custer County:* Stanley Lake. *Blaine County:* Big Wood River (head of); Ketchum. *Clark County:* Birch Creek (mountains east of). *Butte County:* Little Lost River Mountains [=Needle Peak, Lemhi Mountains, 10 mi. SW Kaufman].

Ochotona princeps ventorum Howell
WYOMING PIKA

Ochotona uinta ventorum Howell, Proc. Biol. Soc. Washington, 32:106. May 20, 1919. Type from Fremont Peak, Wind River Mountains, Fremont County, Wyoming.

Synonym.—Lagomys princeps, part, Merriam, 1891:73.

Distribution.—Mountains of the vicinity of Yellowstone National Park.

Description.—Similar to *princeps*, but coloration in summer pelage more buffy and less varied with blackish; skull averaging larger, with longer nasals and broader interpterygoid fossa (Howell, 1924: 18).

Record of occurrence (Merriam, 1891:74).—*Teton County?:* Teton Canyon. Howell *(ibid.)* does not list this specimen in his revision of the pikas. Until otherwise allocated, I feel justified on geographical grounds in referring it to the race *ventorum.*

Ochotona princeps goldmani Howell
LAVA-BEDS PIKA

Ochotona schisticeps goldmani Howell, N. Amer. Fauna, 47:40. August 21, 1924. Type from Echo Crater, Craters of the Moon National Monument, 20 miles southwest of Arco, Butte County, Idaho.

Distribution.—Known only from Craters of the Moon National Monument.

Description.—Similar to *princeps*, but very much darker (darkest race of the genus); skull broader and shorter; nasals broader; auditory bullae larger.

Remarks.—Previously this lava-beds race was known only from Echo Crater and Fissure Crater. This past summer, 1937, we encountered individuals on Recent lava flows near the Government Camp at the north edge of the Monument; also, in the older lava just north of Grassy Cone and in the region near Great Owl Cavern. A number of men whose work with livestock takes them into the country near by say that pikas or "rock rabbits," as they call them, occur in a number of places in the lava fields outside the Monument.

Unlike pikas I have observed in other parts of Idaho, Glidden Lakes and Copenhagen Basin for example, those in the lava fields are extremely wary. Moreover, because of the nearly perfect blending of their color with that of the lava, they are far more difficult to discern. Often I could hear their "bleating" but could not locate it until they moved. Their rate of recovery from fear when molested seemed much slower than that of other races. I observed individuals that remained out of sight for thirty minutes or more when my approach forced them to cover.

Records of occurrence.—Specimens examined, 5, all from the Craters of the Moon National Monument, Butte County, as follows: S. base Grassy Cone, 4; Great Owl Cavern, 1. Additional records (Howell, 1924:41) : *Butte County:* Echo Crater (type locality). *Blaine County:* Fissure Crater.

Ochotona princeps howelli Borell
SEVEN DEVILS PIKA

Ochotona princeps howelli Borell, Jour. Mammalogy, 12:306. August 24, 1931. Type from summit of Smith Mountain, 7500 feet altitude, near head of Bear Creek, south end of Seven Devils Mountains, Adams County, Idaho.

Synonym.—Ochotona princeps lemhi Howell, 1924:18, part.

Distribution.—Known only from the Seven Devils Mountains in west-central Idaho.

Description.—Similar to *princeps* but grayer (less brownish) dorsally, ventrally, on shoulders, and sides; ears blackish brown on inside, rather than light buff; nasals narrow and emarginate posteriorly, rather than broadly truncate. Larger and darker-colored than *lemhi.* External measurements of 5 males and 5 females from the type locality average, respectively, 188-11-31-24 and 191-13-30-23.

Records of occurrence.—Specimens examined, 26, as follows: *Adams County:* ½ mi. E Black Lake, 2; summit Smith Mountain, 24 (all in Ralph Ellis coll.). Additional record (Howell, 1924:18) : Seven Devils Mountains.

Ochotona princeps clamosa Hall and Bowlus
SOUTHEASTERN IDAHO PIKA

Ochotona princeps clamosa Hall and Bowlus, Univ. California Publ. Zool., 42:335. October 12, 1938. Type from N. rim Copenhagen Basin, 8400 ft., Bear Lake County, Idaho.

Distribution.—Bear River Range (Wasatch Range) of southeastern Idaho.

Description.—Hall and Bowlus *(op. cit.)* say: "Color: dark; in fresh summer pelage, near *(c)* Light Ochraceous Buff (capitalized color terms after Ridgway: Color Standards and Color Nomenclature,

1912) mixed with blackish, the latter color predominating; underparts whitish washed with near *(c)* Pinkish Buff. Skull: auditory bullae much inflated; palatal bridge narrow, with anterior border anteriorly concave; lateral margins of nasals straight; interpterygoid space spatulate.

"*Ochotona princeps clamosa* resembles *O. p. ventorum* and *O. p. goldmani* more closely than it does *O. p. uinta* and is judged to be about as closely related to *goldmani* as to *ventorum*. The size is about as in *ventorum* or *uinta* and greater than in *goldmani*. The color below and in worn winter pelage is nearest to that of *goldmani*, but that of the fresh summer pelage is nearest to *uinta* though intermediate toward *goldmani*. The auditory bullae are more inflated than in adjoining races. The palatal bridge is narrower than in *uinta* and about as in *goldmani* and *ventorum*. The anterior margin of the palatal bridge is broadly V-shaped as in *goldmani* and *ventorum*, and not straight as in *uinta*. The lateral margins of the nasals are straight as in *goldmani* rather than concave as in *ventorum* and *uinta*. The interpterygoid fossa is spatulate, or at any rate narrower posteriorly, as in *ventorum*, rather than parallel-sided as in *goldmani* and *uinta*."

Remarks.—In July, 1937, we found several colonies of this pika in the vicinity of Copenhagen Basin in the Wasatch Mountains about midway between Preston, Franklin County, and Montpelier, Bear Lake County. Nearly every rock slide harbored a few individuals and in a few of the larger slides they were abundant. Between July 13 and 23 we observed dozens of half-grown young of the year. None of the females collected was pregnant.

The original describers *(op. cit.)* point out that "the greater inflation of the auditory bullae in *clamosa* than occurs in near-by races is reflected in the following measurements of the distance to which the bullae project below the basioccipital in three of the subspecies studied. Average and extreme measurements in millimeters are as follows: *O. p. clamosa*, 4.5 (4.2-4.9) ; *ventorum*, 3.7 (3.4-4.0) ; *goldmani*, 4.0 (3.8-4.4) ; *uinta*, from Summit County, 4.2 (4.1-4.3). The greater inflation in *clamosa* is apparent also in the horizontal plane.

"The three specimens from Deep Lake, only 15 miles or so south of the type locality of *clamosa*, are slightly lighter colored than *clamosa* and, so far as the damaged skulls permit one to judge, have the interpterygoid space less spatulate. These variations are tendencies toward the conditions obtaining in *uinta*."

Records of occurrence.—Specimens examined, 21, all from the Wasatch Range, as follows: *Bannock County:* ¼ mi. W Copenhagen Basin, 1. *Franklin County:* Wasatch Mts., 2 mi. E Strawberry Cr. R. S., 2. *Bear Lake County:* W. rim Copenhagen Basin, 8; N. rim Copenhagen Basin, 10. Additional records (Hall and Bowlus, 1938): *Bear Lake County:* Deep Lake, Bear River Mountains, 3.

Family LEPORIDAE
HARES and RABBITS

Small- to medium-sized mammals with long ears; hind legs longer than front legs, hind feet large, fully furred; pelage long and soft; tail short, but externally visible. Skull with fenestrations on rostrum and sides of cranium; supraorbital plate bearing anterior and posterior spines; jugal laterally compressed, projecting backward beyond squamosal arm as a spinous process; incisive foramina as long as diastema, or nearly so; palatal bridge short, terminating posteriorly near M^1; pterygoid fossae well developed; bullae large, noncancellous; teeth rootless; dental formula $\frac{2\ 0\ 3\ 3}{1\ 0\ 2\ 3}$; upper tooth rows farther apart than lower rows; clavicle rudimentary; scapula with distinct metacromion process.

This family is divided into two groups, the hares *(Lepus)* and the rabbits *(Sylvilagus* and related forms). Hares are characterized by large size and specialization of the limbs for cursorial habit; the eyes are large; many species are seasonally dichromatic, white in winter, gray or brown in summer. The young at birth are fully furred, have their eyes and ears open, and are precocious. Rabbits are less specialized for running, the hind legs are relatively short; ears short; most of them seek safety under cover; usually not white in winter. The young at birth are blind, naked, and helpless.

Geologically the family is old, the paleontological record reaching back as far as the Oligocene in both the New and the Old worlds. At that time the family was about as well differentiated morphologically as it is today. In Idaho, fossil remains of leporids have been found in Upper Pliocene deposits at Hagerman (see Gazin, 1934), where two now extinct genera, *Hypolagus* and *Alilepus*, occurred. In Pleistocene deposits near American Falls remains of *Lepus* and *Sylvilagus* were found (see Gazin, 1935). These fossil remains illustrate that leporids of one kind or another have occurred in Idaho for thousands of years. Moreover, they show that evolutionary changes have taken place there or in near-by regions.

Because of their antiquity, and usually nomadic habits, the hares are widespread within the areas to which they are adapted. A positive correlation of extent of range with structure and habit is illustrated by comparison of such species as *L. californicus, S. nuttallii,* and *S. idahoensis.* The first-mentioned is large, nomadic, relies upon running to elude enemies, and is capable of traveling great distances; it is most widespread. The cottontail, *S. nuttallii,* is smaller, less adapted to running, and to elude enemies relies upon seeking cover in rock piles or brush thickets; its range is less extensive. The pygmy rabbit, *S. idahoensis,* is smallest, least adapted to running, and is the most sedentary of the three; its range is smallest.

Key to Genera and Species of Adult Rabbits and Hares of Idaho

1 Length of hind foot 120 mm. or more; length of ear 75 mm. or more; general size large. **LEPUS** (hares).

    2 Tail bicolored, black above, white below.

        3 Ear nearly as long as hind foot; general color gray, not seasonally dichromatic. **L. californicus**, p. 357

        3' Ear much shorter than hind foot; seasonally dichromatic, brown in summer, white in winter. **L. bairdii**, p. 355

    2' Tail pure white; seasonally dichromatic, gray in summer, white in winter. **L. townsendii**, p. 354

1' Length of hind foot less than 100 mm.; length of ear usually less than 70 mm.; general size medium to small.

                                      SYLVILAGUS (rabbits).

    4 Undersurface of tail pure white. **S. nuttallii**, p. 360

    4' Undersurface of tail burnt orange buff, never pure white. **S. idahoensis**, p. 363

Genus **Lepus** Linnaeus
Hares

Lepus townsendii townsendii Bachman
WHITE-TAILED JACK RABBIT

Lepus townsendii Bachman, Jour. Acad. Nat. Sci. Philadelphia, 8:90. 1839. Type from Old Fort Walla Walla (near Wallula), Walla Walla County, Washington.

Synonyms.—Lepus campestris, Merriam, 1891:78; *Lepus campestris townsendi*, Nelson, 1909:78.

Distribution.—In Idaho, probably occurs only in the southern half of the state.

Description.—Largest of the hares in Idaho. Color (summer): Upper parts light gray, suffused with blacks and browns; top of head grayish brown, ears white behind, fawn-colored on rim and anterior portions; *tail pure white;* legs and upper surfaces of feet white; underparts plumbeous-white, pure white in mid-ventral portion. Winter (December 27): Pure white except for top of head and ears which are fawn-colored with admixture of white. Young: Grizzled grayish all over except tops of feet, abdomen, and inner surfaces of legs and under surface of tail which are white. External measurements of two females from Mt. Harrison average 605-95-155-110; a male from Bellevue measures 550-80-170-110. Skull: Arched dorsally, supraorbital plates large; lacrimal forming distinct antorbital process; nasals short and wide (greatest width of nasals more than half their greatest length); Pm^2 wider than I^1 (ratio of width of Pm^2 to that of I^1, 14:10); greatest length of skull over 90 mm.; auditory bullae relatively small.

Remarks.—This species is wide ranging in the foothills and higher valleys in southern Idaho. Because it is active the year round and nomadic in habit, populations are not continually isolated, and as a result the species is fairly uniform structurally throughout its range.

At Mt. Harrison it occurs in summer usually above 5000 feet altitude, where it inhabits the more open slopes and ridges in the vicinity of thickets of quaking aspen and fir. In winter, however, it descends into the sage-covered valleys and lower foothills where it associates with the more numerous black-tailed jack rabbit. Mr. Will Wickel, a rancher living near Elba, has encountered both species feeding on his stacked hay in winter. In the upper part of the Snake River Valley, the white-tailed jack rabbit is the species most frequently seen outside the heavily timbered areas.

The breeding season appears to be restricted to late spring and early summer. A female collected June 9 at Conner Canyon, near Elba, contained 8 nearly full-term embryos. They were fully furred and the ears and eyes were open; the rump-crown length of one preserved as a study skin measured 115 mm.; the conventional external measurements of this specimen are 160-15-47-27.

Records of occurrence.—Specimens examined, 10, as follows: *Cassia County:* Conner Canyon, 4 mi. N Elba, 2; Mt. Harrison, 10 mi. S Albion, 2. *Clark County:* Small, 1. *Bannock County:* Barrett's Ranch, 1; 6 mi. E McCammon, 1; 4 mi. S Pocatello, 1; Virginia, 1. *Franklin County:* Strawberry Canyon, 20 mi. NE Preston, 1. Additional records (Merriam, 1891:78, unless otherwise stated): *Lemhi County:* head Lemhi River (sight record); Salmon City (sight record). *Custer County:* Challis Valley (sight record); Pahsimeroi Valley (sight record); 8 mi. W Challis (sight record, Davis, 1936). *Cassia County:* 2 mi. W Elba (sight record, Davis, 1934). *Clark County:* Birch Creek (sight record). *Butte County:* Big Lost River Valley (sight record); Little Lost River Valley (sight record). *Teton County:* Teton Basin (Nelson, 1909:82). *Bear Lake County:* Bear Lake (Nelson, *ibid.*).

Lepus bairdii bairdii Hayden
ROCKY MOUNTAIN SNOWSHOE RABBIT

Lepus bairdii Hayden, Amer. Nat., 3:115. May, 1869. Type from near Fremont Peak, Wind River Mountains, Fremont County, Wyoming.

Synonym.—*Lepus americanus bairdii,* Whitlow and Hall, 1933:270.

Distribution.—In Idaho, occurs in the mountainous portions of the state north and east of the Snake River Plains.

Description.—Medium-sized hare, with large hind feet and relatively short ears. Color (summer): Upper parts from grizzled brownish to wood brown, overcast with blackish on rump; top of head and cheeks fawn-colored; ears conspicuously white-edged; underparts plumbeous-white; forelegs fawn-colored; antiplantar surfaces of hind feet white. Winter: Pure white except for black-rimmed eyes and ears. Young similar to adults, but less brownish, that is, more grayish; tops of hind feet plumbeous, rather than white. External measurements of an adult female from Alturas Lake are 465-59-155-85; of an adult male from Schutt's Mine, 435-35-140-79. Skull smaller than in *Lepus townsendii* and *L. californicus,* greatest length near 75 mm.; nasals long, terminating anteriorly on a plane with incisors, and relatively slender (ratio of greatest length to greatest breadth, 21:10) ; lacrimal bone forming a distinct antorbital process; supra-orbital plate large; incisive foramina terminating posteriorly on a plane with middle of Pm^2.

Remarks.—This hare is typical of alpine meadows, streamside thickets, and forests in the mountainous parts of Idaho. Here it is active the year round and usually under-goes little, if any, altitudinal migration. Like others of the genus, the snowshoe rabbit is largely crepuscular or noctur-nal in habit. In summer much of its foraging is done in the vicinity of shrubbery in which it can seek safety when mo-lested. In winter, however, its forage range is more exten-sive because all shrubbery is covered with snow. At Alturas Lake I had opportunity to note how well the dark summer pelage blended with a background of shrubs in late evening. Unless the animal moved, it was so inconspicuous that one could pass close by without noting its presence. It is well adapted to the rigorous winters of the mountains; the white winter coat makes it inconspicuous, and the large, densely furred, snowshoelike hind feet carry it with ease over loose, soft snow.

Rabbits and hares often are heavily infested with ticks and mites. A male *bairdii* which I collected July 12, 1935, at the head of Big Lost River was so heavily infested with ticks *(Dermacentor parumapterus marginatus)* that it was seriously handicapped. When the animal was flushed about 2:30 P.M. in an open stand of lodgepole pine, it hopped awkwardly a few yards up the side of a hill and sat up. Its nose and ears kept moving constantly. I shot it and discovered that it was completely blind in one eye and nearly so in the other. Thirty engorged female ticks were attached to the skin around the eyes and on the chin. The blinded eye was sealed shut and when the lids were opened, nearly a teaspoonful of pus exuded. The cornea of this eye was opaque and had the animal been able to get rid of the ticks, I doubt that the eye would have become functional. The lids of the other eye were glued nearly shut with dried pus. No ticks were on the ears, the part of the body to which they usually are attached.

Half-grown young were collected at Bear Creek, July

1; a female collected on the same date at Cuddy Mountain contained 3 embryos 6 mm. in rump-crown length. A female collected July 29 at Redfish Lake contained 5 embryos 37 mm. in length; another collected the following day at Alturas Lake contained 5 nearly full-term embryos. These data indicate a long breeding season, at least from May to August, and suggest that more than one litter may be reared yearly. The young at birth are fully furred and precocious.

Records of occurrence.—Specimens examined, 23, as follows: *Bonner County:* 5 mi. W Cocolalla, 2. *Latah County:* Cedar Mountain, 5; Felton's Mill, 1 (all in Chas. R. Conner Mus.). *Clearwater County:* 2 mi. NE Weippe, 2. *Adams County:* 1 mi. N Bear Cr. R. S., 3 (Ralph Ellis coll.); 3 mi. W Payette Lake, 1. *Valley County:* Donnelly, 1. *Washington County:* S.W. slope Cuddy Mountain, 3 (2 in Ralph Ellis coll.). *Custer County:* head Big Lost River, 1; Redfish Lake, 1. *Blaine County:* Alturas Lake, 1; Hailey, 1. *Bannock County:* Schutt's Mine, 1. Additional records (Nelson, 1909:112): *Shoshone County:* Mullan. *Latah County:* Moscow. *Custer County:* Big Lost River Valley (near Thousand Springs) (Merriam, 1891:79). *Blaine County:* Ketchum. *County* questionable: Sinyakwatun Depot. Nelson *(ibid.)* also records specimens from Bitterroot Valley in Idaho. I am of the opinion that this was an error, for that valley lies in Montana, rather than in Idaho.

Lepus californicus deserticola Mearns
DESERT BLACK-TAILED JACK RABBIT

Lepus texianus deserticola Mearns, Proc. U. S. Nat. Mus., 18:564. June 24, 1896. Type from western edge of the Colorado Desert, at east base of Coast Range mountains near Mexican boundary, San Diego County, California.

Synonyms.—*Lepus callotis,* Merriam, 1873:666; *Lepus texianus,* Merriam, 1891:78; *Lepus californicus depressus* Hall and Whitlow, 1932:71-72 (type locality, Pocatello, Bannock County, Idaho); *Lepus californicus wallawalla,* Nelson, 1909:133.

Distribution.—In Idaho, occurs in the lower sage-covered valleys and foothills in the southern half of the state.

Description.—Large, black-tailed hare with relatively long ears and hind feet. Color (summer): Upperparts light grayish, mottled with blackish; head and back of same color; ears iron gray, distinctly edged with buff or white; top of tail distinctly black, under side with admixture of white; tops of hind feet whitish; underparts white, washed with buff along lower sides, in axillary and inguinal regions, and on chin. Winter: Pelage longer; color as in summer, but slightly darker dorsally. Young similar to adults, but slightly grayer. External measurements of 4 adult males from Cassia and Minidoka counties average 534-84-125-123; an adult female from Bannock County measures 550-80-125-120. Skull intermediate in size between *L. townsendii* and *L. bairdii*, greatest length near 85 mm.; nasals relatively long and slender, terminating anteriorly behind incisors (ratio of greatest length to greatest breadth, near 2:1); Pm^2 but little wider than I^1 (ratio 30:28); incisive foramina terminating posteriorly on a plane usually behind Pm^2.

Remarks.—In comparing specimens of *californicus* from Idaho with others from Nevada, northeastern California, and Oregon, I failed to find evidence to validate the existence of more than one race in Idaho. The characters used in naming the race *wallawalla* are chiefly those of color. Jack rabbits in Idaho exhibit varying degrees of intensity of melanistic color when comparable (age, sex, and season) specimens are examined. The same degree of color variation was found in specimens examined from Nevada and California. A May-taken specimen from Alkali Lake, Oregon, that is, in the center of the range assigned to *wallawalla*, is darker dorsally than any specimen examined from Idaho and Nevada. It can be matched, however, by a specimen of *deserticola* from Nixon Springs, Arizona. Moreover, the specimen from Alkali Lake is considerably darker than most of the specimens from northeastern California which have been referred by various authors (Nelson, 1909; Grinnell, 1933) to *wallawalla*. It also is darker than a specimen from Wallula, Washington, near the type locality of *wallawalla*. To me, specimens from Modoc, Siskiyou, and Lassen counties, California, and the one from Wallula, Washington, do not differ appreciably from specimens of similar age and pelage taken in Idaho. Nor do the specimens from Idaho differ appreciably from specimens of *deserticola* from southeastern California. Because of this situation, and in spite of the fact that I have not examined the specimen from the Boise River which Nelson *(ibid.)* referred to *wallawalla*, I see no useful purpose to be served in retaining the name *wallawalla*, at least for specimens from Idaho.

Cranial characters also vary considerably in detail in specimens of comparable age from a single locality and also between localities. This is true of the degree to which the rostrum is depressed, a diagnostic character used in applying the recently proposed name *depressus* to specimens from near Pocatello. The depressed condition of the rostrum is not constant in specimens from the Snake River Valley. Moreover, it occurs also in some specimens from Nevada and southern California. Therefore, I have placed the name *L. c. depressus* Hall and Whitlow in the synonymy of *L. c. deserticola* Mearns.

In southern Idaho jack rabbits fluctuate in numbers over a period of years and also from year to year and from locality to locality. I recall the rabbit drives held on the deserts north of Rupert in 1918 and 1919 when thousands of rabbits were killed. The first drive of the season in 1918 yielded near 20,000 rabbits. In the early part of the last decade, rabbits were relatively scarce in the Snake River Valley, but in 1931 they again were very abundant. Gordon (1932) kept count of rabbits found dead on U. S. Highway 30 (Highway 40 is south of Idaho) in two different years. In 1929, the average number found was 2 a mile; in 1931, however, the average was near 10. His account and one by Sperry (1933) illustrate that local fluctuations in population are common. In 1931 Gordon *(ibid.)* found on the average 100 dead rabbits a mile for nearly three miles in the vicinity of Thousand Springs (near Hagerman). The following year, Sperry *(ibid.)* saw no rabbits along the same piece of highway. In 1935 and 1936 I found jack rabbits extremely abundant in Cassia Creek Valley, whereas in 1933 and 1934 their number was at low ebb.

Rabbit drives were held regularly each week during the summer of 1934 northwest of Paul. They were advertised and well attended; anyone who could walk, shout lustily, and wield a club was eligible to participate. Although none of the drives I witnessed resulted in more than four or five hundred rabbits, the total for the season for one permanently established pen was reported to be well over 10,000. Other pens probably yielded similar numbers. Fully 80 per cent of the dead rabbits that I saw were young of the year. Although the pygmy rabbit and the cottontail occur in the area, I saw none among the dead rabbits examined.

Jack rabbits are preyed upon chiefly by coyotes and raptorial birds. Because of decreased numbers of coyotes, due largely to persistent trapping and poisoning, a portion of the natural check on rabbits has been eliminated. Some of it has been replaced, however, by an increase in the number of hawks. In the winter of 1935-36, American Rough-legged Hawks *(Archibuteo lagopus)* were abundant in the Snake River Valley. Hundreds of them were seen flying over the sage-covered deserts and each of the four collected had fed on rabbit.

A female collected May 20 near Hagerman contained 5 half-term embryos; half-grown young were observed at Homedale in late May, and at Acequia and northwest of Paul in June. These meager data suggest an early, restricted breeding season in Idaho.

Records of occurrence.—Specimens examined, 67, as follows: *Elmore County:* 5 mi. S Mountain Home, 5. *Owyhee County:* 7 mi. S Bruneau, 1; 4 mi. S Murphy, 1; 5 mi. SE Murphy, 1; hills 6 mi. W Murphy, 1; Castle Creek, 4 mi. S Oreana, 1. *Gooding County:* 4 mi. E Gooding, 3; 2 mi. S Hagerman, 3. *Minidoka County:* Acequia, 6; 3-4 mi. NW Paul, 14; 4-6 mi. N Rupert, 9; Snake River, 1 mi. W Heyburn, 1. *Twin Falls County:* 2 mi. E Rogerson, 1. *Cassia County:* 4 mi. NW Albion, 2; 6 mi. S Rupert, 1; 6 mi. W Yale, 1. *Bingham County:* 3 mi. S Springfield, 1. *Power County:* 8-15 mi. W Pocatello, 4; 2-3 mi. NW Michaud, 7. *Bannock County:* near Pocatello, 4. Additional records (Merriam, 1891:78, unless otherwise stated): *Canyon County:* Boise River (Nelson, 1909). *Lemhi County:* Lemhi Valley (sight record). *Custer County:* Challis Valley (sight record); Pahsimeroi Valley (sight record); Thousand Springs Valley (sight record). *Blaine County:* Sawtooth National Forest (Nelson, *ibid.*). *Clark County:* Birch Creek (sight record). *Butte County:* Arco (Nelson, *ibid.*); Little Lost River Valley (sight record). *Bingham County:* Blackfoot (Nelson, *ibid.*).

Genus Sylvilagus Gray
Cottontails and Swamp Rabbits

Sylvilagus nuttallii nuttallii (Bachman)
WASHINGTON COTTONTAIL

Lepus nuttallii Bachman, Jour. Acad. Nat. Sci. Philadelphia, 7: 345. 1837. Type probably from eastern Oregon, near the mouth of Malheur River (see Nelson, 1909:203).

Distribution.—In Idaho, occurs in extreme west-central portion of the state.

Description (Nelson, 1909).—Size small; top of head plain dull buffy fawn color; top of back varying from dull dark buff, tinged with fawn, to dull dark fawn, darkened by a wash of black; sides of head slightly paler and grayer; rump dark iron gray; nape dark rusty rufous; ears dark, edged with black; top of tail dusky brown, white below; tops of hind feet white, tinged with cinnamon; front of forelegs cinnamon; throat ochraceous buff; middle of chest and abdomen nearly pure white; ears short. External measurements of 5 adults average 352-44-90-56. Skull small and light, proportionately short and broad across base with slender rostrum and long, narrow, slightly tapering nasals.

Remarks.—See under *Remarks* in account of *S. n. grangeri.*

Records of occurrence (Nelson, 1909:204).—*Nez Perce County:* Lewiston. *Idaho County:* Fiddle Creek.

Sylvilagus nuttallii grangeri (Allen)
BLACK HILLS COTTONTAIL

Lepus sylvaticus grangeri Allen, Bull. Amer. Mus. Nat. Hist., 7:264. August 21, 1895. Type from Hill City, Pennington County, North Dakota.

Distribution.—In Idaho, occurs in the southern half of the state.

Description.—Similar to *nuttallii*, but, according to Nelson (1909), larger and lighter colored. External measurements of 4 adult females from near Acequia average 348-35-90-62; 3 adult males from Acequia, Elba, and Murphy average 365-48-97-66.

Remarks.—Although I have had available 25 specimens of cottontail from Idaho, four of which are from Crane Creek, near the type locality of *nuttallii*, I have been unable to determine to my complete satisfaction their subspecific status. Considering the four individuals from Crane Creek and one from Walla Walla, Washington, as being typical of *nuttallii*, I have failed to find any characters which distinguish them from the other Idaho-taken specimens. As compared with specimens of comparable age and pelage from Nevada and northeastern California (referred to *grangeri* and *nuttallii* respectively) there are no appreciable differences. The characters used to separate these two races are not apparent in the material studied. As compared with Nelson's measurements (1909:201) of the two races, the Idaho specimens are intermediate. The average external measurements of 7 adults more nearly accord with the published measurements of *nuttallii*, but in cranial characters, except for width of parietal region, they are more like *grangeri*. Because the cranial measurements are closer to those published for *grangeri*, it seems best to refer the cottontails from southern Idaho tentatively to *grangeri*.

Although I have not examined the two specimens which Nelson *(ibid.)* records from the Sawtooth National Forest, I am doubtful of their allocation to *nuttallii*. Specimens that I have examined from west of that locality are in measurements nearer *grangeri* and for this reason I have included the Sawtooth National Forest in the range herein assigned to *grangeri*. The specimen from the South Fork of the Owyhee River was not received until after the other specimens were distributed and hence was not critically studied.

Cottontails are persistently hunted by man because of their tender, delicious meat. Never are they as abundant in Idaho as the black-tailed jack rabbit, and my impression is that they do not fluctuate as much in numbers from year to year. Because of their habit of seeking safety in brush thickets and rock piles, they are not encountered as often as the hares which rely principally upon their running ability to escape enemies. At Acequia in June, 1934, cottontails were inhabiting a pile of loose rocks along a canal bank which was occupied also by marmots. At Elba, cottontails were fairly common among the thickets along Cassia Creek. Although they usually are crepuscular in habit, they do not confine their activities solely to early morning and evening. Near Swan Valley I observed cottontails feeding near shrubbery in midafternoon; at Acequia they were abroad throughout most of the day.

In Idaho, the breeding season appears to be restricted to April, May, and June. A female taken May 2 near Pocatello had active mammae but no embryos, a situation which indicated she was nursing young; a female taken May 25 near Murphy contained 6 embryos 30 mm. in rump-crown length. None of the females taken in summer was pregnant.

Records of occurrence.—Specimens examined, 25, as follows: *Washington County:* Crane Creek, 15 mi. E Midvale, 4 (Ralph Ellis coll.). *Owyhee County:* Homedale, 1; 6 mi. W Murphy, 1; 5 mi. SE Murphy, 1; South Fork Owyhee River, 12 mi. N Nevada Line, 1. *Custer County:* 2 mi. SE Cape Horn, 1. *Gooding County:* 2 mi. S Hagerman, 3. *Minidoka County:* 2 mi. E Acequia, 7. *Twin Falls County:* Salmon Creek, 8 mi. W Rogerson, 1. *Cassia County:* Elba, 2. *Bonneville County:* lava beds, 17 mi. W Idaho Falls, 1. *Bannock County:* 4 mi. E Pocatello, 1; Trail Creek, 3 mi. W Pocatello, 1. Additional records (Nelson, 1909): *Lemhi County:* Lemhi; Lemhi Valley. *Blaine County?:* Sawtooth National Forest. *Butte County:* Big Lost River (near Arco); Lost River Mountains. *Bingham County:* Blackfoot.

Sylvilagus idahoensis (Merriam)
IDAHO PYGMY RABBIT

Lepus idahoensis Merriam, N. Amer. Fauna, 5:76. July 30, 1891. Type from head of Pahsimeroi Valley, near Goldburg, Custer County, Idaho.

Synonyms.—*Brachylagus idahoensis*, Lyon, 1904:323; *Brachylagus idahoensis*, Nelson, 1909:275.

Distribution.—In Idaho, nearly coincident with the distribution of sagebrush *(Artemisia tridentata)* in the southern half of the state.

Description.—Smallest of the Leporidae in Idaho. Ears much shorter than in the cottontail. Color (November): Upperparts buffy gray, nape rich cinnamon buff; ears edged with buff, inside of concha clothed with white hairs; anterior surfaces of legs cinnamon buff; throat patch usually buff; abdomen clear white, often tinged with buff; tail rusty buff above and below. By midwinter (February) the fur has become so worn that the upperparts are nearly silver gray, with a slight indication of the sooty brown deeper color visible. By May the upperparts are much darker, nearly sooty brown with admixture of white-tipped hairs; insides of ears gray, rather than white; underparts plumbeous white. June specimens like those in May but with new grayish buff hairs coming in thickly along sides (no. 72092, Mus. Vert. Zool.); old hair beginning to drop out on sides and flanks. The new coat is acquired in mid- or late-summer. External measurements of 3 adult females from Riddle, Elba, and near Pocatello average 296-20-72-47; a male from near Michaud measures 265-20-70-50. Skull small, occipital region highly arched; anteroposterior length of bullae considerably more than length of maxillary tooth row; second upper premolar narrower than first upper molar; greatest length of skull near 50 mm.

Remarks.—Pygmy rabbits differ markedly from cottontails in smaller size, shorter ears, buff, rather than white undertail coloration, much larger auditory bullae, and weaker and more primitive dentition. The species is homogeneous and widespread throughout the northern portion of the Great Basin (here used in its inclusive meaning), occurring from central Nevada north to southwestern Montana and from eastern Idaho west into Oregon and northeastern California.

In Idaho they occur most frequently in areas where *Sarcobatus* is abundant or where dense stands of sagebrush (*Artemisia tridentata*) grow in the deep soil of hollows and gullies. Near the head of the Pahsimeroi River two were seen in low sage, but there it was the best cover available. Usually the pygmy rabbit can be closely approached, particularly if it is in, or very near, cover. For example, one seen near Idavada, when first observed, was sitting near the mouth of a burrow, but when I approached it moved rather leisurely a few yards into the near-by sage thicket, instead of retreating into the burrow as I had anticipated. I followed and several times was able to approach within ten feet before it retreated. In the Pahsimeroi Valley, where cover was too open for adequate protection, the first impulse of one I encountered was to scurry, ground squirrel fashion, to the entrance of a burrow at the base of a sage bush where it sat, partly concealed by the shrub, and watched me. On closer approach it retreated below ground.

Although usually crepuscular in habit, these rabbits frequently forage by day. At Riddle, I observed them on May 28, 29, and 30, 1934, feeding at 1:30 P.M., 4:30 P.M., and 3:00 P.M. respectively. In each instance the foraging was done among dense, low *Sarcobatus vermiculatus*, rather than in the area of taller *Artemisia tridentata* where their burrows were located. On September 13, 1934, one mile north of Idavada one was foraging at 8:45 A.M. Here the rabbit was occupying a burrow system which had six entrances, each of which was about five inches in diameter. There were none of the usual trenches or depressed runways leading to them, nor were definite runways discernible in the surrounding area. The sage here was about three feet high, not very dense, and covered an area about fifty by seventy-five feet. The surrounding vegetation consisted for the most part of dwarfed sagebrush not over twelve inches high. Evidently these rabbits, like many desert-dwelling mammals, are able to subsist without water, for at this locality the closest available supply was three miles distant.

Most rabbits are infested with ectoparasites as well as endoparasites, and pygmy rabbits are not exceptions, for all that I have collected harbored at least three kinds of ectoparasites, ticks, fleas, and lice. Ticks usually are attached on, or at the bases of, the ears. Two specimens that I collected in late May near Riddle were so heavily infested with fleas that the movements of the insects caused the pelage to appear animated.

Grinnell, Dixon, and Linsdale (1930) have convincingly demonstrated that pygmy rabbits undergo but one annual molt. I might add to their account that molt may begin in early June (no. 7292, Mus. Vert. Zool.) and be completed as early as July 5 (no. 4535, Ralph Ellis coll.). After the old fur has been replaced, subsequent changes in pelage consist chiefly of an increase in the length of individual hairs and in the amount of underfur. The pelage of a male (no. 4537, Ellis coll.) collected July 27 is nearly as long and dense as one taken in October; the latter differs in having longer hairs on the sides. Color changes, as the above authors point out, result from abrasion and fading. Molt begins first on the sides and flanks and proceeds thence to the back and belly.

The breeding season probably extends over several months of spring and summer. A female collected May 2 near Pocatello had active mammae but contained no embryos, a condition which indicates she was nursing young. Each of two females, collected May 28 and 30, 1934, at Riddle, contained six embryos which measured 72 mm. in rump-crown length; three were in each horn of the uterus. Judging from the amount of milk in the mammary glands, the females were parturient, and at this stage of development the young were entirely devoid of visible hair. The latest seasonal record of which I am aware is that mentioned by Anthony (1913), who saw a young one on August 21, in Malheur County, Oregon, that was no larger than a man's fist.

Records of occurrence.—Specimens examined, 10, as follows: *Owyhee County:* 1 mi. S Riddle, 2. *Cassia County:* Elba, 1. *Butte County:* S. base Grassy Cone, Craters of the Moon National Monument, 1. *Power County:* 2 mi. N Michaud, 3. *Bannock County:* 1 mi. W Schutt's Mine, 2; Trail Creek, near Pocatello, 1. Additional records (Nelson, 1909:278, unless otherwise stated): *Lemhi County:* Junction. *Custer County:* Pahsimeroi Valley. *Minidoka County:* Minidoka (Seton, 1929:840). *Cassia County:* Burley (Grinnell, Dixon, and Linsdale, 1930:556). *Clark County:* Birch Creek. *Butte County:* Big Lost River Valley; Lost River Mountains. *County* questionable: Ione Valley (Lyon, 1904:323). (I have been unable to locate an Ione Valley in Idaho; there is one, however, in south-central Nevada. Perhaps the specimens Lyon listed came from Nevada, rather than from Idaho.)

Order ARTIODACTYLA
Even-toed, Hoofed Mammals
Family CERVIDAE
CARIBOU, DEER, ELK, MOOSE

Large to small digitigrade, cursorial, deerlike ungulates; males always, female occasionally, with bony antlers which are shed annually; tail short; four functional hoofed digits on each foot; dental formula $\frac{0\ 0\text{-}1\ 3\ 3}{3\ 1\ 3\ 3}$; cheek teeth selenodont; two lacrimal ducts; gall bladder usually absent.

The most striking feature of modern cervids is the presence in males of antlers, branching structures of solid bone, which grow out from the frontal bones of the head just behind the eyes. During growth, the antlers are covered by skin clothed with fine hair, the velvet, but after the growth has ceased, the blood supply is cut off, the bone hardens, the skin dries up and is rubbed off. The antlers are shed yearly. The following year a new, generally more complex, growth replaces the lost structure.

Today, this family is holarctic in distribution; the genera *Cervus, Alces,* and *Rangifer* occur in both the Old and the New worlds. The family dates back to the Miocene (see Romer, 1933) in North America, and in the Upper Pliocene or Lower Pleistocene deposits near Hagerman, Idaho, fossil remains of an unidentified cervid occur (see Gazin, 1936). Hay (1927) records the genus *Cervus* from Pleistocene deposits in Owyhee and Ada counties. These fossil remains furnish evidence that cervids have lived in Idaho at least since Upper Pliocene. The elk, *Cervus canadensis,* is thought to be a relatively recent migrant from the Old World; the genus *Odocoileus* may have evolved on this continent.

Within historic time cervids occurred commonly on the plains and in lower valleys in Idaho and the West in general, but "civilization" has pushed them farther and farther into the mountainous areas where they are less disturbed. Deer are reported (Merriam, 1891) to have occurred in the Snake River Valley near Twin Falls as late as 1890; today they are absent there. Most members of the family typically browse, subsisting in large part on the tender shoots and leaves of shrubs. Grasses and herbs, however, also constitute a portion of their diet. The young, one or two in number, are born usually in early spring. Except for the moose, the juvenal pelage is more or less spotted in American forms.

Genus **Cervus** Linnaeus
Wapiti or American Elk and Old World Red Deer

Cervus canadensis nelsoni Bailey
ROCKY MOUNTAIN ELK

Cervus canadensis nelsoni Bailey, Proc. Biol. Soc. Washington, 48:188. November 15, 1935. Type from Yellowstone National Park, Wyoming.

Synonyms.—*Cervus canadensis,* Merriam, 1891:80; *Cervus canadensis* subsp.?, Whitlow and Hall, 1933:272.

Distribution.—In Idaho, formerly ranged over most of the state, the deserts probably excepted; now greatly reduced in numbers and restricted largely to the more inaccessible mountainous portions of the state.

Description.—A large member of the deer family, males with massive antlers bearing prominent brow tines; color yellowish gray or tawny, a large conspicuous straw-colored patch on rump, surrounding tail; hair on neck long and shaggy. Adult males may weigh as much as 600 pounds and measure 7 or 8 feet in total length, females smaller. Dental formula $\frac{0\,1\,3\,3}{3\,1\,3\,3}$.

Remarks.—In 1890, Merriam (1891) found these animals to be common in the Sawtooth and Pahsimeroi mountains and not rare in the Lemhi Mountains. He reports them also from the Bruneau and Elk mountains in southern Idaho, and from Henrys Lake and the Blackfoot Mountains in eastern Idaho. In 1843, Fremont (1853) found elk in numbers on the prairie in Bear River Valley near Pegram.

The population of elk in Idaho is estimated (Eckert, 1935) to be near 16,000. Small herds have been reported (Graves and Nelson, 1919) from the following National Forests: Cache, Caribou, Challis, Clearwater, Idaho, Minidoka, Payette, Salmon, Selway, Sawtooth, Targhee, and Weiser. Many of the National Forests have been restocked with elk from time to time. The following cumulative summary (Adams, 1926) of the number of elk in the National Forests of northern Idaho indicates a very material increase between the years 1921 and 1925. Unfortunately, similar data from 1926 to the present are unavailable.

TABLE 1

CUMULATIVE SUMMARY OF ELK IN IDAHO

National Forest	1921	1922	1923	1924	1925
Clearwater	200	180	250	450	500
Coeur d'Alene	0	0	0	3	5
Nezperce	115	237	320	334	309
Selway	600	1,000	1,950	1,650	3,010
St. Joe	60	71	70	65	75

Genus Odocoileus Rafinesque
North American Deer

Odocoileus hemionus hemionus (Rafinesque)
MULE DEER

Cervus hemionus Rafinesque, Amer. Monthly Magazine, 1:436. October, 1817. Type from Sioux River, South Dakota.

Synonym.—Cariacus macrotis, Merriam, 1891:80.

Distribution.—Widely distributed throughout most of the state.

Description.—A large-sized deer with heavy antlers and large ears; tail covered with short hairs, naked on underside, and with black terminal tuft; metatarsal gland nearly 5 inches in length; antlers dichotomously branched. Color (summer): Yellowish brown varying to reddish brown above, rump patch dull white. In winter dark grayish brown above. Total length between 5 and 6 feet; weight between 150 and 425 pounds, average nearer 200 pounds.

Remarks.—Many of the early explorers in Idaho mention deer of this species. Lewis and Clark (Thwaite's ed., 1905) reported deer from Lemhi River, North Fork Salmon River, Lochsa River, and Collins Creek (Lolo Fork of Clearwater). Ross (1855) mentions finding deer along the Salmon River in what is now Custer County and also near Redi's (Boise) River. Townsend (1839) records deer from Big Lost River Valley. Merriam (1891) found deer on the Snake River near Shoshone Falls where a hunter killed 11 in early October; he records them also from the Bruneau Mountains.

Borell (MS) saw many tracks, but no deer, on the brushy, open-timbered slopes of Cuddy Mountain in June, 1930. His impression was that few deer were in that immediate area. At Smith Mountain in July, 1930, he and Gilmore saw three mule deer; tracks were numerous. He reports them also from Black Lake. I, personally, have seen mule deer at Loon Creek, Galena Summit, hills 5 mi. E Elba, Mt. Independence, Mt. Harrison, and in the Pahsimeroi Mountains. According to reports from hunters, most of the deer are concentrated in the mountainous central portion of the state.

The present number of deer in Idaho is estimated at 75,000 (Eckert, 1935). No distinction was made between the two species that occur in the state, but I venture the opinion that fully 75 per cent are mule deer. During the hunting season of 1935, 7,464 deer were reported killed by hunters in Idaho. Most of them were taken in the west central portion of the state in Adams, Boise, Valley, and Washington counties. This number is about half that of the 1934 kill. Favorable weather in the autumn of 1935 permitted the deer to remain longer in the higher parts of the mountains, and consequently they were more difficult to find.

Records of occurrence.—Specimens examined, 2, as follows: *Clark County:* Birch Creek, 2 mi. SE Kaufman, 1. *Bannock County:* Rapid Creek, 9½ mi. E Pocatello, 1.

Odocoileus virginianus ochrourus Bailey
YELLOW-TAILED DEER

Odocoileus virginianus ochrourus Bailey, Proc. Biol. Soc. Washington, 45:43. April 2, 1932. Type from Coolin, south end of Priest Lake, Bonner County, Idaho.

Distribution.—In Idaho, confined largely to the northern part of the state.

Description.—Medium-sized deer with heavy antlers and large, basally wide tail, yellowish above and conspicuously whitened below. Antlers with tines branching from a single main beam; color (summer) bright tawny or light bay, legs only slightly lighter; in winter grayer; underparts white. Metatarsal gland less than one inch in length and with central white hairs.

Remarks.—This deer differs from the mule deer in smaller size; lack of black on dorsal surface of tail; antlers not dichotomously branched; metatarsal gland one-fifth the length of latter.

Records of occurrence.—Specimens examined, 1, from 5 mi. NE Meadow Creek, Boundary County. Additional records: *Bonner County:* Coolin (Bailey, 1932:44). *Shoshone County:* Coeur d'Alene Mountains (Bailey, *ibid.*). A. H. Howell writes me that specimens are in the Biological Survey collections from: *Idaho County:* Packer Meadow. *Custer County:* Mackay.

Genus Alces Gray
Moose and Old World Elk

Alces americanus shirasi Nelson
YELLOWSTONE MOOSE

Alces americanus shirasi Nelson, Proc. Biol. Soc. Washington, 27:72. April 25, 1914. Type from Snake River, 4 miles south of Yellowstone Park, Teton County, Wyoming.

Synonyms.—*Alce americanus*, Merriam, 1873:668; 1891:79.

Distribution.—Formerly distributed over much of the mountainous portion of the state; now reduced in numbers and found mostly near Yellowstone National Park and in northern Idaho.

Description.—Largest of the American deer. Antlers broad, heavy, and palmate; tail short; muzzle inflated, broad, and pendulous; a pendulous growth of skin on the throat (known as the bell); higher at shoulders than at rump; long pointed hoofs, dew claws well developed; general color from blackish brown to pale brown, sexes similar; color below like that above; total length of adult males near 8 feet.

Remarks.—Fayre Kenagy, of Rupert, Idaho, reported *(in litt.)* seeing a moose in the fall of 1935 on the Lochsa River in Idaho County. In 1910 the estimated number of moose in Idaho was 500 (see Palmer and Oldys, 1911). Raymond M. Gilmore *(in litt.,* 1935) is of the opinion they are increasing slowly but steadily in the upper part of the Snake River Valley. Adams (1926) reports 528 moose in 1925 from the National Forests in northern Idaho, 485 of which were found in the Selway National Forest. I venture to estimate the total number in the state now is near 1,000.

Records of occurrence.—*Lemhi County:* Salmon River Mountains (Merriam, 1891:79). *Fremont County:* Warm River (Brooks, 1906: 202). *Teton County?:* Teton Canyon (Merriam, *ibid.).*

Genus **Rangifer** Hamilton Smith
Reindeer and Caribou

Rangifer montanus Seton-Thompson
MOUNTAIN CARIBOU

Rangifer montanus Seton-Thompson, Ottawa Nat., 13:129. August, 1899. Type from Illecillewaet watershed, near Revelstoke, Selkirk Range, British Columbia.

Synonym.—*Rangifer caribou,* Merriam, 1891: 80.

Distribution.—Formerly occurred in northern Idaho south at least as far as Elk City; now probably occurs in small numbers in Nezperce National Forest.

Description.—A large deer with semipalmate antlers in both sexes, those of the female smaller, occasionally lacking entirely; brow tine present, large, laterally compressed; muzzle wide, hairy, heavily built; ears and tail short; mane on neck; tarsal, but no metatarsal glands; hoofs broad and long with dew claws large and reaching nearly to the ground; dental formula $\frac{0\ 1\ 3\ 3}{3\ 1\ 3\ 3}$; greater part of animal dark brown, lighter on head and shoulders, occasionally nearly white.

Remarks.—Merriam (1891:80) states, "Capt. Charles E. Bendire informs me that Caribou are common in northern Idaho and that they occur as far south as the neighborhood of Elk City, in Idaho County. A hunter named N. C. Linsley states that he and his partner killed 25 Caribou on Pend d'Oreille River during the winter of 1888-'89."

Seton (1929, 3:61), quoting George Bird Grinnell (Forest and Stream, Sept. 23, 1911:486), writes, "Thirty years ago (in the 1880's), there were a few caribou in northern Idaho, ... We have seen camps of Kootenai Indians bring in to Sineaqueteen—the old crossing place of the Pend d'Oreille River—fresh skins which they said had been taken but a few miles north of there. There seems to be more reason to think that a small herd of Caribou still ranges over the Cabinet Mountains north of Lake Pend d'Oreille. It is believed that the herd is small, not more than 15 or 20." Grant (1903:191) reports caribou from the mountains of northern Idaho. Recent information (1936) from Mr. Amos Eckert, former State Game Warden of Idaho, leads to the conclusion that this species no longer occurs in the state, although as late as 1925 a small band of 10 was found in the Nezperce National Forest (see Adams, 1926).

Family ANTILOCAPRIDAE
PRONGHORNED ANTELOPE

Form deerlike; horn forked, consisting of a matted hair sheath, shed and renewed annually, surrounding a bony core; pelage of coarse, brittle, erectile hairs; foot consisting of two hoofed digits only; body color tan, with conspicuous white rump patch and two white bands across throat and chest. Dental formula $\frac{0\,0\,3\,3}{3\,1\,3\,3}$; cheek teeth hypsodont, selenodont, rootless.

In structural characters the American antelope or pronghorn is closest to the Bovidae, especially to the goats. The structure of the horns and feet, however, differ so markedly from any living bovid that most systematists agree in placing it in a separate family along with some now extinct genera. The one living genus of the family, *Antilocapra*, dates back at least to Pleistocene. The antelopes of the Old World are true bovids; the horn consists of a keratinous sheath, which is not shed, surrounding a bony core. The family Antilocapridae is today, as perhaps it was in the past, confined to the temperate regions of North America.

Genus **Antilocapra** Ord

Antilocapra americana americana (Ord)
PRONGHORNED ANTELOPE

Antilope americana Ord, Guthrie's Geography, 2d Amer. ed., 2:292 (described on p. 308). 1815. Type from plains and highlands of the Missouri.

Synonyms.—Antilocapra americana, Merriam, 1873:669; 1891:80.

Distribution.—In Idaho, formerly occurred over much of the more arid southern half of the state; now in scattered herds chiefly in Owyhee County and in the Lost River country.

Description.—As for family given above.

Remarks.—Normally the pronghorn inhabits barren rolling hills or plains and avoids timber and broken country. In the last century it was common on the Great Plains, but since has pushed back into the less inhabited portions of the West where it occurs in scattered herds, the largest of which is thought to be in southeastern Oregon. It is one of the most picturesque of North American mammals. Mr. W. Cowell, of Rupert, Idaho, who has hunted pronghorns in the Pahsimeroi Valley, recounts the seeming desire of these animals to exhibit their speed by running parallel to a fast-moving automobile for some distance and then attempting to cross the road in front of the speeding car. They possess a keen sense of curiosity, a circumstance which hunters take advantage of when hunting them.

All the early travelers in Idaho encountered pronghorns in the lower valleys in the southern half of the state. In 1872, Merriam (1891) saw many herds along the route of the Hayden Survey in eastern Idaho; hundreds were seen in the Teton Basin. He records *(op. cit.,* p. 80) that the following year an epidemic disease broke out among them and greatly reduced their numbers. According to reliable reports from old settlers in the region, by 1900 pronghorns were so reduced in numbers that they faced extinction. In 1924, the estimated number in the state was 1,500 (see Nelson, 1925:30), but full protection for a number of years has permitted the herds to increase. In 1935, the estimated number of individuals was 10,500 (see Eckert, 1935:163). In fact, the State Game Department is of the opinion that they now (1937) are sufficiently numerous to permit of a limited number being taken annually. A definite number to be killed might be decided upon in late summer, a special license required, and an impartial drawing of names held to decide which of the many applicants would be allowed to hunt them.

Records of occurrence.—Specimen examined, 1, from the head of Pahsimeroi River, Custer County (shed horn). Additional records (Nelson, 1925:31-32, unless otherwise stated): *Owyhee County:* Duck Valley Indian Reservation; forks of Owyhee River; Juniper Basin; Juniper Mountains; Succor Creek. *Lemhi County:* Lemhi Valley. *Custer County:* Antelope Valley; Big Lost River, near Chilly; Copper Basin, near Mackay; Horse Heaven Pass; Pahsimeroi Valley, near Goldburg. Pahsimeroi Mountains (Biol. Surv. coll.). *Twin Falls County:* Browns Bench. *Clark County:* Birch Creek; Medicine Lodge Creek. *Butte County:* Little Lost River Valley; Snake River desert near Arco. *Fremont County:* Middle Fork of Snake River (Merriam, 1891:80). *Madison County:* Canyon Creek (Merriam, *ibid.*). *Bonneville County:* Iona (Biol. Surv. coll.). The records of specimens in the Biological Survey collections not formerly published were furnished me by A. H. Howell.

Family BOVIDAE
BISON, SHEEP, GOATS, ANTELOPE

Large to small ruminants with both sexes usually horned; horn consisting of hollow, keratinous, unbranched sheath surrounding a bony core, never shed, but added to from year to year until fully developed; feet usually with four hoofed digits, two constituting the so-called dew claws; cheek teeth high crowned; dental formula $\frac{0\;0\;3\;3}{3\;1\;3\;3}$.

Geologically, the family is an old one, dating back at least to the Miocene and perhaps to the Oligocene, in which period it, as well as the deer, giraffe, and pronghorn families, branched from the main stem that gave rise to the primitive living tragulids of the Old World. The Bovidae typically is an Old World family and there it has differentiated into a number of forms, many of which have been domesticated; American forms consist only of the musk-ox, bison, mountain sheep, and mountain goat which probably migrated to this continent in the Pliocene or early Pleistocene; except for introductions by man, the family has not reached South America. In the Pleistocene, bison were exceedingly numerous in North America and, to judge from the fossil record, they branched out into a number of species. The bison inhabiting Idaho during that period *(Bison alleni)* was a species different from the one that occurred there in the last century. In the Pleistocene, the musk-ox, now restricted to the far North, probably occurred in Idaho; fossil remains of it are known from the south in Utah (see Hay, 1927). Mountain sheep and mountain goats are known from the Pleistocene, the latter from cave deposits in California and Nevada, but, so far as I am aware, no fossils are available for Idaho.

Genus **Bison** Hamilton Smith
Bison

Bison bison bison (Linnaeus)
PLAINS BISON

[*Bos*] *bison* Linnaeus, Syst. Nat., ed. 10, 1:72. 1758. Type from Mexico. (See Thomas, Proc. Zool. Soc. London, March, 1911:154.)

Synonym.—*Bison bison*, Merriam, 1891:81.

Distribution.—Formerly, within historic time, occurred in large numbers in southeastern Idaho west as far as Salmon Falls on the Snake River (near Hagerman); now extinct in the state.

Description.—Large, horned in both sexes; horns curved and cylindrical; thoracic vertebrae very high producing a great hump; tail short, covered with short hair, with terminal tuft of long hair; hair long and woolly, especially on fore parts; thick beard on chin; general color blackish brown. Young at birth dull reddish yellow. Adult males may weigh as much as 1800 pounds; females 700 to 1200 pounds.

Remarks.—Bailey (1932b) recently described a new race of bison, *Bison bison oregonus*, from remains found in the dried portions of the former bed of Malheur Lake, Oregon. That buffalo formerly ranged in numbers over portions of eastern Oregon and northeastern California is suggested by Merriam (1926). This race may have occurred in western Idaho. The subspecific name *bison* is here applied to the buffalo formerly found in Idaho on the assumption, based upon the observations and writings of Captain John C. Fremont (1853), that within historic times these animals crossed the Rocky Mountains from the east into the Snake River hydrographic basin.

Concerning this migration, Fremont says (pp. 186-87) : "The information is derived principally from Mr. Fitzpatrick, supported by my own personal knowledge and acquaintance with the country. Our knowledge does not go farther back than the spring of 1824. . . . In travelling through the country west of the Rocky Mountains, observations readily led me to the impression that the buffalo had, for the first time, crossed a few years prior to the period we are considering; and in this opinion I am sustained by Mr. Fitzpatrick, and the older trappers in that country. In the region west of the Rocky Mountains, we never meet with any of the ancient vestiges which, throughout all the country lying upon their eastern waters, are found in the *great highways.* . . , sometimes several feet in depth, which the buffalo have made. . . . The Snake Indians . . . have always been very grateful to the American trappers, for the great kindness (as they frequently expressed it) which they did to them in driving the buffalo so low down the Columbia river."

I believe it is of significance to note that Lewis and Clark made no mention of buffalo in the Lemhi Valley when they visited it in August, 1805, whereas John Work and Alexander Ross encountered them in numbers there in December and May respectively about twenty years later. That buffalo were to be found in great herds in the eastern section of the Snake River Plains is attested to by the writings of several early explorers. Ross reports seeing thousands of them in the Lemhi and Little Lost River valleys in 1823; Work, in 1831-32, reported large herds in Lemhi, Big Lost River, Little Lost River, and upper Salmon River valleys; Townsend, in 1833, describes a hunt on which large herds were encountered in what is now Caribou County, some 70 miles east of Old Fort Hall. Fremont reports (*ibid.*) that by 1843 such a great diminution in the numbers of this game animal had occurred that in areas where it was abundant in 1824 only "an occasional buffalo skull and a few wild antelope were all that remained of the abundance which had covered the country" a few years earlier.

Records of occurrence.—Specimen examined, 1, from 5½ mi. NW Michaud, Power County (weathered skull). Additional records: *Lemhi County:* Lemhi Valley (Ross, 1855:60) : near Junction; Agency Creek (Lewis and Phillips, 1923:136, 138). *Custer County:* Big Lost River Valley; Pahsimeroi Valley; Salmon River, near Challis; Thousand Springs Valley (Lewis and Phillips, 1923:143-149). *Blaine County:* E. fork Little Wood River (Lewis and Phillips, 1923:150). *Camas County:* near mouth of Camas Creek (Lewis and Phillips, 1923:153). *Cassia County:* 20 mi. W Raft River (Fremont, 1853: 222). *Butte County:* Big Lost River Valley (Townsend, 1839:237) ; Little Lost River Valley (Ross, 1855:60). *Bannock County:* Justice Park (Whitlow and Hall, 1933:273) ; Ross Fork Creek (Townsend, 1839:212).

Genus Ovis Linnaeus
Sheep

Ovis canadensis canadensis Shaw
ROCKY MOUNTAIN SHEEP

Ovis canadensis Shaw, Naturalist's Miscell., 15:text to pl. 610. 1804. Type from mountains on Dew River, near Exshaw, Alberta, Canada.

Synonyms.—*Ovis canadensis,* Merriam, 1891:81; *Ovis montana,* Hornaday, 1901:101.

Distribution.—Formerly occurred throughout much of the mountainous portions of the state; now restricted in summer to the higher mountains in the central part of the state, in winter found in the higher valleys.

Description.—A large, wild sheep, the males carrying horns which curve regularly backward, downward, and outward in a spiral; horns with transverse ridges; ears small, pointed, hairy; head broadest between the eyes; body stout, nose narrow, chin beardless; grayish-brown in color with whitish rump patch.

Remarks.—Early accounts of mountain sheep in Idaho indicate that they were widely distributed and numerous. Seton (1929) records that in 1884 thousands of sheep were in the Lost River area; Hornaday (1901) reports that in 1887 trappers encountered 2,000 to 2,500 head on the Middle Fork of the Salmon River; and Merriam (1891) in 1890 found them to be common in the Lemhi and Pahsimeroi mountains and, in smaller numbers, in the Sawtooth Mountains. He also reported them as common in northern Idaho. A recent estimate (Eckert, 1935) places the total number in the state at near 2,000.

Records of occurrence.—Specimens examined, 3, as follows: *Owyhee County:* Silver City. (In May, 1935, I saw the mounted horns of a mountain sheep at Grand View that had been found in the mountains near Silver City. Mountain sheep no longer occur in southwestern Idaho.) *Blaine County:* Copper Creek, 6 mi. N Muldoon, 1 (horn only). *Bannock County:* Mink Creek, 11 mi. SE Pocatello, 1 (weathered horn). Additional records (supplied by A. H. Howell from specimens in the Biological Survey collection, unless otherwise stated): *Idaho County:* Bargamin Creek, 50 mi. SE Grangeville; Meadow Creek, 14 mi. above mouth; Wind River, 40 mi. S Grangeville. *Valley County:* Middle Fork Salmon River, 60 mi. from main Salmon River (Hornaday, 1901:104). *Custer County:* Upper Loon Creek (reported *in litt.* by F. Kenagy, of Rupert, Idaho). *Fremont County:* Henrys Lake (Hornaday, *ibid.*).

Genus **Oreamnos** Rafinesque
Mountain Goats

Oreamnos americanus missoulae Allen
ROCKY MOUNTAIN GOAT

Oreamnos montanus missoulae Allen, Bull. Amer. Mus. Nat. Hist., 20:20. February 10, 1904. Type from Missoula, Missoula County, Montana.

Synonym.—*Mazama montana*, Merriam, 1891:81.

Distribution.—In Idaho, restricted to the more mountainous central and northern portions of the state.

Description.—A large, white goat with black hoofs and horns; horns in both sexes, ridged at base, gently curving backward and outward, those in male larger; neural spines of thoracic vertebrae long, producing a hump in the shoulder area; tail short and almost hidden in long, shaggy body hair; bearded; ears moderately large, clothed with short hairs; color in summer and winter nearly pure white, often tinged with yellowish in summer.

Remarks.—The mountain goat is a sturdy creature with short, stout legs; the squarish hoofs, consisting of soft inner pads each surrounded with a hard, sharp rim, are well adapted to climbing over the rocks and ice in its high mountain habitat. It is a fearless climber, but in many respects lacks the grace and daring of the mountain sheep.

Today, there are perhaps more mountain goats in Idaho than in any other state in the Union. The estimated population in 1922 (see Seton, 1929) was 4,148; a recent estimate (see Eckert, 1935) was 4,000. In Idaho they occur commonly in the Bitterroot Mountains; in the Salmon River and Sawtooth mountains they are less common.

Records of occurrence.—Specimens examined, 2, as follows: *Custer County:* upper Loon Creek, 1. (In 1919, I examined the head and hide of a male that was killed at this locality by the late Harry E. Dunn, of Rupert, Idaho.) *Blaine County:* Boulder Peak, Sawtooth Mountains, 1. (I examined the head and hide of one killed at this locality in 1935 by Mr. Gene Glahn, of Bellevue, Idaho; the feet are in Mus. Vert. Zool.) Additional records: *Lemhi County:* Salmon River Mountains (Merriam, 1891:81). *Custer County:* Stanley Lake (near) (Anthony, 1923:151). *Blaine County:* Sawtooth Mountains near Alturas Lake (Biol. Surv. coll.). (This record was furnished by A. H. Howell.)

ABSTRACT

One hundred and forty-one kinds of mammals, 57 per cent of which are rodents, occur in Idaho; they are divided among 6 orders, 20 families, and 55 genera; each kind is treated separately as to names, type locality, distribution, diagnostic characters, and where known, ecology. They are associated with three faunal areas, (1) the Great Basin, (2) the Pacific Coast, and (3) the Rocky Mountains. Of the 141 kinds, 70 are restricted to small biogeographical areas herein termed "biotic areas." Rodents are regarded as more plastic than other mammals and, therefore, more susceptible to environmental changes; these, and certain birds and plants, constitute the criteria for recognizing biotic areas.

Associations are considered the most fundamental of distributional units; temperature zones are thought to be less limiting, therefore less critical and less fundamental units in Idaho. Snow is an important element in aiding the dispersal of certain nonhibernating mammals, especially in the Great Basin. The lower course of the Snake River is important in limiting the geographic movements of certain kinds of mammals; toward the headwaters, where the individual streams are smaller, it limits their geographic movements little, if at all. Hibernation is thought to be important in determining the distribution of ground squirrels in southern Idaho. Interspecific competition is important in determining occurrence: ecologically similar kinds complement each other geographically.

The mammalian fauna of Idaho is not static; it is changing. It consists of elements which have moved in recently, or are now moving in, plus a core that has been present in the area since the Pleistocene, or earlier. Certain kinds appear to have moved in from the south, others from the north, and still others from the east; the east-west course of the Snake River has influenced greatly the present distribution of recent immigrants.

Taxonomic changes proposed are as follows: (1) The subgenus *Lemmiscus* of the genus *Lagurus*, is raised to full generic rank; (2) *Citellus (townsendii) brunneus* is raised to a full species; (3) the following are reduced to subspecies: *Citellus oregonus* becomes *Citellus beldingi oregonus*, *Citellus idahoensis* becomes *Citellus mollis idahoensis*, *Callospermophilus trepidus* becomes *Callospermophilus lateralis trepidus*, *Callospermophilus lateralis* and *C. chrysodeirus* are considered as conspecific, *Thomomys fuscus* becomes *Thomomys talpoides fuscus*, *Thomomys idahoensis* becomes *Thomomys talpoides idahoensis*, *Thomomys pygmaeus* becomes *Thomomys talpoides pygmaeus;* (4) the following subspecies are named as new: *Citellus elegans aureus*, *Castor canadensis taylori*, *Peromyscus maniculatus serratus*.

LITERATURE CITED

ADAMS, C. C.
1926. The economic and social importance of animals in forestry with special reference to wild life. Roos. Wild Life Bull., 3(4):509-676, pls. 20-21, figs. 153-180.

ALLEN, A. A.
1921. Banding bats. Jour. Mammal., 2(2):53-57, 2 pls.

ALLEN, G. M.
1916. Bats of the genus Corynorhinus. Harvard College, Mus. Comp. Zool. Bull., 60(9):333-356, 1 pl.
1923. The red bat in Bermuda. Jour. Mammal., 4(1):61.

ALLEN, J. A.
1895. Descriptions of new American mammals. Am. Mus. Nat. Hist. Bull., 7(10):327-340.
1898. Revision of the chickarees, or North American red squirrels (subgenus Tamiasciurus). Am. Mus. Nat. Hist. Bull., 10 (14):249-298.

ANDERSON, R. M.
1932. Five new mammals from British Columbia. Canad. Nat. Mus., Ann. Rept., 1931:99-119, pl. V.

ANTHONY, H. E.
1913. Mammals of northern Malheur County, Oregon. Am. Mus. Nat. Hist. Bull., 32:1-27, 2 pls.
1923. White goats of the Sawtooth Mountains. Nat. Hist., 23(2): 142-154, 12 figs.
1928. Field book of North American Mammals. (G. P. Putnam's Sons, New York), i-xxv + 1-625, illustrated.

BACHMAN, J.
1839. Description of several new species of American quadrupeds. Acad. Nat. Sci. Phila. Jour., 8(I):57-74.
1839. The following species must be added to the list of Mr. Townsend's quadrupeds. Acad. Nat. Sci. Phila. Jour., 8(I):101-105.

BAILEY, V.
1897. Revision of the American voles of the genus Evotomys. Biol. Soc. Wash. Proc., 11:113-138, 1 pl.
1900. Revision of the American voles of the genus Microtus. U. S. Dept. Agric., Bur. Biol. Surv., N. Am. Fauna, 17:1-88, 5 pls., 17 figs.
1914. Eleven new species and subspecies of pocket gophers of the genus Thomomys. Biol. Soc. Wash. Proc., 27:115-118.
1915. Revision of the pocket gophers of the genus Thomomys. U. S. Dept. Agric., Bur. Biol. Surv., N. Am. Fauna, 39:1-136, 8 pls., 10 figs.
1917. A new subspecies of meadow mouse from Wyoming. Biol. Soc. Wash. Proc., 30:29-30.
1927. Beaver habits and experiments in beaver culture. U. S. Dept. Agric., Tech. Bull., 21:1-39, 14 pls., 7 figs.
1932. Buffalo of the Malheur Valley, Oregon. Biol. Soc. Wash. Proc., 45:47-48.
1932b. The northwestern white-tailed deer. Biol. Soc. Wash. Proc., 45:43-44.
1936. The mammals and life zones of Oregon. U. S. Dept. Agric., Bur. Biol. Surv., N. Am. Fauna, 55:1-416, 52 pls., 102 figs.

BAILEY, V., AND SPERRY, C. C.
 1929. Life history and habits of the grasshopper mice, genus Ony-
    chomys. U. S. Dept. Agric., Tech. Bull., 145:1-19, 4 pls.
BAIRD, S. F.
 1857. Explorations and surveys for a railroad route from the
    Mississippi River to the Pacific Ocean. Gen. Rept. upon the
    Zool. of the several Pacific R. R. routes, vol. 8, pt. 1:xlviii +
    1-757, 60 pls., 35 figs.
BENSON, S. B.
 1933a. Concealing coloration among some desert rodents of the
    southwestern United States. Calif. Univ. Publ. Zool., 40
    (1):1-70, 2 pls., 8 figs.
 1933b. A new race of beaver from British Columbia. Jour. Mam-
    mal., 14(4):320-325, 1 fig.
BORELL, A. E.
 1931. A new pika from Idaho. Jour. Mammal., 12(3):306-308.
BORELL, A. E., AND ELLIS, R.
 1934. Mammals of the Ruby Mountains region of northeastern
    Nevada. Jour. Mammal., 15(1):12-44, 6 pls., 1 fig.
BROOKS, H.
 1906. The Idaho moose. New York Zool. Soc. Rep., 10:201-216,
    4 figs.
BUWALDA, J. P.
 1924. The age of the Payette Formation and the old erosion sur-
    face in Idaho. Science, n. s., 60:572-573.
CARY, M.
 1911. A biological survey of Colorado. U. S. Dept. Agric., Bur.
    Biol. Surv., N. Am. Fauna, 33:1-256, 39 figs., 1 map.
CLARK, H. W.
 1937. Association types in the north coast ranges of California.
    Ecology, 18(2):214-230, 5 figs.
COPE, E. D.
 1868. Observations on some specimens of Vertebrata presented by
    Wm. M. Gabb, of San Francisco which were procured by
    him in western Nevada and the northern part of Lower
    California. Acad. Nat. Sci. Phila. Proc., 1868:2.
COWAN, I. McT.
 1936. Nesting habits of the flying squirrel Glaucomys sabrinus.
    Jour. Mammal., 17(1):58-60.
DAVIS, W. B.
 1934a. Notes on the Utah chipmunk. Murrelet, 15:20-22.
 1934. A study of the Idaho jumping mice of the genus Zapus, with
    remarks on a few specimens from British Columbia. Jour.
    Mammal., 15(3):221-227, 1 fig.
 1935. Mammals of the Ross expedition (1824) in Idaho. Murrelet,
    16(1):7-10.
 1937. Variations in Townsend pocket gophers. Jour. Mammal.,
    18(2):145-158, 5 figs.
ECKERT, A. H.
 1935. [Discussion, pp. 163-164] in The Taylor Grazing Act and
    wildlife in the west [by] A. Funk, Am. Game Conf., 21st
    Trans., pp. 155-165.
EDSON, J. M.
 1932. Hibernation of the northwest jumping mouse. Murrelet,
    13(2):55-56.

ELFTMAN, H. O.
1931. Pleistocene mammals of Fossil Lake, Oregon. Am. Mus. Nov., 481:1-21, 10 figs.

ELLIOT, D. G.
1898. List of species of mammals, principally rodents, obtained... in the states of Iowa, Wyoming, Montana, Idaho, Nevada and California with descriptions of new species. Field Col. Mus. Publ., 27, Zool. ser., 1(10):193-221.
1899. Catalogue of mammals from the Olympic Mountains Washington with descriptions of new species. Field Col. Mus. Publ., 32, Zool. ser., 1(13):241-276, pls. 50-57.

ENGELS, W. L.
1936. Distribution of races of the brown bat (Eptesicus) in western North America. Am. Mid. Nat., 17(3):653-660, 1 fig.

FLOWER, H. W., AND LYDEKKER, R.
1891. An introduction to the study of mammals living and extinct. (Adam and Charles Black), London, i-xvi + 1-763, 357 figs.

FREMONT, J. C.
1853. The exploring expedition to the Rocky Mountains, Oregon and California. (Derby, Orton and Mulligan, Buffalo), pp. 1-456.

FROTHINGHAM, E. H.
1909. Douglas fir: a study of the Pacific Coast and Rocky Moun-·tain forms. U. S. Dept. Agric., For. Serv. Circ., 150:1-38, 3 figs.

GAUSE, G. F.
1937. Experimental populations of microscopic organisms. Ecology, 18(2):173-179.

GAZIN, C. L.
1933. New felids from the Upper Pliocene of Idaho. Jour. Mammal., 14(3):251-256, 3 figs.
1933b. A new shrew from the Upper Pliocene of Idaho. Jour. Mammal., 14(2):142-144, 1 fig.
1934. Fossil hares from the late Pliocene of southern Idaho. U. S. Nat. Mus. Proc., 83(2976):111-121, 5 figs.
1935. Annotated list of Pleistocene Mammalia from American Falls, Idaho. Wash. Acad. Sci. Jour., 25(7):297-302.
1936. A study of the fossil horse remains from the Upper Pliocene of Idaho. U. S. Nat. Mus. Proc., 83(2985):281-320, pls. 23-33, figs. 21-24.

GOLDMAN, E. A.
1910. Revision of the wood rats of the genus Neotoma. U. S. Dept. Agric., Bur. Biol. Surv., N. Am. Fauna, 31:1-124, 8 pls., 14 figs.
1917. Two new pocket mice from Wyoming. Biol. Soc. Wash. Proc., 30:147-148.
1922. A new pocket mouse from Idaho. Biol. Soc. Wash. Proc., 35:105-106.
1931. Two new desert foxes. Wash. Acad. Sci. Jour., 21(11): 249-251.
1935. New American mustelids of the genera Martes, Gulo, and Lutra. Biol. Soc. Wash. Proc., 48:175-186.
1937. The wolves of North America. Jour. Mammal., 18(1):37-45.
1937b. The Colorado River as a barrier in mammalian distribution. Jour. Mammal., 18(4):427-435.

GORDON, K.
1932. Rabbits killed on an Idaho Highway. Jour. Mammal., 13 (2) :169.

GRANT, M.
1903. The caribou. New York Zool. Soc. Rep., 7:175-196, 33 figs.

GRAVES, H. S., AND NELSON, E. W.
1919. Our national elk herds. U. S. Dept. Agric., Dept. Circ., 51:1-34, 19 figs.

GRIFFIN, D. R.
1936. Bat banding. Jour. Mammal., 17(3) :235-239.

GRINNELL, H. W.
1918. A synopsis of the bats of California. Calif. Univ. Publ. Zool., 17(12) :223-404, pls. 14-24, 24 figs.

GRINNELL, J.
1914. An account of the mammals and birds of the Lower Colorado Valley, with especial reference to the distributional problems presented. Calif. Univ. Publ. Zool., 12(4) :51-294, pls. 3-13, 9 figs.
1922. A geographical study of the kangaroo rats of California. Calif. Univ. Publ. Zool., 24(1) :1-124, pls. 1-7, 24 figs.
1923. The burrowing rodents of California as agents in soil formation. Jour. Mammal., 4(3) :137-149, 3 pls.
1926. The pocket gopher of Honey Lake Valley. Calif. Univ. Publ. Zool., 30(1) :1-6, 1 pl.
1933. Review of the Recent mammal fauna of California. Calif. Univ. Publ. Zool., 40(2) :71-234.

GRINNELL, J., AND DIXON, J.
1924. Revision of the genus Lynx in California. Calif. Univ. Publ. Zool., 21(13) :339-354, pl. 11, 1 fig.

GRINNELL, J., DIXON, J., AND LINSDALE, J. M.
1930. Vertebrate natural history of a section of northern California through the Lassen Peak region. Calif. Univ. Publ. Zool., 35:v + 1-594, 181 figs.

HAHN, W. L.
1908. Some habits and sensory adaptations of cave-inhabiting bats. Biol. Bull., 15(3-4) :135-193, 1 fig., 4 tables.

HALL, E. R.
1928. Notes on the life history of the sage-brush meadow mouse (Lagurus). Jour. Mammal., 9(3) :201-204.
1931. Critical comments on mammals from Utah, with descriptions of new forms from Utah, Nevada and Washington. Calif. Univ. Publ. Zool., 37(1) :1-13.
1934. Mammals collected by T. T. and E. B. McCabe in the Bowron Lake Region of British Columbia. Calif. Univ. Publ. Zool., 40(9) :363-386, 1 fig.
1934b. Two new rodents of the genera Glaucomys and Zapus from Utah. Mich. Univ. Mus. Zool. Occas. Papers, 296:1-6.
1935. Nevadan races of the Microtus montanus group of meadow mice. Calif. Univ. Publ. Zool., 40(12) :417-428, 1 fig.
1936. Mustelid mammals from the Pleistocene of North America. ... Carnegie Inst. Wash., Publ. 473:41-119, 5 pls., 6 figs.

HALL, E. R., AND BOWLUS, H. L.
1938. A new pika (mammalian genus Ochotona) from southeastern Idaho with notes on near-by subspecies. Calif. Univ. Publ. Zool., 42(6) :335-339, 1 fig.

HALL, E. R., AND HATFIELD, D. M.
1934. A new race of chipmunk from the great basin of western United States. Calif. Univ. Publ. Zool., 40(6):321-326, 1 fig.

HALL, E. R., AND WHITLOW, W. B.
1932. A new black-tailed jack-rabbit from Idaho. Biol. Soc. Wash. Proc., 45:71-72.

HAMILTON, W. J., JR.
1934. The life history of the rufescent woodchuck *Marmota monax rufescens* Howell. Carnegie Mus. Ann., 23:85-178, 20 pls., 9 figs.

HARLAN, R.
1825. Fauna Americana.... Anthony Finley, Philadelphia, i-x + 11-318.

HATFIELD, D. M.
1935. A natural history study of Microtus californicus. Jour. Mammal., 16(4):261-271, 1 fig.
1936. A revision of the Pipistrellus hesperus group of bats. Jour. Mammal., 17(3):257-262, 1 fig.

HATT, R. T.
1929. The red squirrel: its life history and habits, with special reference to the Adirondacks of New York and the Harvard forest. Roos. Wild Life Ann., 2(1b):1-146, 52 figs., 1 map.

HAY, O. P.
1921. Descriptions of species of Pleistocene Vertebrata, types or specimens of most of which are preserved in the United States National Museum. U. S. Nat. Mus. Proc., 59:599-642, pls. 116-124.
1927. The Pleistocene of the western region of North America and its vertebrated animals. Carnegie Inst. Wash., Publ. 322 B: 1-346, 12 pls., 19 figs., 21 maps.

HILL, J. E.
1937. Morphology of the pocket gopher mammalian genus Thomomys. Calif. Univ. Publ. Zool., 42(2):81-172, 26 figs.

HINTON, M. A. C.
1926. Monograph of the voles and lemmings (Microtinae) living and extinct. Brit. Mus. Nat. Hist., London, xvi + 1-488, 15 pls., 110 figs.

HOLLISTER, N.
1911. A systematic synopsis of the muskrats. U. S. Dept. Agric., Bur. Biol. Surv., N. Am. Fauna, 32:1-47, 6 pls.
1914. A systematic account of the grasshopper mice. U. S. Nat. Mus. Proc., 47(2057):427-489, pl. 15, 3 figs.

HORN, E. E.
1923. Some notes concerning the breeding habits of Thomomys townsendii, observed near Vale, Malheur County, Oregon, during the spring of 1921. Jour. Mammal., 4(1):37-39, 1 pl.

HORNADAY, W. T.
1901. Notes on the mountain sheep of North America, with a description of a new species. New York Zool. Soc. Rep., 5:77-122, 18 figs., 1 map.

HOWELL, A. B.
1926. Voles of the genus Phenacomys.... U. S. Dept. Agric., Bur. Biol. Surv., N. Am. Fauna, 48:iv + 1-66, 7 pls., 11 figs.
1932. The saltatorial rodent Dipodomys: the functional and comparative anatomy of its muscular and osseous systems. Am. Acad. Arts and Sci. Proc., 67(10):377-536, 28 figs.

HOWELL, A. B., AND GERSH, I.
1935. Conservation of water by the rodent Dipodomys. Jour. Mammal., 16(1):1-9.

HOWELL, A. H.
1901. Revision of the skunks of the genus Chincha. U. S. Dept. Agric., Bur. Biol. Surv., N. Am. Fauna, 20:1-62, 8 pls.
1914. Revision of the American harvest mice (genus Reithrodontomys). U. S. Dept. Agric., Bur. Biol. Surv., N. Am. Fauna, 36:1-97, 7 pls., 6 figs.
1915. Revision of the American marmots. U. S. Dept. Agric., Bur. Biol. Surv., N. Am. Fauna, 37:1-80, 15 pls., 3 figs.
1915b. Descriptions of a new genus and seven new races of flying squirrels. Biol. Soc. Wash. Proc., 28:109-114.
1918. Revision of the American flying squirrels. U. S. Dept. Agric., Bur. Biol. Surv., N. Am. Fauna, 44:1-64, 7 pls., 4 figs.
1924. Revision of the American pikas (genus Ochotona). U. S. Dept. Agric., Bur. Biol. Surv., N. Am. Fauna, 47:iv + 1-57, 6 pls., 4 figs.
1928. Descriptions of six new North American ground squirrels. Biol. Soc. Wash. Proc., 41:211-214.
1929. Revision of the American chipmunks (genera Tamias and Eutamias). U. S. Dept. Agric., Bur. Biol. Surv., N. Am. Fauna, 52:1-157, 10 pls., 9 figs.
1931. Preliminary descriptions of four new North American ground squirrels. Jour. Mammal., 12(2):160-162.
1938. Revision of the North American ground squirrels with a classification of the North American Sciuridae. U. S. Dept. Agric., Bur. Biol. Surv., N. Am. Fauna, 56:1-256, 32 pls., 20 figs.

JACKSON, H. H. T.
1928. A taxonomic review of the American long-tailed shrews (genera Sorex and Microsorex). U. S. Dept. Agric., Bur. Biol. Surv., N. Am. Fauna, 51:vi + 1-238, 13 pls., 24 figs.

LEWIS AND CLARK
1904-1905. Original journals of the Lewis and Clark expedition, 1804-1806. (R. G. Thwaites, ed., 7 vols., separately paged, Dodd, Mead and Co.)

LEWIS, W. S., AND PHILLIPS, P. C.
1923. The Journal of John Work.... (A. H. Clark Co., Cleveland), pp. 1-209, 6 pls.

LIVINGSTON, B. E., AND SHREVE, F.
1921. The distribution of vegetation in the United States, as related to climatic conditions. Carnegie Inst. Wash., Publ. 284:xvi + 1-590, 73 pls., 74 figs.

LYON, M. W., JR.
1904. Classification of the hares and their allies. Smiths. Misc. Coll., 45:321-447, pls. 74-100.

MATTHEW, W. D.
1915. Climate and evolution. New York Acad. Sci. Ann., 24:171-318, 33 figs.

MERRIAM, C. H.
1873. Report on the mammals and birds of the expedition (pp. 661-715), in 6th ann. rept. U. S. Geol. Surv. of the Territories ... 1872, pp. xi + 1-844.
1890. Descriptions of twenty-six new species of North American mammals. U. S. Dept. Agric., Div. Ornith. and Mammal., N. Am. Fauna, 4:1-55, 3 pls., 3 figs.

1891. Results of a biological reconnoissance of south-central Idaho. U. S. Dept. Agric., Div. Ornith. and Mammal., N. Am. Fauna, 5:vii + 1-127, 4 pls., 4 figs.

1895a. Occurrence of the Siberian lemming-vole (Lagurus) in the United States. Am. Nat., 29:758-759.

1895. Synopsis of the American shrews of the genus Sorex. U. S. Dept. Agric., Div. Ornith. and Mammal., N. Am. Fauna, 10:57-98, pls. 4-12.

1897. Notes on the chipmunks of the genus *Eutamias* occurring west of the east base of the Cascade-Sierra System, with descriptions of new forms. Biol. Soc. Wash. Proc., 11:189-212.

1913. Six new ground squirrels of the *Citellus mollis* group from Idaho, Oregon, and Nevada. Biol. Soc. Wash. Proc., 26: 135-138.

1918. Review of the grizzly and big brown bears of North America (genus Ursus) with description of a new genus, Vetularctos. U. S. Dept. Agric., Bur. Biol. Surv., N. Am. Fauna, 41:1-136, 16 pls.

1926. The buffalo in northeastern California. Jour. Mammal., 7 (3):211-214.

MERRIAM, J. C., AND SINCLAIR, W. J.
1907. Tertiary faunas of the John Day region. Calif. Univ. Bull. Dept. Geol., 5:171-205.

MERRIAM, J. C., AND STOCK, C.
1932. The *Felidae* of Rancho La Brea. Carnegie Inst. Wash., Publ. 422:xvi + 1-231, 42 pls., 152 figs.

MILLER, G. S., JR.
1896. Genera and subgenera of voles and lemmings. U. S. Dept. Agric., Bur. Biol. Surv., N. Am. Fauna, 12:1-78, 39 figs., 3 pls.

1912. Catalogue of the mammals of Western Europe (Europe exclusive of Russia) in the collection of the British Museum. Brit. Mus. Nat. Hist., pp. xv + 1-1019, 213 figs.

1924. List of North American Recent mammals, 1923. U. S. Nat. Mus. Bull., 128:xvi + 1-673.

MILLER, G. S., JR., AND ALLEN, G. M.
1928. The American bats of the genera Myotis and Pizonyx. U. S. Nat. Mus. Bull., 144:viii + 1-218, 1 pl., 1 fig., 13 maps.

MOORE, A. W.
1928. Zapus princeps princeps in Utah. Jour. Mammal., 9(2): 154-155.

MOSSMAN, H. W., LAWLAH, J. W., AND BRADLEY, J. A.
1932. The male reproductive tract of the Sciuridae. Am. Jour. Anat., 51(1):89-155, 7 pls., 16 figs.

MURIE, O. J., AND MURIE, A.
1931. Travels of Peromyscus. Jour. Mammal., 12(3):200-209, 1 fig.

NELSON, E. W.
1909. The rabbits of North America. U. S. Dept. Agric., Bur. Biol. Surv., N. Am. Fauna, 29:1-314, 13 pls., 19 figs.

1925. Status of the pronghorned antelope, 1922-1924. U. S. Dept. Agric., Dept. Bull., 1346:1-64, 6 pls., 21 figs.

ORR, R. T.
1933. Aquatic habits of Peromyscus maniculatus. Jour. Mammal., 14(2):160-161.

OSGOOD, W. H.
1900. Revision of the pocket mice of the genus Perognathus. U. S. Dept. Agric., Bur. Biol. Surv., N. Am. Fauna, 18:1-72, 4 pls., 15 figs.
1909. Revision of the mice of the American genus Peromyscus. U. S. Dept. Agric., Bur. Biol. Surv., N. Am. Fauna, 28:1-285, 8 pls., 12 figs.

PALMER, T. S., AND OLDYS, H.
1911. Progress of game protection in 1910. U. S. Dept. Agric., Bur. Biol. Surv., Circ. 80:1-36, 1 fig.

PREBLE, E. A.
1899. Revision of the jumping mice of the genus Zapus. U. S. Dept. Agric., Bur. Biol. Surv., N. Am. Fauna, 15:1-42, 1 pl., 4 figs.

RAFINESQUE, C. S.
1817. Descriptions of seven new genera of North American quadrupeds. Amer. Monthly Magazine, 2:44-46.

RHOADS, S. N.
1897. A revision of the west American flying squirrels. Acad. Nat. Sci. Phila. Proc., 1897:314-327.
1898. Contributions to a revision of the North American beavers, otters and fishers. Am. Philos. Soc. Trans., n. s., 19:417-439, pls. 21-25.
1902. Synopsis of the American martens. Acad. Nat. Sci. Phila. Proc., 54(2):443-460.

ROMER, A. S.
1933. Vertebrate paleontology (Chicago Univ. Press), pp. vii + 1-491, 359 figs.

ROSS, A.
1855. The fur hunters of the far West; a narrative of adventure in the Oregon and Rocky Mountains (Smith Elder and Co., London), 2 vols., separately paged.

SAUNDERS, A. A.
1921. A distributional list of the birds of Montana.... Cooper Ornith. Club, Pac. Coast Avif., 14:1-194, 35 figs.

SETON, E. T.
1929. Lives of game animals (Doubleday, Doran and Co., New York), 4 vols., separately paged, 1500 figs., 50 maps.

SHAW, W. T.
1924. The home life of the Columbian ground squirrel. Canad. Field-Nat., 38(7-8):128-130, 151-153, 6 figs.
1925. The seasonal differences of north and south slopes in controlling the activities of the Columbian ground squirrel. Ecology, 6(2):157-162, 2 figs.
1925b. Duration of the æstivation and hibernation of the Columbian ground squirrel (Citellus columbianus) and sex relation of the same. Ecology, 6(1):75-81, 2 figs.
1925c. Breeding and development of the Columbian ground squirrel. Jour. Mammal., 6(2):106-113, 12 figs.
1925d. The Columbian ground squirrel as a handler of earth. Sci. Monthly, 20:483-490, 8 figs.
1925e. The food of ground squirrels. Am. Nat., 59:250-264, 5 figs.
1925f. A life history problem and a means for its solution. Jour. Mammal., 6(3):157-162, 4 figs.
1925g. Observations on the hibernation of ground squirrels. Jour. Agric. Research, 31(8):761-769, 6 figs.
1925h. The hibernation of the Columbian ground squirrel. Canad. Field-Nat., 39(3-4):56-61, 79-82, 11 figs.

SMITH, C. F.
1936. Notes on the habits of the long-tailed harvest mouse. Jour. Mammal., 17(3):274-278.

SPERRY, C. C.
1933. Highway mortality of rabbits in Idaho. Jour. Mammal., 14(3):260.

STIRTON, R. A.
1935. A review of the Tertiary beavers. Calif. Univ. Publ. Geol., 23(13):391-458, 142 figs., 1 map, 2 charts.

SUMNER, E. L., JR.
1927. Notes on the San Bernardino flying squirrel. Jour. Mammal., 8(4):314-316.

SVIHLA, A.
1932. A comparative life history study of the mice of the genus *Peromyscus*. Mich. Univ. Mus. Zool., Misc. Publ., 24:1-39.
1933. Notes on the deer-mouse, *Peromyscus maniculatus oreas* (Bangs). Murrelet, 14(1):13-14.

SVIHLA, R. D.
1936. Breeding and young of the grasshopper mouse (Onychomys leucogaster fuscogriseus). Jour. Mammal., 17(2):172-173.

SVIHLA, A., AND SVIHLA, R. D.
1933. Notes on the jumping mouse Zapus trinotatus trinotatus Rhoads. Jour. Mammal., 14(2):131-134.

SWARTH, H. S.
1936. Origins of the fauna of the Sitkan district, Alaska. Calif. Acad. Sci. Proc., 23(3):59-79, 1 fig.

TAYLOR, W. P.
1910. Two new rodents from Nevada. Calif. Univ. Publ. Zool., 5(6):283-302, pls. 27-29.
1911. Mammals of the Alexander Nevada expedition of 1909. Calif. Univ. Publ. Zool., 7(7):205-307.
1916. The status of the beavers of western North America, with a consideration of the factors in their speciation. Calif. Univ. Publ. Zool., 12(15):413-495, 22 figs.
1935. Ecology and life history of the porcupine *(Erethizon epixanthum)* as related to the forests of Arizona and the southwestern United States. Ariz. Univ. Bull. 6(5), (Biol. Sci. Bull., 3):1-177, 9 pls., 18 figs.

TAYLOR, W. P., AND SHAW, W. T.
1929. Provisional list of land mammals of the state of Washington. Washington State College, Chas. R. Conner Mus., Occ. Papers, 2:1-32.

THOMAS, O.
1912. On mammals from Central Asia, collected by Mr. Douglas Carruthers. Ann. and Mag. Nat. Hist., 9(8):391-408.
1921. Bats on migration. Jour. Mammal., 2(3):167.

TOWNSEND, J. K.
1839. Narrative of a journey across the Rocky Mountains, to the Columbia River.... (Reprint in Early Western Travels, 1748-1846, R. G. Thwaites, ed., A. H. Clark Co., Cleveland, 1905).

WEBER, M.
1927. Die Saügetiere. (Gustav Fischer, Jena), 2 vols., separately paged, illustrated. Vol. 1, 1927; vol. 2, 1928.

WHEELER, O. D.
1904. The trail of Lewis and Clark, 1804-1904; .... (G. P. Putnam's Sons, New York and London), 2 vols., separately paged, 197 figs. Vol. 2 treats Idaho.

WHITLOW, W. B., AND HALL, E. R.
1933. Mammals of the Pocatello region of southeastern Idaho. Calif. Univ. Publ. Zool., 40(3):235-276, 3 figs.

WILSON, R. W.
1933. A rodent fauna from later Cenozoic beds of southwestern Idaho. Carnegie Inst. Wash., Publ. 440:117-135, 2 pls., 8 figs.

WOOD, A. E.
1935. Evolution and relationship of the heteromyid rodents.... Carnegie Mus. Ann., 24:73-262, 157 figs.

YOUNG, F. G.
1899. The correspondence and journals of Captain Nathaniel J. Wyeth 1831-6; .... (Univ. Ore. Press), Sources of History of Oregon, 1:xix + 1-262, 3 maps.

Transmitted July, 1937.

INDEX